Regulation of Bacterial Differentiation

Regulation of Bacterial Differentiation

Edited by

Patrick Piggot
Temple University School of Medicine
Philadelphia, Pennsylvania

Charles P. Moran, Jr.
Emory University School of Medicine
Atlanta, Georgia

Philip Youngman
University of Georgia
Athens, Georgia

American Society for Microbiology
Washington, D.C.

Cover figures illustrate compartmentalized expression of *spoIIIG-lacZ* in the forespore and *gerE-lacZ* in the mother cell, using a fluorescent probe for β-galactosidase. (Courtesy J. E. Bylund, M. A. Haines, P. J. Piggot, and M. L. Higgins.)

Library of Congress Cataloging-in-Publication Data

Regulation of bacterial differentiation / edited by Patrick Piggot, Charles P. Moran, Jr., Philip Youngman
p. cm.
Review articles based on the eleventh International Spores Conference, held at Woods Hole, Mass., May 1992
Includes bibliographical references and index.
ISBN 1-55581-066-7
1. Microbial differentiation. 2. Bacteria, Sporeforming. I. Piggot, Patrick. II. Moran, Charles. III. Youngman, Philip. IV. International Spores Conference (11th: 1992: Woods Hole, Mass.)
QR73.5.R44 1993
589.9′0876—dc20 93-29794
CIP

Printed in the United States of America

CONTENTS

PREFACE

Since 1956 the publication of the proceedings of periodic international conferences on bacterial sporulation has served to summarize the progress in this field. Participants in the Eleventh International Spores Conference, held at Woods Hole, Massachusetts, in May 1992 found that the study of bacterial sporulation continues to offer unique insights into fundamental biological problems. Included among these are several aspects of cell differentiation, the control of cell division and morphogenesis, the repair of DNA damage, and the function of multiple types of transcription factors found in a wide variety of bacteria (e.g., RNA polymerase sigma factors, anti-sigma factors, and phosphorylated DNA binding proteins). These studies are important to a wide range of microbiologists. Therefore, in order to include background literature as well as recent developments this volume follows the format that was introduced with the tenth volume in the "Spores" series, i.e., it contains a small number of review articles, rather than a series of short research papers by all of the conference participants.

Since the last meeting three of our colleagues have passed away: Ernst Freese, A. T. (Gan) Ganesan, and Kissel Szulmajster. Each made substantial contributions to the study of bacilli and spore formation. We mourn the passing of these three friends; they are sorely missed.

The organizers of this conference—P. J. Piggot, P. Youngman, C. P. Moran, Jr., C. W. Price, P. Setlow, R. A. Slepecky, and I. Smith—express their appreciation to the International Spores Conference Advisory Council, R. Dedonder, A. L. Demain, R. H. Doi, A. Galizzi, H. O. Halvorson, F. Kawamura, A. Keynan, H. Levinson, W. Murrell, J. R. Norris, G. Rapoport, H. Saito, V. Vinter, W. M. Waites, and M. Yudkin. The conference was made possible by generous support from the National Science Foundation, the National Institutes of Health, Abbott Laboratories, DuPont, Eniricerche, Entotech, Fujisawa, Genencor, Campbell Soup, Bristol-Myers Squibb, Johnson & Johnson, Lab Line, and Merck Research Laboratories.

The editors express their gratitude to the authors for submitting articles of high quality which required very little editing and they thank their scientific colleagues for helpful discussions and insights regarding the preparation of this book. They give special thanks to Patrick Fitzgerald and Eleanor Tupper of the ASM Publications Department for their patience and assistance in the editing of the book.

Patrick Piggot
Department of Microbiology and Immunology
Temple University School of Medicine
Philadelphia, PA 19140

Charles P. Moran, Jr.
Department of Microbiology and Immunology
Emory University School of Medicine
Atlanta, GA 30322

Philip Youngman
Department of Genetics
University of Georgia
Athens, GA 30602

A NOTE ON NOMENCLATURE

We have not obtained consistency in nomenclature for three terms in common use in the sporulation literature: forespore, prespore, and sporangium. Different authors have used the terms differently for many years. Early soundings by the editors indicated that they were unlikely to achieve a standard usage here. Various usages are outlined below. It is hoped that this cautionary note will reduce confusion for the reader.

"Forespore" and "prespore" are often used interchangeably to mean the cell destined to become the mature spore. Most authors use one rather than the other; "forespore" is more common in North America and "prespore" in Europe. A separate usage reserves "prespore" as the name for the smaller cell present between stages II (septation) and III (engulfment) of sporulation, and "forespore" as the name for the engulfed prespore.

Some authors use "sporangium" to mean the cell that engulfs the forespore/prespore. Thus it has the same meaning as "mother cell." Other authors use "sporangium" to mean mother cell plus forespore/prespore.

Regulation of Bacterial Differentiation
Edited by P. Piggot et al.

Chapter 1

Signal Transduction Network Controlling Degradative Enzyme Synthesis and Competence in *Bacillus subtilis*

Frank Kunst, Tarek Msadek, and Georges Rapoport

Requirements for bacterial survival include the continuous monitoring of changes in the cytoplasm of the cell as well as in its extracellular environment. Signals perceived by sensory proteins or sensor kinases are transmitted to the transcription apparatus, allowing the bacterium to adapt gene expression to the needs of the cell. This adaptation process is called signal transduction. Since two regulatory proteins play a central role in this process, the system has been referred to as a "two-component system," although in many cases more than two regulatory proteins are involved. Such two-component systems have been the subject of several reviews (see references in references 26 and 36).

Typically, the first component is either a membrane-bound or a cytoplasmic histidine protein kinase receiving a signal from the extracellular environment or from the cytoplasm, respectively. The N-terminal part of the protein is probably involved in receiving the signal, which is subsequently transduced via the carboxy-terminal domain of the kinase to the second component, the response regulator, which is generally a transcriptional activator. The common mechanism underlying this signal transduction process involves a phosphotransfer reaction between the two proteins. The protein kinase is first autophosphorylated at a conserved histidine residue in an ATP-dependent reaction. In a second step, the phosphoryl group is transferred to an aspartate residue in the amino-terminal domain of the response regulator. Regulation may therefore take place by modulating either the kinase activity or the phosphatase activity of the

Frank Kunst, Tarek Msadek, and Georges Rapoport, Unité de Biochimie Microbienne, Centre National de la Recherche Scientifique, URA 1300, Institut Pasteur, 25 rue du Docteur Roux, 75724 Paris Cedex 15, France.

protein kinase. However, for reasons of simplicity, members of this family will be designated only as "kinases" in this chapter.

In *Bacillus subtilis* two-component systems have been identified affecting phosphate assimilation (PhoR/PhoP) (41, 42), degradative enzyme synthesis and competence for transformation by exogenous DNA (ComP/ComA and DegS/DegU) (18, 22, 24, 47, 51, 53), chemotaxis (CheA/CheY) (4, 13), and sporulation (two kinases, KinA and KinB, and two response regulators, Spo0F and Spo0A, are involved) (see Chapter 3, this volume).

Proteins in the histidine kinase family possess a conserved C-terminal domain of approximately 250 amino acids involved in autophosphorylation of the protein at a histidine residue (19). PhoR, KinB, and ComP appear to be membrane-bound kinases, whereas DegS, KinA, and CheA are cytoplasmic kinases.

Proteins in the response regulator family possess a highly conserved amino-terminal phosphoacceptor domain. The ComA and DegU response regulators contain carboxy-terminal domains presenting similarities with the UhpA subfamily of response regulators from gram-negative bacteria. Likewise, PhoP belongs to the OmpR subfamily (26, 46). Spo0A is part of a separate subclass, since this protein does not show any similarities in its C-terminal domain with other response regulators. The CheY and Spo0F response regulators lack a carboxy-terminal domain.

REGULATORY GENES (*comP, comA, degS, degU, degQ, degR*)

As mentioned above, two pairs of regulatory proteins, ComP/ComA and DegS/DegU, control the expression of competence genes as well as the synthesis of degradative enzymes, including an intracellular protease and several enzymes which are secreted into the culture medium, such as levansucrase, β-glucanase(s), α-amylase, xylanase, and proteases (1, 3, 23).

The DegU response regulator has been shown to be phosphorylated by the DegS kinase (9, 10, 29, 48) (see below). ComP and ComA show amino acid similarities with the histidine protein kinase and response regulator families, respectively. Additional evidence indicating that ComA is a response regulator was obtained by Roggiani and Dubnau (37a), who showed that ComA could be phosphorylated using acetylphosphate as a phosphate donor. The activities of the DegS and ComP kinases are thought to be modulated by signals from the environment. Some preliminary data, which may eventually be helpful for the subsequent identification of the signal perceived by the ComP protein, will be discussed below. Such a signal may come from the extracellular environment, since the ComP protein has eight potential membrane-spanning segments in the amino-terminal part of the protein (53). The signal perceived by the cytoplasmic DegS protein may originate either from the cytoplasm or from the extracellular environment. In the latter case, one may postulate the existence of an additional transmembrane protein acting as a "sensor" and transmitting a signal to the DegS kinase. A similar case of a cytoplasmic kinase (CheA) receiving signals from membrane receptors (Tar, Tsr, Trg, and Tap) has been described in *Escherichia coli* (for reviews, see references 6 and 45).

The *degS* and *degU* genes are both required for the synthesis of degradative enzymes in *B. subtilis* 168. These two essential regulatory genes as well as two additional accessory regulatory genes, *degQ* and *degR*, encoding small polypeptides of 46 and 60 amino acids, respectively, act at the level of transcription (for reviews, see references 20, 21, 26, and 43). The presence of *degQ* or *degR* on high-copy-number plasmids leads to increased production of degradative enzymes, but deletion of these genes does not lead to any recognizable phenotype (43, 56, 57). The *comP* and *comA* genes are dispensable for degradative enzyme synthesis in the wild-type background of *B. subtilis* 168, but contribute to the expression of degradative enzymes in certain mutants such as *mecA, mecB*, or *degQ*(Hy) mutants (see below). The *degU, comP*, and *comA* genes, but not the *degS* gene, are required for the expression of competence. These genetic data together with in vitro biochemical evidence (see below) indicate that phosphorylated DegU is required for degradative enzyme synthesis, whereas phosphorylated ComA is required for the expression of competence. The effect of DegU on competence is complex and will be discussed below.

TARGET GENES

In addition to competence genes and genes encoding degradative enzymes, other genes have been described as being controlled by the *degS/degU* and *comP/comA* signal transduction pathways. Sporulation regulatory genes and genes involved in flagellar synthesis are probable target genes, since *degU*(Hy) mutants which hyperproduce degradative enzymes are devoid of flagella and are able to sporulate in the presence of glucose. In addition, it has been shown that both *comP* and *degS* can play a role in the sporulation signal transduction system under certain conditions, presumably through crosstalk with the sporulation response regulators (44).

Expression of the *degQ* gene was shown to be controlled by both the ComP/ComA and DegS/DegU two-component systems (25). Recently, Yasbin and coworkers (7, 57a, 58) showed that the competence-specific induced expression of the *recA* gene is also controlled by the *degS/degU* and *comP/comA* systems. The *comP/comA* system controls the expression of *gsiA*, a glucose-starvation-inducible gene (27, 28) and of *srfA*, an operon involved in surfactin biosynthesis (14, 30, 31). Target sites of ComA-dependent regulation have been located through deletion analysis, and a consensus target sequence could be proposed after comparison of DNA regions located upstream from the following *comP/comA* controlled genes: *degQ*, *srfA*, and *gsiA*. A 16-bp region of imperfect dyad symmetry (TTGCGGNN-TCCCGCAN) has been suggested as the likely ComA target site. Site-directed mutagenesis studies have indeed revealed that alteration of positions 3 and 4 of the CCGCAA motif prevent ComA-dependent transcription of *srfA* (31). Furthermore, Roggiani and Dubnau (37a) have shown that phosphorylated ComA binds directly to the *srfA* promoter region.

Precise target sites for DegU-dependent regulation have not as yet been identified. Neither has it been established whether the DegU protein acts directly on genes encoding degradative enzymes or whether this protein exerts its effect indirectly via an intermediate regulatory gene or genes. However, *degU*(Hy) and *degQ*(Hy) mutations leading to hyperproduction of degradative enzymes have been used to locate *cis*-acting target sequences upstream from the promoters of *sacB* (encoding levansucrase) and *aprE* (encoding alkaline protease). Regions essential for transcriptional activation by DegS/DegU or DegQ were located between positions –117 and –96 and positions –164 and –141 with respect to the transcriptional start sites of *sacB* and *aprE*, respectively (15–17). No biochemical evidence yet exists, however, for specific binding of phosphorylated DegU to these target sites. The DegU response regulator controls *sacB* expression at an additional level by increasing the expression of the *sacXY* operon encoding a pair of regulatory genes mediating levansucrase induction (8).

PHOSPHORYLATION OF THE DegU RESPONSE REGULATOR

The presence and the conformation of the DegU response regulator determine the phenotypic changes observed in different *degS* and *degU* mutants. The study of these mutants, described below, led to the characterization of three phenotypically distinct classes:

i. The DegU response regulator is present, but mainly or only in its unphosphorylated form. In this case, degradative enzyme synthesis is deficient but competence is not diminished compared to the wild-type strain (25) (see below).

ii. The DegU response regulator presents an increased rate of phosphorylation or a decreased rate of dephosphorylation. This results in the accumulation of the phosphorylated form of DegU, leading to hyperproduction of degradative enzyme synthesis (Hy phenotype) and to deficiency of competence using the classical procedure (2, 24).
iii. The *degU* gene product is absent, leading to deficiency of both competence and degradative enzyme synthesis (24, 38, 47).

The *degU146* mutant, belonging to class (i), encodes the DegU D56N response regulator, modified within the putative phosphorylation site. This protein was purified, and we showed that it could no longer be phosphorylated by DegS, suggesting that the Asp-56 residue is indeed the phosphorylation site of the DegU protein (9, 10). Expression of competence in this strain, either monitored with the use of a *comG'-'lacZ* fusion or measured as the transformation frequency, was essentially the same as in the wild type in our *B. subtilis* 168 genetic background (25; see below).

A low level or the absence of DegU phosphorylation may also be the consequence of deficiency of DegS kinase activity, as shown after purification of modified DegS proteins from *degS* mutants. The DegS E300K protein is no longer autophosphorylated (48), whereas the DegS A193V protein is still autophosphorylated but is strongly diminished in the subsequent catalytical step, phosphoryltransfer to DegU (10). In both these class (i) mutants degradative enzyme synthesis is abolished, and competence is at the level of the wild-type strain.

degU(Hy) mutants encoding the DegU T98I and DegU V131L response regulators seem to belong to class (ii). This was deduced from preliminary phosphoryltransfer experiments, which consisted of incubating crude extracts containing either wild-type or mutant proteins in the presence of purified DegS and radioactive ATP. A stronger phosphorylation signal was obtained with the modified DegU T98I and DegU V131L proteins as compared to the wild-type DegU protein under these conditions (9). Another class (ii) mutant, *degU32*(Hy), encodes the DegU H12L response regulator, which is phosphorylated by DegS, but has a significantly decreased rate of dephosphorylation as compared to the wild-type DegU protein, with a half-life of 120 min rather than 18 min as determined in vitro (10). This strongly increased stability is consistent with the Hy phenotype of the DegU H12L mutant. Increased stability of phosphorylated DegU may also result from an alteration of the DegS kinase, which also acts as a DegU phosphatase. The DegS G218E and DegS A193V kinases produced by class (ii) *degS*(Hy) mutants are deficient in DegU phosphatase activity (10, 48). This defect is thought to lead to hyperproduction of degradative enzymes.

The role of phosphorylation may be indirect, since mutations have been found in other two-component systems which trigger function in the absence of phosphorylation (for a review, see reference 6). Evidence has been obtained that it is not phosphorylation per se, but rather the multimerization of the phosphorylated effector that induces a conformational change to the active conformation (40, 54). The possible existence of DegU as an oligomer could explain the results obtained by Podvin and Steinmetz (37). These authors introduced a recombinant SPβ phage carrying a wild-type *degU* allele into a *degU32*(Hy) strain. The resulting strain carrying two different *degU* alleles had a lower level of *sacB′-′lacZ* expression as compared to the reference strain containing a single *degU32*(Hy) allele, indicating partial suppression of the hyperproduction phenotype associated with *degU32*. An alternative hypothesis is that the suppression could be the result of competition between wild-type and mutant DegU proteins at the target site. Finally, it cannot be ruled out that, even though phosphorylated DegU is very likely to be an activator of degradative enzyme genes, the unphosphorylated form may have an additional negative effect (37).

Little is known about the putative environmental signal(s) triggering DegU phosphorylation. However, some data are now available concerning the signal(s) triggering expression of *comP/comA*-controlled target genes, as discussed below.

ENVIRONMENTAL CONDITIONS AFFECTING COMPETENCE

Competence responds to signals that are at least in part nutritional. A typical medium used for the development of competence consists of salts, glucose, and amino acids. Competence develops postexponentially in such a medium (see below; for a review, see reference 11). Alternatively, cells can be made competent by growth in defined minimal medium (S7 medium; see references 49 and 50) supplemented with glucose and glutamate. Cells grown in S7 medium appear to be competent throughout growth, with a peak toward the end of the exponential growth phase (Dubnau as cited in reference 39). Competence gene expression is decreased by either the addition of glutamine or the substitution of glycerol for glucose in the competence medium (38). However, competence gene expression is no longer downregulated under these conditions in certain strains in which *comP* is inactivated. This has been shown in a *comP* mutant overexpressing *comA* and in *mec* strains (38; see below). From these data it was deduced that the *comP/comA* system may be involved in detecting the availability of carbon and nitrogen sources (53). Another possibility is that the *comP/comA* system may merely detect the exhaustion of a nitrogen source and that the presence of an efficiently metabolized carbon source such as glucose simply enhances the effect of nitrogen source starvation by producing a more severe imbalance between carbon and nitrogen source utilization.

In addition to the expression of late competence genes such as *comG*, *comC*, and *comDE* (11), the *comP/comA* regulatory system also affects *degQ*, *gsiA*, and *srfA* gene expression as mentioned above. It could thus be expected that *comG'-'lacZ*, *degQ'-'lacZ*, *gsiA'-'lacZ*, and *srfA'-'lacZ* expression might respond similarly under certain growth conditions. This has indeed been observed. For instance, *srfA'-'lacZ* and late competence gene expression are stimulated by glucose and severely repressed by addition of both glucose and glutamine (32–34). In addition, the expression of *comG'-'lacZ* and that of *degQ'-'lacZ* were strongly increased in response to amino acid starvation (see below) (25) and also, but to a lesser degree, in response to ammonium ion starvation (performed as described in references 22a, 27, and 28). Finally, *gsiA'-'lacZ* expression increased in response to both amino acid and ammonium ion starvation (27, 28). Nevertheless, differential regulation of ComA-controlled target genes suggests that additional regulatory systems also control these genes. For instance, glucose has an opposite effect on *degQ'-'lacZ* expression as compared to *srfA'-'lacZ* and *comG'-'lacZ*, since glucose represses the expression of *degQ'-'lacZ*. Moreover, phosphate starvation leads to an increase of *degQ'-'lacZ* expression as opposed to that of *comG'-'lacZ*, which is not affected (Table 1). This result seems to indicate that additional regulatory pathways, which appear to be involved in catabolite repression and phosphate regulation (25), control the expression of *degQ*.

The importance of the nature of the nitrogen source on the expression of late competence genes was further studied by monitoring *comG'-'lacZ* expression in glucose minimal media supplemented with different nitrogen sources. In a minimal medium containing glucose and phosphate in excess as well as casein hydrolysate as the limiting nitrogen source, the expression of *comG'-'lacZ* increases postexponentially (Table 1). This increase may be due to the exhaustion of amino acids. It was also observed (Table 1) that this increase was much stronger under similar conditions using a different medium: glucose minimal medium with potassium glutamate as the sole nitrogen source. This result suggests again that glutamate appears to play an important role in competence gene expression. We compared this result with the classical one-step (5, 55) and two-step (2) procedures used for the development of competence. In the two-step procedure, cells were grown to the early stationary phase in a first medium containing casein hydrolysate, ammonium sulfate, and glucose. The culture was then subjected to a nitrogen shiftdown by dilution in a second

TABLE 1. Dependence of postexponential expression of *comG* and *degQ* on the growth medium containing limiting amounts of nitrogen or phosphate

Gene fusion	Limiting nutrient source in minimal medium[a]	β-Galactosidase (units/mg protein)[c]	
		Exponential phase	Stationary phase
comG'-'lacZ	Casein hydrolysate (0.1%)[a]	20	450
comG'-'lacZ	Potassium glutamate (0.2%)[a]	90	1,700
comG'-'lacZ	Casein hydrolysate (0.1%)[a] + potassium glutamate (0.2%)	20	3,600
comG'-'lacZ	Phosphate[b]	<10	10
degQ'-'lacZ	Casein hydrolysate (0.1%)[a] + potassium glutamate (0.2%)	150	2,300
degQ'-'lacZ	Phosphate[b]	50	1,350

[a]Cells were grown in minimal medium containing 100 mM potassium phosphate at pH 7, 3 mM trisodium citrate, 3 mM $MgSO_4$, 2% glucose, 22 mg/liter ferric ammonium citrate, 50 mg/liter L-tryptophan as the auxotrophic requirement, and the indicated nitrogen sources.

[b]Phosphate starvation experiments were performed as described in reference 25.

[c]The figures represent the mean values of at least three experiments.

minimal medium containing ammonium sulfate as the sole nitrogen source as well as glucose. This procedure was subsequently refined by using a one-step protocol in a medium containing both efficient nitrogen sources (a mixture of nine amino acids) and a poor nitrogen source (ammonium sulfate) (5, 55). We have now developed a similar one-step protocol in which ammonium sulfate is replaced by glutamate, since this amino acid has a stimulatory effect on competence. Cells were grown in a glucose minimal medium (see footnote *a* to Table 1) containing both casein hydrolysate (0.1%) and potassium glutamate (0.2%). Competence in this medium (referred to as modified competence medium or MC medium) reached a maximal value at 60 min after T_0. The effectiveness of this procedure seems to be based on a shift from efficient to poor nitrogen metabolism, as is the case for the classical procedures. However, the growth rate in the modified medium was higher and the observed transformation frequency was systematically higher than that obtained with the classical two-step procedure (2). Apparently, the transition from efficient to slow nitrogen metabolism may be at least one of the signals triggering competence development. This signal may be sensed by the putative ComP kinase or a protein interacting with this kinase.

Using MC medium, we reexamined the competence of three strains: the reference strain 168, a *degU146* strain, and a *degU32*(Hy) mutant. The obtained transformation frequencies were 0.2% for the reference strain, 0.25% for the *degU146* strain (QB4469), and 0.1% for the *degU32*(Hy) strain (QB4664). These frequencies are not significantly different, indicating that all three strains are competent under these conditions, in contrast to strain QB4487, in which the *degU* gene is disrupted (its transformation frequency was reduced 10^3- to 10^4-fold as compared to the reference strain). These results indicate that the *degU32*(Hy) mutant now develops competence in this MC medium in contrast with the results obtained using the classical procedure. In the latter case, the transformation frequency of a *degU32*(Hy) strain was found to be reduced 1000-fold as compared to the reference strain *B. subtilis* 168 (24). This striking phenomenon is as yet not understood and is presently under study.

In conclusion, the results concerning the effect of the *degU* gene and its different mutant alleles on competence may be summarized as follows:

i. The *degU* gene product is required for the development of competence in all conditions we have tested.
ii. The *degU146* allele leading to the synthesis of unphosphorylated DegU allows competence in our genetic background of *B. subtilis* 168. However, using a different genetic background, Dubnau and Hahn (11b) showed that competence was decreased in the IS75 derivative BD1512 (38) carrying the *degU146* mutation as compared to its counterpart carrying the wild-type *degU* allele. These results indicate that the effect of the *degU146* mutation apparently depends on the genetic background used.
iii. The *degU32*(Hy) mutation leads to a decreased genetic competence using the classical procedure both in our genetic background of *B. subtilis* 168 and in the genetic background of IS75 derivatives used by Dubnau and coworkers (38). However, this competence defect depends on the growth medium used for the development of competence, since a *degU32*(Hy) strain could be transformed using the MC medium described above.

At this stage it seems premature to present a specific interpretation of the role of DegU on competence gene expression, which needs to be further investigated at the molecular level. For instance, DNA binding assays may be carried out in order to determine the direct target(s) of this regulatory protein.

REGULATORY NETWORK INCLUDING *comP/comA* AND *degS/degU*

The *comP/comA* regulatory pathway contains additional regulatory genes: *comQ*, *srfA* (also called *comL*) and *comK* (for a review, see reference

11). The *comQ* gene is located just upstream from the *comP* and *comA* genes (25, 52). Possibly, in response to a nitrogen starvation signal, ComP could act in conjunction with ComQ to phosphorylate ComA and allow expression of *srfA* (Fig. 1). This appears to be the major role of the ComP, ComA, and ComQ proteins in the development of competence (14, 35).

Most of the genes which have been identified to date as being controlled by the *degS/degU* two-component system are also controlled by the *comP/comA* system. Examples are *comG, comC, srfA, degQ,* and *recA*. An exception to this pattern is the *gsiA* gene, which is only controlled by *comP/comA* (27). The *degS/degU* and *comP/comA* systems thus seem to act as two parallel regulatory pathways which frequently interact and often appear to form a regulatory network.

Another gene which is controlled by both *comP/comA* and *degS/degU* is the regulatory gene *comK* encoding a competence transcriptional regulator (48b). Since *comK* is a target of both two-component systems affecting degradative enzyme synthesis and competence, we reasoned that both systems might exert their effects via this single intermediate regulatory gene, *comK*. But this is not the case, since a deletion of the *comK* gene did not diminish the level of *sacB'-'lacZ* expression in a *degU32*(Hy) mutant or in the wild-type strain (Table 2, strains QB4719 and QB4632). Therefore, the *degU* gene acts independently from *comK* by increasing the expression of the *sacB* gene and also by activating expression of the *sacXY* operon (8, 25).

In addition to the *degU32* mutation, a *degQ36* mutation increasing the promoter strength of the *degQ* gene leads to hyperproduction of degradative enzymes (25, 56). A second question then arose: is the Hy phenotype due to the *degQ36* mutation affected by the *comK* deletion? Again, no effect was found (22a). Apparently, the *degQ* gene also acts independently from *comK*, at least with respect to the Hy phenotype, despite the fact that its action requires the presence of functional *degS/degU* and *comP/comA* regulatory pairs (25).

PROPERTIES OF *mecA* AND *mecB* MUTANTS

Competence is subject to several levels of control (11):

i. Competence develops in glucose-minimal salts medium and not in complex medium.
ii. Competence develops after the time of transition from the exponential to the stationary phase of growth (T_0).
iii. Maximally competent cultures can be resolved on density gradients into noncompetent and competent cell fractions.

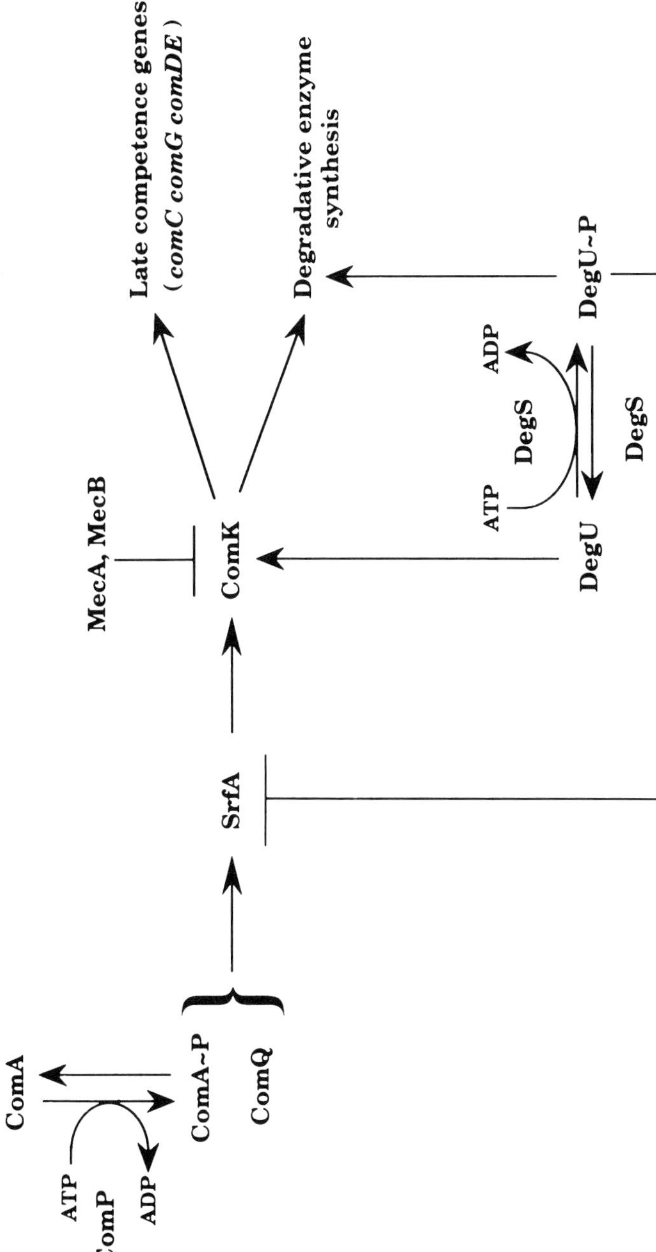

FIGURE 1. Provisional scheme of the regulatory network affecting degradative enzyme synthesis and competence (modified from reference 11). Arrows and perpendicular bars indicate positive and negative regulation, respectively.

TABLE 2. Expression of *sacB′-′lacZ* in different genetic backgrounds[a]

Strain	Relevant genotype		β-Galactosidase (units/mg protein)
QB4624	*amyE*::*sacB′-′lacZ erm*		30
QB4632	*amyE*::*sacB′-′lacZ erm*	Δ *comK*::Cm	30
QB4662	*amyE*::*sacB′-′lacZ erm*	Δ *mecA*::Km	2,100
QB4666	*amyE*::*sacB′-′lacZ erm*	Δ *mecA*::Km Δ *comK*::Cm	160
QB4667	*amyE*::*sacB′-′lacZ erm*	Δ *mecA*::Km *comA124*::Cm	60
QB4664	*amyE*::*sacB′-′lacZ erm*	*degU32*(Hy)	11,000
QB4659	*amyE*::*sacB′-′lacZ erm*	*degU32*(Hy) Δ *mecA*::Sp	5,900
QB4719	*amyE*::*sacB′-′lacZ erm*	*degU32*(Hy) Δ *comK*::Cm	11,000
QB4665	*amyE*::*sacB′-′lacZ erm*	Δ (*degS degU*)::Km	7
QB4658	*amyE*::*sacB′-′lacZ erm*	Δ (*degS degU*)::Km Δ *mecA*::Sp	2,600

[a]Cells were grown in minimal medium containing 2% sucrose, 1% glucose, 100 mM potassium phosphate at pH 7, 25 mM $(NH_4)_2SO_4$, 0.2% potassium glutamate, 0.015% yeast extract, 0.5 mM $MgSO_4$, 0.01 mM $MnSO_4$, 22 mg/liter ferric ammonium citrate, and 50 mg/liter L-tryptophan as the auxotrophic requirement. β-Galactosidase activities were determined 1 h after the end of the exponential growth phase. Double colons indicate gene disruptions by chloramphenicol (Cm), kanamycin (Km), or spectinomycin (Sp) resistance cassettes.

Genetic competence in *B. subtilis* depends on several gene products that mediate binding, processing, and uptake of transforming DNA. The synthesis of these late products depends on regulatory proteins that are encoded by the early competence genes. Among these early genes, *comP, comA, degS,* and *degU* are expressed throughout growth and in all media. The expression of the late genes mirrors the regulation of competence: these genes are not expressed in complex media and are turned on after T_0 and only in the competent cell fraction.

Dubnau and coworkers (12, 38) isolated mutants capable of expressing late competence genes in complex medium, which were called *mec* mutants (for medium-independent expression of competence). The *mec* mutations were mapped on the *B. subtilis* chromosome at two distinct loci: *mecA* was located between *spo0K* and *comK* (11a, 13a) and *mecB* was linked by transformation to the *cysA, spo0H,* and *rpoB* genes. The *mecA* gene appears to act as a negative regulator, since disruption of the gene bypasses the requirement of the early regulatory genes *comP, comA, degS,* and *degU* for the expression of late competence genes (20a). However, it does not bypass the need for *comK* (22a, 48a). These results seem to indicate that the *mecA* gene product may act downstream from the ComP, ComA, DegS, and DegU regulatory proteins, but also that it probably acts prior to ComK

(Fig. 1). This conclusion is supported by recent work demonstrating that *mecA* is in fact a negative regulator of *comK* expression (11b).

Since regulation of competence gene expression and degradative enzyme synthesis are apparently interwoven in *B. subtilis,* we decided to examine the effect of *mecA* and *mecB* mutations on degradative enzyme synthesis. By analogy with late competence gene expression, in which the need for the *degS/degU* regulatory pair was bypassed by *mecA* and *mecB* mutations, we examined whether these mutations would also bypass the requirement of *degS/degU* for *sacB′-′lacZ* expression. This turned out to be the case: β-galactosidase synthesis driven by the *sacB* promoter occurred in the absence of *degS* and *degU* in strain QB4658 due to the deletion of the *mecA* gene (Table 2). Furthermore, the level of *sacB′-′lacZ* expression in this strain was about 80-fold higher than that of the reference (*mecA*$^+$) strain QB4624. We propose that this high level of *sacB′-′lacZ* expression was the consequence of overproduction of the ComK protein, which, in turn, could be ascribed to inactivation of the MecA repressor. Support for this hypothesis came from the observation that *sacB′-′lacZ* expression was low in strain QB4666, in which both *mecA* and *comK* were deleted (Table 2). Although evidence has been obtained that the ComK protein may be a DNA binding protein recognizing targets upstream from late competence genes (11a, 48a), this has not as yet been shown for potential target genes encoding degradative enzymes.

The result that the simultaneous disruption of both the *comA* and *mecA* genes prevents the high level expression of *sacB′-′lacZ* in strain QB4667 (Table 2), despite the absence of a functional MecA repressor, is more difficult to interpret. The *comA* gene is indeed thought to act prior to *mecA* in the regulatory cascade presented in Fig. 1. This was deduced from the result obtained by Dubnau and coworkers (12, 38) that *mecA* and *mecB* mutations completely bypass the need of *comP/comA* for the expression of late competence genes. On the contrary, *comA* is apparently still required to bring about a high level of *sacB′-′lacZ* expression in the absence of a functional *mecA* gene. To explain this difference in regulation of degradative enzyme synthesis and competence expression, which in both cases is thought to be mediated by the ComK protein, one may consider different hypotheses. A trivial hypothesis is that our knowledge of the regulatory cascade is incomplete and that additional (unknown) regulatory genes possibly interact with *comK* to allow differential regulation of degradative enzyme synthesis and competence expression via the *comP, comA, comK* regulatory branch. Another hypothesis is that the ComK protein may bind to sites upstream from the late competence genes as well as to a site upstream from *sacB,* although at a lower affinity in the latter case. A *comA* knockout mutation might then lower the ComK concentration, leading to dissociation of the ComK protein from the weak binding site and thus lowering *sacB* expression. Late competence gene expression would not be affected, since ComK, although present at a lower concentration, would still be able to bind to the high-affinity sites. It should be stressed that these are only working hypotheses and that the available data are not sufficient to clarify this question.

The effects of both *mecA* and *mecB* mutations on both degradative enzyme synthesis and late competence gene expression underscore the pleiotropic nature of these mutations. An additional phenotype was found after we noticed that *mecA* and *mecB* mutants grew in competence minimal medium (2), which contains glucose, ammonium sulfate, and casein hydrolysate (0.02%), but attained a lower optical density compared to the wild-type strain. This suggested a growth defect, which we subsequently identified: a mutant in which *mecA* was disrupted was unable to grow in glucose minimal medium with ammonium sulfate as the sole nitrogen source (Fig. 2). After addition of casein hydrolysate (0.1%) to this medium, growth occurred, albeit at a somewhat slower rate compared to the wild-type strain: generation times of about 60 and 40 min were determined for a *mecA* mutant and a *mecA*$^+$ counterpart, respectively. The growth defect of the *mecA* mutant appears to be related to ComK overproduction, since a mutant in which both *mecA* and *comK* were disrupted grew normally in minimal medium containing ammonium sulfate as the sole nitrogen source and glucose (Fig. 2). However, it is not known whether ComK, when overproduced, has a general toxic effect which is detrimental to the

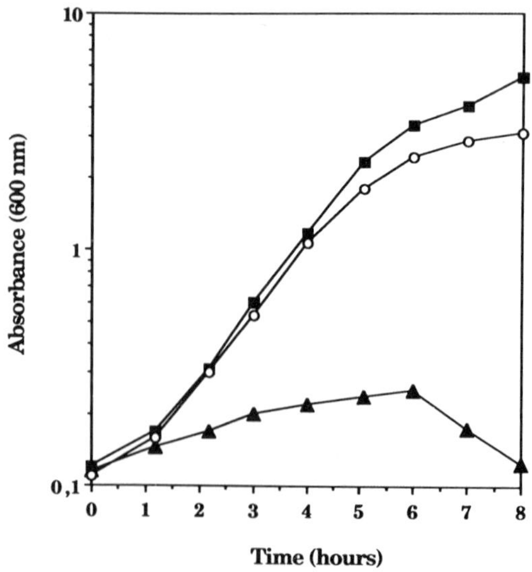

FIGURE 2. Growth defect of a *mecA* mutant in glucose minimal medium. Strains QB4462 (▲) (relevant genotype: Δ*mecA*), QB4666 (○) (relevant genotype: Δ*mecA* Δ*comK*), and 168 (■) (reference strain) were grown in C mineral medium containing 1% glucose, 3 mM trisodium citrate, 20 mM $(NH_4)_2SO_4$, potassium phosphate buffer at pH 7, 3 mM $MgSO_4$, 22 mg/liter ferric ammonium citrate, and 50 mg/liter L-tryptophan as the auxotrophic requirement.

cell, or whether ComK has a more specific negative regulatory effect on the utilization of certain nitrogen sources.

CONCLUSIONS AND PERSPECTIVES

The regulatory network affecting competence expression and degradative enzyme synthesis is composed of at least two regulatory branches, one including the *degS/degU* two-component system and a second one including the *comP/comA* two-component system and the *srfA* operon. In response to an unidentified signal the DegS kinase phosphorylates the DegU response regulator, whose phosphorylated form acts positively on degradative enzyme synthesis and negatively on the expression of late competence genes. The requirement of both *comP* and *comA* to stimulate degradative enzyme synthesis as well as competence under certain conditions, especially in the case of *degQ*(Hy) and *mecA* mutants, seems to indicate that phosphorylated ComA has a positive effect on these two cellular processes. As also suggested by Dubnau (11), we propose that the putative ComP kinase may phosphorylate ComA in response to a nitrogen source starvation signal. How such a signal could be perceived by ComP, whether additional sensor proteins are involved, or whether a nitrogen source starvation signal is the unique signal perceived by ComP remain unanswered questions.

Downstream from ComA in the regulatory cascade affecting late competence gene expression, the *srfA* operon and the *comK* gene have been identified. Likewise, we wondered whether intermediate regulatory genes may exist between DegU and target genes such as *sacB*. This was a particularly attractive hypothesis, since preliminary gel retardation experiments were unsuccessful in showing binding of phosphorylated DegU to the DNA region upstream from *sacB*. This may be due to the fact that DegU may bind upstream from the *sacXY* operon and possibly to an unknown regulatory gene, the products of which would then activate the *sacB* promoter. A preliminary search for mutations in an additional regulatory gene, which would allow expression of *sacB'-'lacZ* in a strain devoid of both *degU* and *comK*, was, however, unsuccessful.

Future efforts are necessary to permit a better understanding of this regulatory network. Experiments will be designed in order to address the following questions:

i. What is the exact nature of the signals to which the DegS/DegU and ComP/ComA systems respond?
ii. What is the DNA target of the DegU protein?
iii. What is the nature of the *mecB* mutations?

Work in progress in different laboratories will no doubt provide information concerning these issues in the near future.

We wish to thank D. Cheo, D. Dubnau, J. Hahn, L. Kong, M. Roggiani, D. van Sinderen, and R. Yasbin for many helpful discussions and for providing us with unpublished data. We are grateful to Joëlle Bignon for expert technical assistance and Christine Dugast for excellent secretarial assistance. Work in our laboratory was supported by funds from the Institut Pasteur, Centre National de la Recherche Scientifique, and Université Paris 7.

REFERENCES

1. **Amory, A., F. Kunst, E. Aubert, A. Klier, and G. Rapoport.** 1987. Characterization of the *sacQ* genes from *Bacillus licheniformis* and *Bacillus subtilis*. *J. Bacteriol.* **169:**324–333.
2. **Anagnostopoulos, C., and J. Spizizen.** 1961. Requirements for transformation in *Bacillus subtilis*. *J. Bacteriol.* **81:**741–746.
3. **Aymerich, S., G. Gonzy-Tréboul, and M. Steinmetz.** 1986. 5′-Noncoding region *sacR* is the target of all identified regulation affecting the levansucrase gene in *Bacillus subtilis*. *J. Bacteriol.* **166:**993–998.
4. **Bischoff, D. S., and G. W. Ordal.** 1991. Sequence and characterization of *Bacillus subtilis* CheB, a homolog of *Escherichia coli* CheY, and its role in a different mechanism of chemotaxis. *J. Biol. Chem.* **266:**12301–12305.
5. **Bott, K. F., and G. A. Wilson.** 1968. Metabolic and nutritional factors influencing the development of competence for transfection of *Bacillus subtilis*. *Bacteriol. Rev.* **32:**370–378.
6. **Bourret, R. B., K. A. Borkovich, and M. I. Simon.** 1991. Signal transduction pathways involving protein phosphorylation in prokaryotes. *Annu. Rev. Biochem.* **60:**401–441.
7. **Cheo, D. L., K. W. Bayles, and R. E. Yasbin.** 1992. Molecular characterization of regulatory elements controlling expression of the *Bacillus subtilis* $recA^{+}$ gene. *Biochimie* **74:**755–762.
8. **Crutz, A. M., and M. Steinmetz.** 1992. Transcription of the *Bacillus subtilis sacX* and *sacY* genes, encoding regulators of sucrose metabolism, is both inducible by sucrose and controlled by the DegS-DegU signalling system. *J. Bacteriol.* **174:**6087–6095.
9. **Dahl, M. K., T. Msadek, F. Kunst, and G. Rapoport.** 1991. Mutational analysis of the *Bacillus subtilis* DegU regulator and its phosphorylation by the DegS protein kinase. *J. Bacteriol.* **173:**2539–2547.
10. **Dahl, M. K., T. Msadek, F. Kunst, and G. Rapoport.** 1992. The phosphorylation state of the DegU response regulator acts as a molecular switch allowing either degradative enzyme synthesis or expression of genetic competence in *Bacillus subtilis*. *J. Biol. Chem.* **267:**14509–14514.
11. **Dubnau, D.** 1991. Genetic competence in *Bacillus subtilis*. *Microbiol. Rev.* **55:**395–424.

11a. **Dubnau, D.** Personal communication.

11b. **Dubnau, D., and J. Hahn.** Personal communication.

12. **Dubnau, D., and M. Roggiani.** 1990. Growth medium-independent genetic competence mutants of *Bacillus subtilis*. *J. Bacteriol.* **172:**4048–4055.

13. **Fuhrer, D. K., and G. W. Ordal.** 1991. *Bacillus subtilis* CheN, a homolog of CheA, the central regulator of chemotaxis in *Escherichia coli. J. Bacteriol.* **173:**7443–7448.
13a. **Grossman, A.** Personal communication.
14. **Hahn, J., and D. Dubnau.** 1991. Growth stage signal transduction and the requirements for *srfA* induction in development of competence. *J. Bacteriol.* **173:**7275–7282.
15. **Henner, D. J., E. Ferrari, M. Perego, and J. A. Hoch.** 1988. Location of the targets of the *hpr-97, sacU32*(Hy), and *sacQ36*(Hy) mutations in upstream regions of the subtilisin promoter. *J. Bacteriol.* **170:**296–300.
16. **Henner, D. J., E. Ferrari, M. Perego, and J. A. Hoch.** 1988. Upstream activating sequences in *Bacillus subtilis,* p. 3–9. *In* A. T. Ganesan and J. A. Hoch (ed.), *Genetics and Biotechnology of Bacilli,* vol. 2. Academic Press, Inc., San Diego, Calif.
17. **Henner, D. J., M. Yang, L. Band, H. Shimotsu, M. Ruppen, and E. Ferrari.** 1987. Genes of *Bacillus subtilis* that regulate the expression of degradative enzymes, p. 81–90. *In* M. Alacevic, D. Hranueli, and Z. Toman (ed.), *Genetics of Industrial Microorganisms.* Proceedings of the Fifth International Symposium on the Genetics of Industrial Microorganisms. Pliva, Zagreb, Yugoslavia.
18. **Henner, D. J., M. Yang, and E. Ferrari.** 1988. Localization of *Bacillus subtilis sacU*(Hy) mutations to two linked genes with similarities to the conserved procaryotic family of two-component signaling systems. *J. Bacteriol.* **170:** 5102–5109.
19. **Hess, J. F., R. B. Bourret, and M. I. Simon.** 1988. Histidine phosphorylation and phosphoryl group transfer in bacterial chemotaxis. *Nature* (London) **336:**139–143.
20. **Klier, A., T. Msadek, and G. Rapoport.** 1992. Positive regulation in the Gram-positive bacterium: *Bacillus subtilis. Annu. Rev. Microbiol.* **46:**429–459.
20a. **Kong, L., K. Jaacks Siranosian, A. D. Grossman, and D. Dubnau.** 1993. Sequence and properties of *mecA,* a negative regulator of genetic competence in *Bacillus subtilis. Mol. Microbiol.* **9:**365–373.
21. **Kunst, F., A. Amory, M. Débarbouillé, I. Martin, A. Klier, and G. Rapoport.** 1988. Polypeptides activating the synthesis of secreted enzymes, p. 27–31. *In* A. T. Ganesan and J. A. Hoch (ed.), *Genetics and Biotechnology of Bacilli,* vol. 2. Academic Press, Inc., San Diego, Calif.
22. **Kunst, F., M. Débarbouillé, T. Msadek, M. Young, C. Mauël, D. Karamata, A. Klier, G. Rapoport, and R. Dedonder.** 1988. Deduced polypeptides encoded by the *Bacillus subtilis sacU* locus share homology with two-component sensor-regulator systems. *J. Bacteriol.* **170:**5093–5101.
22a. **Kunst, F., T. Msadek, and G. Rapoport.** Unpublished data.
23. **Kunst, F., M. Pascal, J. Lepesant-Kejzlarová, J.-A. Lepesant, A. Billault, and R. Dedonder.** 1974. Pleiotropic mutations affecting sporulation conditions and the synthesis of extracellular enzymes in *Bacillus subtilis* 168. *Biochimie* **56:**1481–1489.
24. **Msadek, T., F. Kunst, D. Henner, A. Klier, G. Rapoport, and R. Dedonder.** 1990. Signal transduction pathway controlling synthesis of a class of degradative enzymes in *Bacillus subtilis:* expression of the regulatory genes and analysis of mutations in *degS* and *degU. J. Bacteriol.* **172:**824–834.
25. **Msadek, T., F. Kunst, A. Klier, and G. Rapoport.** 1991. DegS-DegU and ComP-ComA modulator-effector pairs control expression of the *Bacillus subtilis* pleiotropic regulatory gene *degQ. J. Bacteriol.* **173:**2366–2377.

26. **Msadek, T., F. Kunst, and G. Rapoport.** 1993. Two-component regulatory systems, p. 729–745. *In* A. L. Sonenshein, J. A. Hoch, and R. Losick (ed.), *Bacillus subtilis and Other Gram-Positive Bacteria: Biochemistry, Physiology, and Molecular Genetics*. American Society for Microbiology, Washington, D.C.
27. **Mueller, J. P., G. Bukusoglu, and A. L. Sonenshein.** 1992. Transcriptional regulation of *Bacillus subtilis* glucose starvation-inducible genes: control of *gsiA* by the ComP-ComA signal transduction system. *J. Bacteriol.* **174:**4361–4373.
28. **Mueller, J. P., C. Mathiopoulos, F. J. Slack, and A. L. Sonenshein.** 1991. Identification of *Bacillus subtilis* adaptive response genes by subtractive differential hybridization. *Res. Microbiol.* **142:**805–813.
29. **Mukai, K., M. Kawata, and T. Tanaka.** 1990. Isolation and phosphorylation of the *Bacillus subtilis degS* and *degU* gene products. *J. Biol. Chem.* **265:**20000–20006.
30. **Nakano, M. M., R. Magnuson, A. Myers, J. Curry, A. D. Grossman, and P. Zuber.** 1991. *srfA* is an operon required for surfactin production, competence development, and efficient sporulation in *Bacillus subtilis*. *J. Bacteriol.* **173:**1770–1778.
31. **Nakano, M. M., L. A. Xia, and P. Zuber.** 1991. Transcription initiation region of the *srfA* operon, which is controlled by the *comP-comA* signal transduction system in *Bacillus subtilis*. *J. Bacteriol.* **173:**5487–5493.
32. **Nakano, M. M., and P. Zuber.** 1989. Cloning and characterization of *srfB*, a regulatory gene involved in surfactin production and competence in *Bacillus subtilis*. *J. Bacteriol.* **171:**5347–5353.
33. **Nakano, M. M., and P. Zuber.** 1990. Identification of genes required for the biosynthesis of the lipopeptide antibiotic surfactin in *Bacillus subtilis*, p, 397–405. *In* M. M. Zukowski, A. T. Ganesan, and J. A. Hoch (ed.), *Genetics and Biotechnology of Bacilli*, vol. 3. Academic Press, Inc., San Diego, Calif.
34. **Nakano, M. M., and P. Zuber.** 1990. Molecular biology of antibiotic production in *Bacillus*. *Crit. Rev. Biotechnol.* **10:**223–240.
35. **Nakano, M. M., and P. Zuber.** 1991. The primary role of ComA in establishment of the competent state in *Bacillus subtilis* is to activate expression of *srfA*. *J. Bacteriol.* **173:**7269–7274.
36. **Parkinson, J. S., and E. C. Kofoid.** 1992. Communication modules in bacterial signaling proteins. *Annu. Rev. Genet.* **26:**71–112.
37. **Podvin, L., and M. Steinmetz.** 1992. A *degU*-containing SPβ prophage complements superactivator mutations affecting the *Bacillus subtilis degSU* operon. *Res. Microbiol.* **143:**559–567.
37a. **Roggiani, M., and D. Dubnau.** 1993. ComA, a phosphorylated response regulator protein of *Bacillus subtilis*, binds to the promoter region of *srfA*. *J. Bacteriol.* **175:**3182–3187.
38. **Roggiani, M., J. Hahn, and D. Dubnau.** 1990. Suppression of early competence mutations in *Bacillus subtilis* by *mec* mutations. *J. Bacteriol.* **172:**4056–4063.
39. **Rudner, D. Z., J. R. LeDeaux, K. Ireton, and A. D. Grossman.** 1991. The *spo0K* locus of *Bacillus subtilis* is homologous to the oligopeptide permease locus and is required for sporulation and competence. *J. Bacteriol.* **173:**1388–1398.
40. **Scarlato, V., A. Prugnola, B. Aricó, and R. Rappuoli.** 1990. Positive transcriptional feedback at the *bvg* locus controls expression of virulence factors in *Bordetella pertussis*. *Proc. Natl. Acad. Sci. USA* **87:**6753–6757.

41. **Seki, T., H. Yoshikawa, H. Takahashi, and H. Saito.** 1987. Cloning and nucleotide sequence of *phoP,* the regulatory gene for alkaline phosphatase and phosphodiesterase in *Bacillus subtilis. J. Bacteriol.* **169:**2913–2916.
42. **Seki, T., H. Yoshikawa, H. Takahashi, and H. Saito.** 1988. Nucleotide sequence of the *Bacillus subtilis phoR* gene. *J. Bacteriol.* **170:**5935–5938.
43. **Smith, I.** 1993. Regulatory proteins that control late-growth development, p. 785–800. *In* A. L. Sonenshein, J. A. Hoch, and R. Losick (ed.), *Bacillus subtilis and Other Gram-Positive Bacteria: Biochemistry, Physiology, and Molecular Genetics.* American Society for Microbiology, Washington, D.C.
44. **Smith, I., E. Dubnau, M. Predich, U. Bai, and R. Rudner.** 1992. Early *spo* gene expression in *Bacillus subtilis:* the role of interrelated signal transduction systems. *Biochimie* **74:**669–678.
45. **Stock, J. B., G. S. Lukat, and A. M. Stock.** 1991. Bacterial chemotaxis and the molecular logic of intracellular signal transduction networks. *Annu. Rev. Biophys. Biophys. Chem.* **20:**109–136.
46. **Stock, J. B., A. J. Ninfa, and A. M. Stock.** 1989. Protein phosphorylation and regulation of adaptive responses in bacteria. *Microbiol. Rev.* **53:**450–490.
47. **Tanaka, T., and M. Kawata.** 1988. Cloning and characterization of *Bacillus subtilis iep,* which has positive and negative effects on production of extracellular proteases. *J. Bacteriol.* **170:**3593–3600.
48. **Tanaka, T., M. Kawata, and K. Mukai.** 1991. Altered phosphorylation of *Bacillus subtilis* DegU caused by single amino acid changes in DegS. *J. Bacteriol.* **173:**5507–5515.
48a. **Van Sinderen, D.** Personal communication.
48b. **Van Sinderen, D., and D. Dubnau.** Personal communication.
49. **Vasantha, N., and E. Freese.** 1979. The role of manganese in growth and sporulation of *Bacillus subtilis. J. Gen. Microbiol.* **112:**329–336.
50. **Vasantha, N., and E. Freese.** 1980. Enzyme changes during *Bacillus subtilis* sporulation caused by deprivation of guanine nucleotides. *J. Bacteriol.* **144:** 1119–1125.
51. **Weinrauch, Y., N. Guillen, and D. A. Dubnau.** 1989. Sequence and transcription mapping of *Bacillus subtilis* competence genes *comB* and *comA,* one of which is related to a family of bacterial regulatory determinants. *J. Bacteriol.* **171:**5362–5375.
52. **Weinrauch, Y., T. Msadek, F. Kunst, and D. Dubnau.** 1991. Sequence and properties of *comQ,* a new competence regulatory gene of *Bacillus subtilis. J. Bacteriol.* **173:**5685–5693.
53. **Weinrauch, Y., R. Penchev, E. Dubnau, I. Smith, and D. Dubnau.** 1990. A *Bacillus subtilis* regulatory gene product for genetic competence and sporulation resembles sensor protein members of the bacterial two-component signal-transduction systems. *Genes Dev.* **4:**860–872.
54. **Weiss, V., F. Claverie-Martin, and B. Magasanik.** 1992. Phosphorylation of nitrogen regulator-I of *Escherichia coli* induces strong cooperative binding to DNA essential for activation of transcription. *Proc. Natl. Acad. Sci. USA* **89:** 5088–5092.
55. **Wilson, G. A., and K. F. Bott.** 1968. Nutritional factors influencing the development of competence in the *Bacillus subtilis* transformation system. *J. Bacteriol.* **95:**1439–1449.
56. **Yang, M., E. Ferrari, E. Chen, and D. J. Henner.** 1986. Identification of the pleiotropic *sacQ* gene of *Bacillus subtilis. J. Bacteriol.* **166:**113–119.

57. **Yang, M., H. Shimotsu, E. Ferrari, and D. J. Henner.** 1987. Characterization and mapping of the *Bacillus subtilis prtR* gene. *J. Bacteriol.* **169:**434–437.

57a. **Yasbin, R. E., and D. Cheo.** Personal communication.

58. **Yasbin, R. E., D. L. Cheo, and K. W. Bayles.** 1992. Inducible DNA repair and differentiation in *Bacillus subtilis:* interactions between global regulons. *Mol. Microbiol.* **6:**1263–1270.

Regulation of Bacterial Differentiation
Edited by P. Piggot et al.

Chapter 2

Regulation of Gene Expression at the Onset of Stationary Phase in *Escherichia coli*

Gjalt Huisman and Roberto Kolter

In the presence of ample nutrients and optimal conditions, *Escherichia coli* is able to grow with a generation time of 20 to 30 min. In principle, 24 h of unrestricted growth at such a rate would yield over 1,000 tons of biomass starting from a single cell. However, because of constraints in the amount of substrate that can be made available to such a culture, nutrient limitation will retard growth and eventually growth will stop completely. In the natural environment bacteria seldom are able to sustain prolonged periods of growth but rather spend most of their existence alternating between long periods of nongrowth and short periods of growth.

In order to survive *E. coli* must be able to adapt to conditions found in two ecosystems. In the intestinal tract of mammals the availability of growth substrate is related to the feeding pattern of the host. Whereas physical conditions for growth, such as temperature and pH, are near optimal in this environment, nutrient limitation often prevents growth. In contrast the other *E. coli* habitat, the environment outside the host, is extremely variable in physical conditions, since temperature, pH, and osmolarity change rapidly. In addition, the supply of nutrients usually undergoes drastic fluctuations.

The variable conditions *E. coli* encounters require an adequate and sensitive system which allows fast adjustment in order to prepare for and survive harsh conditions. To do so, *E. coli* redirects its metabolism from one that sustains growth to one that maintains viability during starvation conditions. This redirection is accomplished through the induction of a set of proteins at the onset of starvation (26, 46). An equally important adapta-

---

Gjalt Huisman and Roberto Kolter, Department of Microbiology and Molecular Genetics, Harvard Medical School, 200 Longwood Avenue, Boston, Massachusetts 02115.

tion is the ability to resume growth when conditions once again permit it. This step also requires the expression of a specific set of proteins (64).

PHYSIOLOGICAL CHANGES IN A STARVED *E. COLI* CULTURE

Cessation of growth can be brought about in many different ways. However, starvation by exhaustion of a specific nutrient such as nitrogen, carbon, phosphate, sulfate, oxygen, or micronutrients is intrinsically different from growth cessation due to physical challenges such as heat shock, osmotic shock, oxidative shock, or pH shock. Nutritional starvation conditions tend to be encountered by a population in a gradual fashion and do not necessarily lead to damage of essential macromolecules like that generated by the sudden impact of physical challenges. Growing cells are able to respond quickly to physical stresses by induction of specific stress regulons such as OxyR, SoxRS, and alternative sigma factors such as σ^{32}. However, during prolonged starvation, cells cannot rapidly build up protection against physical stresses because of their low metabolic capacity. It thus makes sense that at the onset of starvation cells prepare in advance by inducing multiple increased resistances for the possibility of encountering environmental assaults.

When cultures enter stationary phase because of exhaustion of carbon, nitrogen, or phosphate, the synthesis of at least fifty to seventy proteins is induced (26). Although each specific starvation condition leads to the induction of a specific set of proteins, a core set of proteins has been found to be always induced during starvation, regardless of which nutrient is exhausted (46). It is likely that some of these proteins are important for the development of increased resistance to several physical stresses that is characteristic of starved *E. coli* (36). It has been shown that synthesis of new proteins in stationary phase requires the degradation of existing ones (55). Degradation of proteins synthesized during carbon starvation is Clp-dependent (16). When the cells are not able to synthesize amino acids efficiently de novo, they utilize proteins and peptides as a reservoir of amino acids.

The *E. coli* cell undergoes dramatic changes when growth ceases (Fig. 1). In the cell envelope, unsaturated fatty acids of phospholipids are converted to the cyclopropyl derivatives (13). The physiological implications of this change remain unknown. Overexpression of the *cfa* gene, which encodes the cyclopropane fatty acid synthase, results in the formation of the corresponding fatty acids during growth but does not cause any anomalies in the growth of the strain nor in a number of stationary-phase phenotypes (27, 28). The phospholipid composition of the membranes is

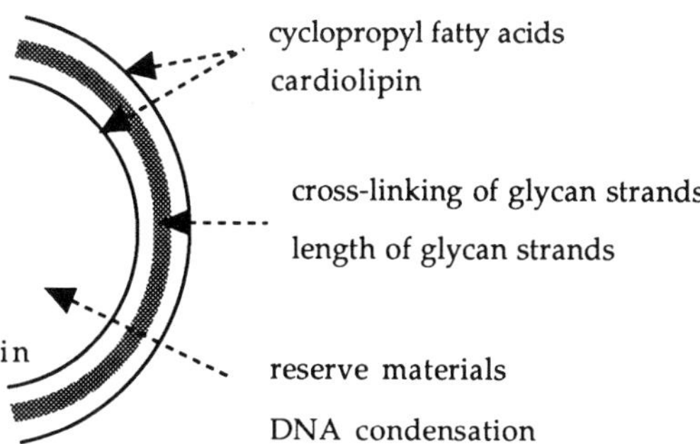

FIGURE 1. Schematic of the major cellular components that undergo changes upon entry into stationary phase.

also altered. The phosphatidylethanolamine concentration decreases concomitant with an increase in cardiolipin during early stationary phase (14). Changes in the cell wall are apparent in starved cells as well (74). Chemostat studies showed an increase in glycan strand cross-linking and shorter glycan strands as a result of large decreases in the growth rate. These changes were correlated with increases in the amounts of disaccharide tripeptides due to increased levels of penicillin binding proteins (PBP) 3, 5, and 6. At the same time disaccharide tetrapeptide and *bis*-disaccharide tetrapeptide fractions decreased as a result of a decline in the levels of PBPs 1a, 1b, and 4.

One of the most remarkable intracellular processes initiated at the onset of stationary phase is the deposit of reserve materials. Depending on the cause of growth cessation, microorganisms accumulate polymeric materials like glycogen, poly(3-hydroxyalkanoate)s (PHB, PHV, PHA), polyphosphate, or polysulfur (67). Glycogen metabolism has been well-studied in *E. coli* on both the physiological and the genetic level (53, 58). A detailed model for its synthesis and degradation is now available and has proven helpful in the manipulation of starch-synthesizing plants such as potato or maize (66).

The structural alterations in the envelope of stationary-phase cells and the accumulation of reserve materials exemplify the strategy that gram-negative bacteria utilize to ensure survival by encapsulating in a protective shell with intracellular energy supplies. Thus protected against diverse stresses, they are more likely to survive for longer periods of time.

SURVIVAL OF *E. COLI* IN STATIONARY PHASE: ISOLATION OF *sur* GENES

The existence of genes whose products are involved in survival of stationary phase in rich medium was supported by the isolation of the mutants that, while appearing normal during logarithmic growth, failed to survive prolonged periods in stationary phase (71). One such mutant strain, harboring a mutation in *surA,* distinguishes itself from the wild type in that it loses viability completely within a 5-day period after reaching stationary phase in LB medium (71). In contrast, the viability of the wild-type strain stabilizes at about 10^8 CFU/ml, after reaching a maximum of about 5×10^9 CFU/ml after overnight incubation. The *surA1* mutation was mapped to minute 1 of the *E. coli* chromosome, where it forms an operon with *pdxA, ksgA, apaG,* and *apaH.* The primary structure of the SurA protein as deduced from the nucleotide sequence of *surA* suggests that the protein may be localized to the periplasm. In addition, the properties of dying *surA1* cells suggest that the primary defect in these mutants is in the cell wall (4a).

In a search for mutants unable to survive glucose starvation we identified the *surB* locus (64). The phenotype of cells harboring null mutations in *surB* is very interesting because viability per se is not affected. The mutants remain viable during starvation, but having entered stationary phase, they are unable to exit it (aerobically) at high temperatures (≥37°C). The function of the *surB* gene product appears to be related to the proper assembly of cytochrome *d* (64). The *surB* gene is located in minute 18 of the *E. coli* chromosome and encodes a cytoplasmic membrane protein that contains an ATP-binding cassette typical of many membrane proteins involved in diverse translocation processes (34). One possibility is that SurB functions to translocate and properly localize the heme *d* moiety of the cytochrome complex and that this step is necessary for the proper sensing of nutritional changes under the conditions tested. Although the primary defect in *surB* mutants is their inability to resume growth, analysis of the *surB1* mutant indicates that the ability to recover from starvation depends on events that occur when cells are entering stationary phase. The ability to exit from stationary phase and resume normal growth depends on proper SurB function early during stationary phase, because the temperature-sensitive phenotype of the mutant depends on whether cells enter stationary phase at the permissive or nonpermissive temperature.

THE σ^s REGULON

Identification of *rpoS*

In their studies on expression of different catalases in *E. coli,* Loewen and coworkers isolated mutants that did not express a starvation-induced catalase (44). *E. coli* is equipped with two catalases, HPI and HPII. The first enzyme is encoded by the *katG* gene and is expressed as a member of the *oxyR* regulon (12). Expression thus depends on induction by reactive oxygen species, such as hydrogen peroxide. HPII is expressed during stationary phase and is independent of the *oxyR* regulon. The genetic approach to identifying the gene that encodes HPII resulted in the identification of two genes, *katE* and *katF*. *katE* encodes the structural gene for the hydrogen peroxidase HPII and is located at minute 37 in the *E. coli* genetic map. The *katF* gene was mapped in minute 59 (44). The predicted amino acid sequence of the *katF* product shows extensive similarities to the major sigma factor, σ^{70}, suggesting its function as an alternative sigma factor (48). Independent studies on the regulation of expression of the acid phosphatase gene, *appA*, identified *appR* as a regulatory locus (73). This locus was later shown to be identical to *katF* and to encode an important regulator of stationary-phase gene expression (41). These observations have been extended by the identification of many starvation-inducible genes whose expression is under the control of this locus. More recently, Ishihama and coworkers have provided biochemical evidence indicating that the *katF* gene product acts as a sigma factor with core RNA polymerase (69). Thus we refer to the gene as *rpoS* and its product as σ^s.

Analysis of protein synthesis in an *rpoS* mutant and its isogenic parent identified at least 32 proteins whose synthesis during carbon starvation depends on σ^s (47a). In addition, synthesis of approximately 10 proteins appears to be repressed by σ^s during stationary phase.

Members (and Classes) of the σ^s Regulon

The number of identified genes whose expression depends on σ^s continues to increase. In addition to those mentioned in the preceding section, σ^s also regulates *mcc* (19), *xthA* (59), *dps* (4), *glgS* (30), *treA* (31), *otsAB* (23, 31), *osmB* (38), *osmE* (28a), *osmY* (77), *bolA* (8, 40), and *ftsQ* (72a). Based on the biological function and patterns of expression of these genes, it appears that several classes of σ^s-dependent genes exist.

General Stress Resistance. Analysis of an *rpoS* mutant strain under a series of stresses demonstrated that the *rpoS* gene product is involved in resistance against pH, oxidative, and heat shocks in starved cells (41, 47a). The *katE, xth, dps, appA,* and *mcc* genes comprise a class that encodes proteins involved in such general starvation-induced stress resistances. As discussed above, *katE* encodes a hydrogen peroxidase (43). The *xthA* gene encodes exonuclease III and is involved in DNA repair after damage by hydrogen peroxide and thus, indirectly, near-UV irradiation (56). *appA* encodes an acid phosphatase (17). The *mcc* genes are the plasmid-borne genes required for the production of the peptide antibiotic microcin C7 (51). The *dps* gene encodes a highly expressed DNA binding protein that appears to protect the DNA from attack by hydrogen peroxide in vivo (4). The conservation of amino acid sequence between Dps and proteins from *Treponema pallidum, Anabaena variabilis,* and *Streptomyces aureofaciens* suggests that proteins with a similar role are well-conserved among eubacteria.

Osmolarity Protection. *treA, otsBA, osmB, osmE,* and *osmY* are all involved in responding to osmotic challenge and constitute a second class of σ^s-dependent genes. The *ots* genes encode enzymes that synthesize trehalose in the cytoplasm (23). Trehalose is subsequently exported to the periplasm and the *treA* gene product is a trehalase that acts in that compartment (9). *treA* is not induced by the presence of trehalose, but only by changes in osmolarity. Whereas a *treA::TnphoA* fusion is still induced in an *rpoS* insertion mutant, the *otsAB* genes are completely σ^s-dependent. Thus the induction of these genes is always σ^s-dependent and expression in the exponential growth phase after osmotic shock is a demonstration that σ^s can be active during growth (32). It is known that trehalose has protective properties on proteins and membranes and as such increases the thermotolerance of a variety of organisms (7, 75). Because of the dual regulation of the genes involved in its metabolism, trehalose appears to be not just an osmoprotectant, but a general stress protectant. The *csi-5* locus has been identified as a *lacZ* fusion induced in stationary phase (29). The product of *csi-5* was shown to be identical to OsmY, a periplasmic protein which is in addition induced under hyperosmotic conditions (77). OsmB is an outer membrane lipoprotein expressed upon both osmotic shock and starvation (38). The *osmB* gene is preceded by two transcriptional start sites. The major promoter allows basal levels of expression and further elevation upon osmotic shock or stationary-phase conditions. The minor promoter is only functional when both inducing conditions are present at the same time. It must be emphasized, however, that not all genes induced by high osmolarity are σ^s-dependent (15). For example, *proU, betT,* and *betB,* as well as *ompC,* do not depend on σ^s.

Morphogenes and Cell Division. A third group of σ^s-dependent genes is formed by *bolA* and *ftsQAZ,* which are involved in cell morphology and cell division. Obviously, cell division is a major process which is altered when growth ceases. Cells from a stationary-phase culture are often smaller in size and more spherical than growing cells (40). The *bolA* gene was isolated as a gene that, when overexpressed, resulted in the formation of small spherical cells. This phenotype is similar to what is observed when PBP5, a D-alanine carboxypeptidase, is overexpressed or PBP2 is not active (1). Analysis of a *bolA* mutant identified another D-alanine carboxypeptidase (PBP6) as one of the proteins which is likely to be expressed in a BolA-dependent fashion and which may confer the spherical phenotype. The *ftsQ* gene is part of the *ftsQAZ* operon in a cell division gene cluster at minute 2.5 of the *E. coli* map. Expression of *ftsQ* partly results from transcription of a σ^s-dependent promoter (72a). The function of FtsQ is not known, but the protein is thought to participate in septation through interaction with other proteins, among them FtsA and FtsZ (72). FtsA has been shown to interact with the periplasmic PBP3, and its primary structure shows sequence similarity with a class of ATPases (10). FtsZ is a GTP binding protein that is able to form contracting rings at the site of cell division (18, 54). Homologs of *ftsA* and *ftsZ* have been characterized from *Bacillus subtilis,* in which they are involved in septation in vegetative cells as well as in the formation of the asymmetric septum during sporulation (25).

The *ftsQ* gene is preceded by a so-called "gearbox promoter" consensus sequence (2). This sequence, CTGCAA-N_{14-17}-CGGCAAGT, has been proposed as a consensus sequence for some stationary-phase inducible genes. Indeed the sequence is also present upstream of genes *bolA, mcbA,* and *ftsAZ* (2). However, this sequence does not define the σ^s consensus because the *mcbA* gene contains one and its expression is σ^s-independent (8, 40). Instead *mcbA* expression requires the vegetative sigma factor σ^{70}.

Stationary-Phase Induction Independent of σ^s

It is clear that σ^s is not the only regulatory molecule controlling the induction of transcription during stationary phase. Induction of approximately twenty of the proteins induced by carbon starvation is *rpoS*-independent, as judged by two-dimensional gel electrophoresis (47). Three heat shock proteins (DnaK, GroEL, and HtpG) are induced during starvation, but their expression depends on σ^{32} rather than on σ^s (65).

Expression of several genes that are induced in response to glucose starvation depends on cAMP and is independent of the *rpoS* gene product (46). An example of this class of genes is *cstA. cstA* is located at minute 14 and encodes a 60-kDa protein whose primary structure suggests an involvement in peptide uptake (62). In coupled transcription/translation experiments *cstA* is expressed in the presence of cAMP by an RNA polymerase containing σ^{70}. Deletion of the cAMP receptor protein binding site upstream of *cstA* abolishes induction by carbon depletion. Although not directly involved in the development of increased resistance during starvation, the *cst* genes have to be considered as potential stationary-phase exit pathways. Cst proteins may increase the chances for the cell to scavenge any potential carbon source when concentrations are low. Similar nutrient scavenging systems are turned on during nitrogen and phosphate starvation (68).

In addition, the stationary-phase induction of the glycogen biosynthetic genes *glgB* and *glgC* is cAMP- and ppGpp-dependent and under the control of a negative regulatory molecule, the product of the *csrA* gene (57, 58). Recently, *glgS* has been identified as a σ^s-controlled gene involved in glycogen synthesis, because its gene product may act as a proteinaceous primer (30). At the first step in the biosynthetic pathway leading to glycogen accumulation, expression of the *pckA* gene, encoding phosphoenolpyruvate carboxykinase, is also growth-phase-controlled (24). This enzyme catalyzes the first reaction in gluconeogenesis and as such plays an important role in the assimilation of scarce carbon sources into essential molecules. Its expression is cAMP-dependent, suggesting that it is independent of σ^s.

Microcin B17 is a ribosomally synthesized antibiotic whose production requires the *mcbA-G* genes (21, 22, 60). Although microcin B17 production is induced during stationary phase, transcription of the *mcb* genes is not dependent on σ^s (8, 40). In fact, the *mcbA* transcription is stimulated by the OmpR activator (33) and requires σ^{70}-RNA polymerase in vitro (8). Deletion analysis has shown that the OmpR activation site is located between positions –117 and –54 from the start of transcription whereas stationary-phase induction is exerted through the sequences located between –54 and +11. From these results we conclude that expression of genes during stationary phase is not always stimulated by σ^s. In fact it has been found that *mcbA* expression is slightly repressed by σ^s; its induced levels increase twofold in an *rpoS* mutant strain (8).

REGULATION OF THE σ^s-DEPENDENT STATIONARY-PHASE RESPONSE

Analysis of *lacZ* Fusions

One explanation for the observed induction of σ^s-dependent genes during the onset of stationary phase is that active σ^s is not present in growing cells. If this is indeed the case, there must be regulation of σ^s activity during the transition from exponential growth to stationary phase. Genetic evidence is accumulating suggesting that the level of active σ^s in the cell may be regulated at various levels: transcriptional, translational, and posttranslational. Most of this evidence comes from studies of *lacZ* fusions to *rpoS* and different σ^s-dependent genes.

Transcriptional fusions are available for *katE, bolA, osmB, osmE, treA, otsBA, mccC, ftsQ,* and *glgS*. Analysis of β-galactosidase activity as a function of time for a growing culture shows that transcription of these genes initiates during the transition between exponential growth and stationary phase. Expression of these genes coincides with the appearance of functional gene products, supporting the notion that most of the regulation in this regulon is at the level of transcription. In contrast, the regulation of expression of *rpoS* itself appears to be different.

Studies by different laboratories using transcriptional and translational *rpoS-lacZ* fusions have led to somewhat different and slightly conflicting results (41, 45, 47, 49, 61). Analysis of transcriptional *lacZ* fusions to *rpoS* demonstrated that regulation of *rpoS* transcription is complex. Several groups have shown that in rich medium *rpoS* transcription initiates during the late exponential phase and increases until stationary phase has been reached (41, 49). The induction of the σ^s-dependent transcription of a *katE-lacZ* fusion is slightly delayed relative to *rpoS* transcription, suggesting that transcription of *rpoS* is not all that is needed to activate at least some members of the regulon (49). Examination of *rpoS-lacZ* transcriptional fusions in minimal medium with glucose or succinate as a carbon source indicates that under such conditions *rpoS* expression increases throughout exponential growth (49). Expression of *katE* follows that of *rpoS*, but does not reach the levels obtained in rich medium.

A point of controversy, however, is the overall effect of glucose on *rpoS* expression. Mulvey et al. report expression of an *rpoS-lacZ* fusion in M9-glucose minimal medium to levels higher than in LB medium (49). Lange and Hengge-Aronis on the other hand show a complete absence of induction of their *rpoS-lacZ* fusion upon glucose exhaustion in M9-glucose minimal medium (41). In addition, expression of *rpoS* and *bolA* (indirectly through σ^s) is repressed upon addition of cAMP.

Not surprisingly, medium composition has a clear impact on the expression of the σ^s regulon. A further illustration of the role of the medium in the regulation of the σ^s regulon comes from transcriptional studies under different nutrient limitation conditions. In an experiment in which growth ceased because of either nitrogen or carbon limitation, different non-correlating levels of expression of the *katE* and *rpoS* fusion were observed (49). Upon transfer of exponentially growing cells to medium lacking a carbon source, *rpoS* was induced up to 45% of the levels obtained when cells enter stationary phase because of exhaustion of the medium. However, under these conditions *katE* was induced up to only 6% of its fully induced level. In contrast, transfer to a medium without a nitrogen source resulted in full induction of both fusions.

Using different metabolites, Mulvey et al. and Schellhorn and Stones attempted to identify an extracellular inducer for the σ^s regulon (49, 61). In both studies weak acids were found to stimulate the regulon. However, whereas the studies by Schellhorn and Stones identified acetate and propionate among the inducers, Mulvey et al. found no effect with these compounds. As discussed below, for theoretical reasons acetate is an attractive candidate to initiate some kind of signaling pathway in the induction of the σ^s regulon.

The lag time between transcription of *rpoS* and that of its dependent genes is partly caused by delayed translation of the messenger (45, 47). This temporal delay is expanded when *rpoS* transcription is induced by the supplementation of sodium benzoate as an inducer. In its presence expression of the *rpoS* transcriptional fusion is observed during growth, whereas σ^s-dependent genes are not expressed until stationary phase (45).

In conclusion, studies on transcription and translation of *rpoS* from different laboratories show that *rpoS* expression is complex. Analysis of the data shows that many factors are involved in σ^s-dependent transcription and that additional studies are required to reconcile the differences observed and to understand the mechanism of σ^s regulation.

Possible Metabolic Triggers of the σ^s Regulon

The induction of the σ^s regulon at the onset of stationary phase requires a signal (or signals) that triggers *rpoS* expression in response to starvation. The question is whether all nutrient limitations elicit the same signal to initiate the response or whether different signals are converted to a common σ^s regulon start point. Several possible triggers have been suggested to date.

Methylation of elongation factor Tu (EF-Tu) has been shown to occur at the end of exponential growth when nutrients are depleting (78, 79). The current view on the function of EF-Tu methylation is that nutrient exhaustion is sensed by some nutrient sensor in the membrane and that this signal is subsequently transduced to the membrane-bound EF-Tu molecule. (The sensing of exhaustion of different nutrients could be funneled through a mechanism able to sense the subtle fluctuations in the components of the proton motive force [ΔpH and $\Delta\psi$] that occur at the onset of starvation [63].) As a consequence, methylated EF-Tu is released from the membrane and exerts its regulatory control either on the level of translation or as a repressor of transcription. Similar results have been obtained from analysis of the methylation of EF-Tu in *B. subtilis* and imply a role of the protein in sporulation (79). Interestingly, the primary structure shares significant sequence similarity with several eukaryotic GTP-binding proteins, such as H-*ras* p21 (79). The structural homology together with functional homologies in autophosphorylation of EF-Tu and H-*ras* p21 suggests a fundamental role for this enzyme in bacteria as a sensor of changing growth conditions.

The concentration of the phosphonucleotides guanosine tetraphosphate (ppGpp) and diadenosine tetraphosphate (ApppppA) changes drastically in response to stress (11, 37). When *E. coli* cells are exposed to heat shock or to oxidative shock the intracellular levels of ApppppA increase at least 100-fold (37). Since mutants deficient in ApppppA hydrolase (*apaH*) do not constitutively express heat shock proteins and overexpression of ApaH does not affect induction of these genes, ApppppA is considered a modulator of this stress response (37). As a modulator it may regulate activities of proteins like DnaK and GroEL to which it binds. This process could in turn lead to fluctuations in the phosphorylation state of DnaK, which have been related to the activity of the heat shock response sigma factor, σ^{32} (42). In an analogous way, but through the modification of another protein, ApppppA and ppGpp could act to modulate σ^{s} activity. The fact that mutants deficient in ppGpp synthesis and breakdown (*relA spoT*) (22a) as well as mutants deficient in ApppppA breakdown (*apaH*) express some of the phenotypes of mutants lacking σ^{s} is consistent with this hypothesis (37).

Another molecule that could modulate the activation of the σ^{s} regulon is acetate. Acetate is secreted into the medium at the end of exponential growth and is subsequently taken up and metabolized (70). As acetyl-CoA, acetate is a central molecule in the metabolic pathways of *E. coli* as it is the entrance compound for the tricarboxylic acid cycle, which supplies the cell with energy and amino acid precursors. The net reaction of the tricarboxylic acid cycle is the conversion of acetate to carbon dioxide and energy through the formation of reducing equivalents (NADH). The complete loss of carbon atoms in cells growing on acetate is prevented by partially shutting off the tricarboxylic acid cycle and routing acetate through the glyoxylate shunt (50). In this way carbon is preserved for cellular building blocks and may enter the glycogen biosynthetic pathway. This regulation of carbon metabolism could be a key indicator which signals the cell's nutritional limitation. Evidence that the acetyl moiety of acetate, acetyl phosphate, and acetyl-CoA is involved in the control of the phosphate regulon (76) indicates that this molecule may have a general regulatory role in central metabolism. Another factor which is present in cells which cease growing is the universal stress protein UspA (52). Its expression is independent of known regulatory proteins, such as OmpR, PhoB, RelA/SpoT, and σ^{s}.

Allelic Variation of *rpoS*

The analysis of *rpoS* alleles from different *E. coli* strains indicates that this gene is not very stable. The initial discovery of this gene as a regulator of acid phosphatase was based on the observation that different laboratory strains produced different levels of the phosphatase. The locus responsible for this variability was mapped and named *appR* (73). As described above, *appR* was later shown to be the same as *rpoS*. In a similar fashion, strains that synthesized reduced levels of trehalose and whose phenotype could be suppressed by amber suppressor tRNAs were found to carry a nonsense codon in *rpoS* (39). This analysis of the natural variation of the *rpoS* gene has been extended by Eisenstark and colleagues, who sequenced a large number of *rpoS* genes from laboratory strains and found a large degree of allelic variation (35). These observations lead us to hypothesize that the *rpoS* gene is unknowingly being placed under a variety of selective pressures in the laboratory, as strains are kept in stationary phase under different conditions. Interestingly, similar selection for different *rpoS* alleles may occur in the natural environment. Normark and coworkers have identified different allelic states of *rpoS*, depending on the location from where the natural isolates were obtained (50a).

In analyses from our own laboratory strains we often encounter changes in the expression of the σ^s-dependent hydrogen peroxidase HPII. This phenotype is easily screened for by the dropwise addition of 30% H_2O_2 to patches of cells grown on solid media. Strains harboring the wild-type *rpoS* allele will bubble vigorously because of the evolution of oxygen resulting from the rapid breakdown of H_2O_2 (Fig. 2). Strains harboring null mutations in *rpoS* exhibit no bubbling reaction. But many strains show an intermediate phenotype with delayed and much reduced bubbling. We

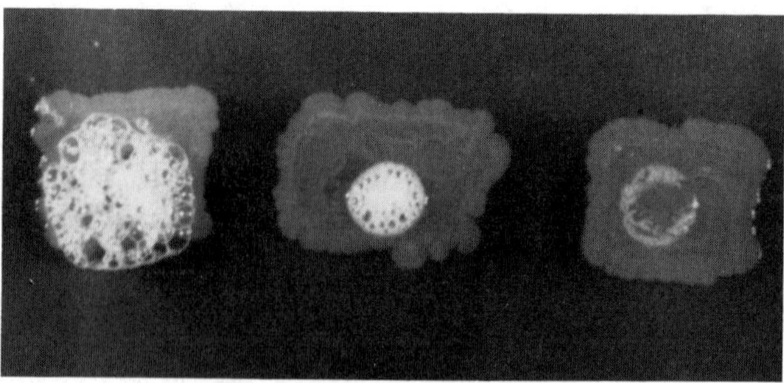

FIGURE 2. The H_2O_2 "bubbling" phenotype of *E. coli*. From left to right: wild-type, intermediate, and null phenotypes resulting from variations in the *rpoS* gene.

have correlated this reduced bubbling phenotype with allelic variation in *rpoS* (80).

In studies in our laboratory aimed at understanding the differences between a 1-day-old *E. coli* culture and a similar culture which had been in stationary phase for 12 days we observed changes in the *rpoS* allele (80). When a 12-day-old culture is mixed with a 1-day-old culture at a dilution of $1{:}10^3$, the number of cells originating from the older culture increases while the cells from the young culture die. We demonstrated that cells in the older culture carried an advantageous mutation not present in cells from the younger culture. Molecular genetic analysis revealed that a short duplication in the *rpoS* gene at the C terminus of the coding sequence resulted in this phenotype. This mutation results in the lowered expression of the σ^s regulon since expression of a *bolA*::*lacZ* fusion and expression of the KatE-dependent bubbling phenotype decreases.

Hierarchical Regulation in the σ^s Regulon

A number of genes within the σ^s regulon encode regulatory proteins (Fig. 3). The *bolA* gene was described as a gene which when overexpressed causes the cells to become spherical (3). The sequence of the gene predicts a protein with a helix-turn-helix motif, suggesting that BolA is a DNA binding protein. One of the genes allegedly regulated by BolA is *dacC*, which encodes PBP6. The levels of PBP6 increase 20-fold at the onset of stationary phase. In addition, in two-dimensional gels additional spots are absent from *bolA* mutant strains.

A second regulator under the control of σ^s is AppY (6). In a search for clones that express the stationary-phase-specific *appA* gene, a plasmid was isolated that did not contain the *appA* gene, but clearly affected its level of transcription. This putative positive regulatory gene was designated *appY*. Based on its function in the synthesis of acid phosphatase and the presence of a DNA binding motif, it is presumed that AppY is a transcriptional activator in the expression of *appA* (29).

A third protein which affects gene expression after it has been expressed itself by σ^s is Dps (4). In two-dimensional gel analysis of proteins synthesized after 3 days of starvation, a number of protein spots are absent from

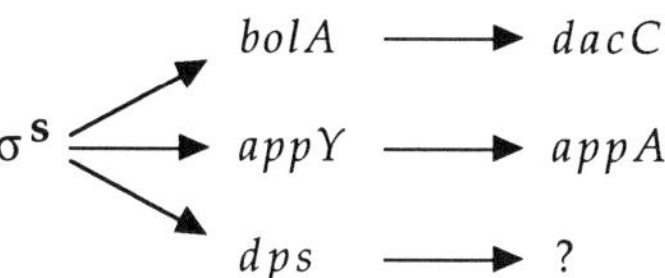

FIGURE 3. Hierarchy in the σ^S regulon. Different σ^S-dependent genes affect the expression of downstream genes.

a *dps* mutant strain compared to the isogenic wild-type strain, whereas the mutant synthesizes a number of proteins absent from the wild type. Dps may constitute a global regulator that only influences gene expression after prolonged periods of starvation, well after the initial induction of the σ^s regulon.

A MODEL FOR THE σ^s REGULON AND ITS POTENTIAL APPLICATION

As the information on metabolism in stationary-phase cultures and the regulation of gene expression under such conditions accumulates, it is clear that metabolism in nongrowing cells is very different from that in exponentially growing cells. Although this fact has gone unrecognized for a long period of time, bacteria in a stationary-phase culture are metabolically very active and may even grow. Bacteria sense growth-restraining conditions and respond by synthesizing new enzymes to scavenge any minor nutrient and to prepare for a period of dormancy. Energy conservation is an important incentive for nongrowing cells, and it is in fact not until stationary phase that *E. coli* grown on glucose gets its tricarboxylic acid cycle running completely (5).

Stationary-phase-specific responses are initiated when starvation generates signals (which remain undefined) that are sensed and translated to induce stationary-phase gene expression via either σ^s or a σ^s-independent pathway. Since the transition between growth and nongrowth can involve a wide spectrum of metabolic changes, induction and expression of stationary-phase responses must be subtle and reversible. Different levels of control are therefore expected, and as yet our understanding of such mechanisms is limited. Knowing that transcriptional, translational, and posttranslational control may be exerted on the σ^s activity, it is now time to identify factors involved in these processes (Fig. 4).

For decades, stationary-phase *Streptomyces* spp. have been used in the production of antibiotics. With the emerging understanding of gene expression in stationary phase, similar processes now become available for the production of other chemicals and proteins of industrial importance. The recent discovery that σ^s is also involved in the virulence of *Salmonella typhimurium* in mice suggests that the study of its regulon will make major contributions to the field of bacterial pathogenesis as well (20). The application of such new physiological insights in clinical and industrial microbiology will lead to some exciting years in the studies on stationary-phase gene expression.

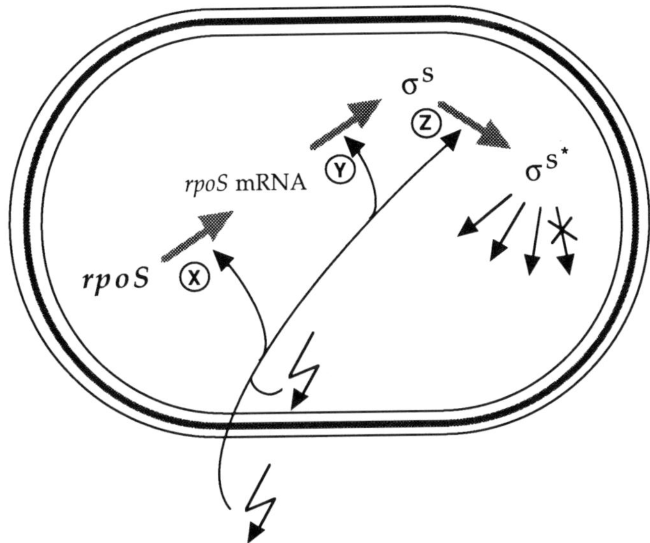

FIGURE 4. Hypothetical model for the activation of σ^S function. X, Y, and Z represent potential targets for the action of regulatory factors.

We gratefully acknowledge the many colleagues who sent us published and unpublished material to help in the writing of this review. Work on various aspects of stationary phase has been supported by a grant (MCB-9207323) from the National Science Foundation to R.K. R.K. is also the recipient of an American Cancer Society Faculty Research Award.

REFERENCES

1. **Aldea, M., T. Garrido, C. Hernandez-Chico, M. Vicente, and S. R. Kushner.** 1989. Induction of a growth-phase-dependent promoter triggers transcription of *bolA,* an *E. coli* morphogene. *EMBO J.* **8:**3923–3931.
2. **Aldea, M., T. Garrido, J. Pla, and M. Vicente.** 1990. Division genes in *Escherichia coli* are expressed coordinately to cell septum requirements by gearbox promoters. *EMBO J.* **9:**3787–3794.
3. **Aldea, M., C. Hernández-Chico, A. G. de la Campa, S. R. Kushner, and M. Vicente.** 1988. Identification, cloning, and expression of *bolA,* an *ftsZ*-dependent morphogene of *Escherichia coli. J. Bacteriol.* **170:**5169–5176.
4. **Almirón, M., A. Link, D. Furlong, and R. Kolter.** 1992. A novel DNA binding protein with regulatory and protective roles in starved *E. coli. Genes Dev.* **6:**2646–2654.

4a. **Almirón, M. A., A. Tormo, S. Lazar, and R. Kolter.** Unpublished data.

5. **Amarasingham, C. R., and B. D. Davis.** 1965. Regulation of α-ketoglutarate dehydrogenase formation in *Escherichia coli. J. Biol. Chem.* **240:**3664–3668.
6. **Atlung, T., A. Nielsen, and F. G. Hansen.** 1989. Isolation, characterization, and nucleotide sequence of *appY,* a regulatory gene for growth-phase-dependent gene expression in *Escherichia coli. J. Bacteriol.* **171:**1683–1691.

7. **Back, J. F., D. Oakenfull, and M. B. Smith.** 1979. Increased thermal stability of proteins in the presence of sugars and polyols. *Biochemistry* **18:**5191–5196.
8. **Bohannon, D. E., N. Connell, J. Keener, A. Tormo, M. Espinosa-Urgel, M. M. Zambrano, and R. Kolter.** 1991. Stationary-phase-inducible "gearbox" promoters: differential effects of *katF* mutations and the role of σ^{70}. *J. Bacteriol.* **173:**4482–4492.
9. **Boos, W., U. Ehmann, E. Bremer, A. Middendorf, and P. Postma.** 1987. Trehalase of *Escherichia coli*. *J. Biol. Chem.* **262:**13212–13218.
10. **Bork, P., C. Sander, and A. Valencia.** 1992. An ATPase domain common to prokaryotic cell cycle proteins, sugar kinases, actin, and hsp70 heat shock proteins. *Proc. Natl. Acad. Sci. USA* **89:**7290–7294.
11. **Cashel, M., and K. E. Rudd.** 1987. The stringent response, p. 1410–1438. *In* F. C. Neidhardt, J. L. Ingraham, K. B. Low, B. Magasanik, M. Schaechter, and H. E. Umbarger (ed.), *Escherichia coli and Salmonella typhimurium: Cellular and Molecular Biology*. American Society for Microbiology, Washington, D.C.
12. **Christman, M. F., R. W. Morgan, F. S. Jacobson, and B. N. Ames.** 1985. Positive control of a regulon for defences against oxidative stress and some heat-shock proteins in *Salmonella typhimurium*. *Cell* **41:**753–762.
13. **Cronan, J. E.** 1968. Phospholipid alterations during growth of *Escherichia coli*. *J. Bacteriol.* **95:**2054–2061.
14. **Cronan, J. E., and C. O. Rock.** 1987. Biosynthesis of membrane lipids, p. 474–497. *In* F. C. Neidhardt, J. L. Ingraham, K. B. Low, B. Magasanik, M. Schaechter, and H. E. Umbarger (ed.), *Escherichia coli and Salmonella typhimurium: Cellular and Molecular Biology*. American Society for Microbiology, Washington, D.C.
15. **Czonka, L. N., and A. D. Hanson.** 1991. Prokaryotic osmoregulation: genetics and physiology. *Annu. Rev. Microbiol.* **45:**569–606.
16. **Damerau, K., and A. C. St. John.** 1993. Role of Clp protease subunits in degradation of carbon starvation proteins in *Escherichia coli*. *J. Bacteriol.* **175:**53–63.
17. **Dassa, E., M. Cahu, B. Desjoyaux-Cherel, and P. L. Bouquet.** 1982. The acid phosphatase with optimum pH of 2.5 of *Escherichia coli*, physiological and biochemical study. *J. Biol. Chem.* **257:**6669–6676.
18. **de Boer, P., R. Crossley, and L. Rothfield.** 1992. The essential bacterial cell-division protein FtsZ is a GTPase. *Nature* (London) **359:**254–256.
19. **Diaz-Guerra, L., F. Moreno, and J. L. S. Millan.** 1989. *appR* gene product activates transcription of microcin C7 plasmid genes. *J. Bacteriol.* **171:**2906–2908.
20. **Fang, F., S. J. Libby, N. A. Buchmeier, P. C. Loewen, J. Switala, J. Harwood, and D. G. Guiney.** 1992. The alternative σ factor KatF (RpoS) regulates *Salmonella* virulence. *Proc. Natl. Acad. Sci. USA* **89:**11978–11982.
21. **Garrido, M. C., M. Herrero, R. Kolter, and F. Moreno.** 1988. The export of the DNA replication inhibitor microcin B17 provides immunity for the host cell. *EMBO J.* **7:**1853–1862.
22. **Genilloud, O., F. Moreno, and R. Kolter.** 1989. DNA sequence, products, and transcriptional pattern of the genes involved in production of the DNA replication inhibitor microcin B17. *J. Bacteriol.* **171:**1126–1135.

22a. **Gentry, D., and M. Cashel.** Personal communication.

23. **Giaever, H. M., O. B. Styrvold, I. Kaasen, and A. R. Strom.** 1988. Biochemical and genetic characterization of osmoregulatory trehalose synthesis in *Escherichia coli*. *J. Bacteriol.* **170:**2841–2849.

24. **Goldie, H.** 1984. Regulation of transcription of the *Escherichia coli* phosphoenolpyruvate carboxykinase locus: studies with *pck-lacZ* fusions. *J. Bacteriol.* **159:**832–836.
25. **Gonzy-Treboul, G., C. Karmazyn-Campelli, and P. Stragier.** 1992. Developmental regulation of transcription of the *Bacillus subtilis ftsAZ* operon. *J. Mol. Biol.* **224:**967–979.
26. **Groat, R. G., J. E. Schultz, E. Zychlinsky, A. Bockman, and A. Matin.** 1986. Starvation proteins in *Escherichia coli:* kinetics of synthesis and role in starvation survival. *J. Bacteriol.* **168:**486–493.
27. **Grogan, D. W., and J. E. Cronan.** 1984. Cloning and manipulation of the fatty acid synthase gene of *Escherichia coli:* physiological aspects of enzyme overproduction. *J. Bacteriol.* **158:**286–295.
28. **Grogan, D. W., and J. E. Cronan.** 1984. Genetic characterization of the *Escherichia coli* cyclopropane fatty acid (*cfa*) locus and neighboring loci. *Mol. Gen. Genet.* **196:**367–372.
28a. **Gutierrez, C.** Personal communication.
29. **Hengge-Aronis, R.** 1993. Survival of hunger and stress: the role of *rpoS* in early stationary phase gene regulation in *Escherichia coli. Cell* **72:**165–168.
30. **Hengge-Aronis, R., and D. Fischer.** 1992. Identification and molecular analysis of *glgS,* a novel growth-phase-regulated and *rpoS*-dependent gene involved in glycogen synthesis in *Escherichia coli. Mol. Microbiol.* **6:**1877–1886.
31. **Hengge-Aronis, R., W. Klein, R. Lange, M. Rimmele, and W. Boos.** 1991. Trehalose synthesis genes are controlled by the putative sigma factor encoded by *rpoS* and are involved in stationary phase thermotolerance in *Escherichia coli. J. Bacteriol.* **173:**7918–7924.
32. **Hengge-Aronis, R., R. Lange, N. Henneberg, and D. Fischer.** 1993. Osmotic regulation of *rpoS*-dependent genes in *Escherichia coli. J. Bacteriol.* **175:**259–265.
33. **Hernandez-Chico, C., J. L. San Millan, R. Kolter, and F. Moreno.** 1986. Growth phase and OmpR regulation of transcription of the microcin B17 genes. *J. Bacteriol.* **167:**1058–1065.
34. **Higgins, C. F.** 1992. ABC transporters: from microorganisms to man. *Annu. Rev. Cell. Biol.* **8:**67–113.
35. **Ivanova, A., M. Renshaw, R. V. Guntaka, and A. Eisenstark.** 1992. DNA base sequence variability in *katF* (putative sigma factor) gene of *Escherichia coli. Nucleic Acids Res.* **20:**5479–5480.
36. **Jenkins, D. E., S. A. Chaisson, and A. Matin.** 1990. Starvation-induced cross protection against osmotic challenge in *Escherichia coli. J. Bacteriol.* **172:**2779–2781.
37. **Johnstone, D. B., and S. B. Farr.** 1991. AppppA binds to several proteins in *Escherichia coli* including the heat shock and oxidative stress proteins DnaK, GroEL, E89, C45, C40. *EMBO J.* **10:**3897–3904.
38. **Jung, J. U., C. Gutierrez, F. Martin, M. Ardourel, and M. Villarejo.** 1990. Transcription of *osmB,* a gene encoding an *Escherichia coli* lipoprotein, is regulated by dual signals. *J. Biol. Chem.* **265:**10574–10581.
39. **Kaasen, I., P. Falkenberg, O. B. Styrvold, and A. R. Strom.** 1992. Molecular cloning and physical mapping of the *otsAB* genes, which encode the osmoregulatory trehalose pathway of *Escherichia coli:* evidence that transcription is activated by KatF (AppR). *J. Bacteriol.* **174:**889–898.
40. **Lange, R., and R. Hengge-Aronis.** 1991. Growth phase-regulated expression of *bolA* and morphology of stationary-phase *Escherichia coli* cells are controlled by the novel sigma factor σ^s. *J. Bacteriol.* **173:**4474–4481.

41. **Lange, R., and R. Hengge-Aronis.** 1991. Identification of a central regulator of stationary phase gene expression in *E. coli. Mol. Microbiol.* **5:**49–59.
42. **Liberek, K., T. P. Galitski, M. Zylicz, and C. Georgopoulos.** 1992. The DnaK chaperone modulates the heat shock response of *Escherichia coli* by binding the σ^{32} transcription factor. *Proc. Natl. Acad. Sci. USA* **89:**3516–3520.
43. **Loewen, P. C.** 1984. Isolation of catalase-deficient *Escherichia coli* mutants and mapping of *katE,* a locus that affects catalase activity. *J. Bacteriol.* **157:**622–626.
44. **Loewen, P. C., and B. L. Triggs.** 1984. Genetic mapping of *katF,* a locus that with *katE* affects the synthesis of a second catalase species in *Escherichia coli. J. Bacteriol.* **160:**668–675.
45. **Loewen, P. C., I. von Ossowski, J. Switala, and M. R. Mulvey.** 1993. KatF (σ^s) synthesis in *Escherichia coli* is subject to posttranscriptional regulation. *J. Bacteriol.* **175:**2150–2153.
46. **Matin, A.** 1991. The molecular basis of carbon-starvation-induced general resistance in *Escherichia coli. Mol. Microbiol.* **5:**3–10.
47. **McCann, M. P., C. D. Fraley, and A. Matin.** 1993. The putative σ factor KatF is regulated posttranscriptionally during carbon starvation. *J. Bacteriol.* **175:**2143–2149.
47a. **McCann, M. P., J. P. Kidwell, and A. Matin.** 1991. The putative σ factor KatF has a central role in development of starvation-mediated general resistance in *Escherichia coli. J. Bacteriol.* **173:**4188–4194.
48. **Mulvey, M. R., and P. C. Loewen.** 1989. Nucleotide sequence of *katF* of *Escherichia coli* suggests KatF protein is a novel σ transcription factor. *Nucleic Acids Res.* **17:**9979–9991.
49. **Mulvey, M. R., J. Switala, A. Borys, and P. C. Loewen.** 1990. Regulation of transcription of *katE* and *katF* in *Escherichia coli. J. Bacteriol.* **172:**6713–6720.
50. **Nimmo, H. G.** 1987. The tricarboxylic acid cycle and anapleurotic reactions, p. 156–169. *In* F. C. Neidhardt, J. L. Ingraham, K. B. Low, B. Magasanik, M. Schaechter, and H. E. Umbarger (ed.), *Escherichia coli and Salmonella typhimurium: Cellular and Molecular Biology.* American Society for Microbiology, Washington, D.C.
50a. **Normark, S.** Personal communication.
51. **Novoa, M. A., L. Diíz-Guerra, J. L. SanMillán, and F. Moreno.** 1986. Cloning and mapping of the genetic determinants for microcin C7 production and immunity. *J. Bacteriol.* **168:**1384–1391.
52. **Nystrom, T., and F. C. Neidhardt.** 1992. Cloning, mapping and nucleotide sequencing of a gene encoding a universal stress protein in *Escherichia coli. Mol. Microbiol.* **6:**3187–3198.
53. **Preiss, J., and T. Romeo.** 1989. Physiology, biochemistry and genetics of bacterial glycogen synthesis, p. 183–233. *In* A. H. Rose and D. Tempest (ed.), *Advances in Microbial Physiology,* vol. 30. Academic Press, London.
54. **RayChaudhuri, D., and J. T. Park.** 1992. *Escherichia coli* cell-division gene *ftsZ* encodes a novel GTP-binding protein. *Nature* (London) **359:**251–254.
55. **Reeve, C. A., P. S. Amy, and A. Matin.** 1984. Role of protein synthesis in the survival of carbon-starved *Escherichia coli* K-12. *J. Bacteriol.* **160:**1041–1046.
56. **Rogers, S. G., and B. Weiss.** 1980. Exonuclease III of *Escherichia coli* K-12, an AP endonuclease. *Methods Enzymol.* **65:**201–211.
57. **Romeo, T., M. Gong, M. Y. Liu, and A. M. Brun.** 1993. Characterization of *csrA,* a gene that affects glycogen biosynthesis, gluconeogenesis, cell size and

surface properties: evidence for a new global regulon in *Escherichia coli* K-12. *J. Bacteriol.* **175:**4744–4755.

58. **Romeo, T., and J. Preiss.** 1989. Genetic regulation of glycogen biosynthesis in *Escherichia coli:* in vitro effects of cyclic AMP and guanosine 5′-diphosphate 3′-diphosphate and analysis of in vivo transcripts. *J. Bacteriol.* **171:**2773–2782.
59. **Sak, B. D., A. Eisenstark, and D. Touati.** 1989. Exonuclease III and the hydroperoxidase II in *Escherichia coli* are both regulated by the *katF* product. *Proc. Natl. Acad. Sci. USA* **86:**3271–3275.
60. **San Millán, J. L., R. Kolter, and F. Moreno.** 1985. Plasmid genes involved in microcin B17 production. *J. Bacteriol.* **163:**1016–1020.
61. **Schellhorn, H. E., and V. L. Stones.** 1992. Regulation of *katF* and *katE* in *Escherichia coli* K-12 by weak acids. *J. Bacteriol.* **174:**4769–4776.
62. **Schultz, J. E., and A. Matin.** 1991. Molecular and functional characterization of a carbon starvation gene of *Escherichia coli. J. Mol. Biol.* **218:**129–140.
63. **Siegele, D. A., and R. Kolter.** 1992. Life after log. *J. Bacteriol.* **174:**345–348.
64. **Siegele, D. A., and R. Kolter.** Studies on an *E. coli* mutant unable to reinitiate growth after starvation. Submitted for publication.
65. **Spence, J., A. Cegielska, and C. Georgopoulos.** 1990. Role of *Escherichia coli* heat shock proteins DnaK and HtpG (C62.5) in response to nutritional deprivation. *J. Bacteriol.* **172:**7157–7166.
66. **Stark, D. M., K. P. Timmerman, G. F. Barry, J. Preiss, and G. M. Kishore.** 1992. Regulation of the amount of starch in plant tissues by ADP glucose pyrophosphorylase. *Science* **258:**287–292.
67. **Steinbuchel, A., and H. G. Schlegel.** 1991. Physiology and molecular genetics of poly(β-hydroxyalkanoic acid) synthesis in *Alcaligenes eutrophus. Mol. Microbiol.* **5:**535–542.
68. **Stock, J. B., A. J. Ninfa, and A. M. Stock.** 1989. Protein phosphorylation and regulation of adaptive responses in bacteria. *Microbiol. Rev.* **53:**450–490.
69. **Tanaka, K., N. Fujita, A. Ishihama, and H. Takahashi.** 1993. Heterogeneity of principal sigma factor in *Escherichia coli:* the *rpoS* gene product, σ^{38}, is a principal sigma factor of RNA polymerase in stationary phase *Escherichia coli. Proc. Natl. Acad. Sci. USA* **90:**3511–3515.
70. **Tempest, D. W., and O. M. Neijssel.** 1987. Growth yield and energy distribution, p. 797–806. *In* F. C. Neidhardt, J. L. Ingraham, K. B. Low, B. Magasanik, M. Schaechter, and H. E. Umbarger (ed.), *Escherichia coli and Salmonella typhimurium: Cellular and Molecular Biology.* American Society for Microbiology, Washington, D.C.
71. **Tormo, A., M. Almirón, and R. Kolter.** 1990. *surA,* an *Escherichia coli* gene essential for survival in stationary phase. *J. Bacteriol.* **172:**4339–4347.
72. **Tormo, A., J. A. Ayala, M. A. de Pedro, M. Aldea, and M. Vicente.** 1986. Interaction of FtsA and PBP3 proteins in the *Escherichia coli* septum. *J. Bacteriol.* **166:**985–992.

72a. **Tormo, A., and R. Kolter.** Unpublished data.

73. **Touati, E., E. Dassa, and P. L. Boquet.** 1986. Pleiotropic mutations in *appR* reduce pH 2.5 acid phosphatase expression and restore succinate utilization in CRP-deficient strains of *Escherichia coli. Mol. Gen. Genet.* **202:**257–264.
74. **Tuomanen, E., and R. Cozens.** 1987. Changes in peptidoglycan composition and penicillin-binding proteins in slowly growing *Escherichia coli. J. Bacteriol.* **169:**5308–5310.

75. **van Laere, A.** 1989. Trehalose, reserve and/or stress metabolite? *FEMS Microbiol. Rev.* **63:**201–210.
76. **Wanner, B. L., and M. R. Wilmes-Riesenberg.** 1992. Involvement of phosphotransacetylase, acetate kinase, and acetyl phosphate synthesis in control of the phosphate regulon in *Escherichia coli. J. Bacteriol.* **174:**2124–2130.
77. **Yim, H. H., and M. Villarejo.** 1992. *osmY,* a new hyperosmotically inducible gene, encodes a periplasmic protein in *Escherichia coli. J. Bacteriol.* **174:**3637–3644.
78. **Young, C. C., J. D. Alvarez, and R. W. Bernlohr.** 1990. Nutrient-dependent methylation of a membrane-associated protein of *Escherichia coli. J. Bacteriol.* **172:**5147–5153.
79. **Young, C. C., and R. W. Bernlohr.** 1991. Elongation factor Tu is methylated in response to nutrient deprivation in *Escherichia coli. J. Bacteriol.* **173:**3096–3100.
80. **Zambrano, M. M., D. A. Siegele, M. Almirón, A. Tormo, and R. Kolter.** 1993. Microbial competition: *Escherichia coli* mutants that take over stationary phase cultures. *Science* **259:**1757–1760.

Regulation of Bacterial Differentiation
Edited by P. Piggot et al.

Chapter 3

The Phosphorelay Signal Transduction Pathway in the Initiation of Sporulation

James A. Hoch

Control of growth and cellular differentiation has been, and continues to be, an area of intense scientific interest in organisms as diverse as bacteria and man. Sporulation in bacteria has long been viewed as a simple system of cellular differentiation, which was amenable to study with the genetic tools available at the time. It is doubtful that *Bacillus subtilis* would have reached its present prominence without this impetus to understand the biochemical mechanisms of development of the spore. The early studies in this field, before the advent of recombinant DNA technology, utilized genetic analyses of sporulation-deficient mutants. These mutants were loosely classified as either early or late, with early being blocked at stage 0 of sporulation and late being blocked after stage 0. This classification was readily apparent from colonial morphology and whether the mutant was capable of producing certain key enzymes (e.g., proteases). Genetic studies of early and late mutants which formed the basis for the research being carried out today revealed that sporulation genes were scattered on the genetic map but tended to cluster in several areas (14, 34). By comparing the phenotypic and morphological properties of mutants, it was possible to classify mutants as to the stage of sporulation they reached before the process was blocked (36). However, despite the best efforts of many investigators, the biochemical basis for the mutations remained obscure. The advent of molecular cloning allowed the isolation and purification of the protein products of sporulation genes. In some cases it was possible to use the homology of the deduced protein product of the gene to predict its function (e.g., Spo0H to sigma factors). Of even greater importance, this

James A. Hoch, Department of Molecular and Experimental Medicine, The Scripps Research Institute, 10666 North Torrey Pines Road, La Jolla, CA 92037.

technology allowed the high-level expression of the products of *spo0* genes, which led to purification of proteins for biochemical analysis.

Yet sporulation poses unsolved problems in three major areas: the biochemical mechanisms responsible for controlling the decision to either continue growth or sporulate; the genetic mechanism regulating the order and timing of biochemical events over the 4- to 6-h period required to make a finished spore; and the macromolecular interactions required to construct faithfully a complicated spore. This chapter will focus on the first of these areas. An overview of all aspects of sporulation can be found in Errington (8).

spo0 MUTANTS AND THE PHOSPHORELAY

The decision to either continue cell division or initiate sporulation is tied directly to nutrient availability through an interwoven network of regulatory controls. Each cell must evaluate its environment and metabolic potential and condense this information into a decision. If cell division is chosen, the cell is committed to completing this process before again having the opportunity to initiate sporulation (21). The diverse environmental and metabolic signals assessed by the organism must be converted or transduced into an effector molecule recognized by the cell as responsible for this decision. What signals are recognized as important indicators for this decision, how are they recognized, and how is this information converted into action? The answers to these questions were thought to lie in the gene products defined by the "early" sporulation genes in which a mutation blocks sporulation at stage 0. Such *spo0* mutants seem to be locked in exponential growth in that they produce large colonies that do not express functions normally associated with stationary phase. Conceivably these Spo0 proteins could comprise the sensing, signal transducing, and effector functions required for initiation of sporulation.

Classical genetic studies identified several genes in which mutations caused initiation-defective sporulation and gave rise to the stage 0 phenotype: *spo0A, spo0B, spo0E, spo0F, spo0H, spo0J,* and *spo0K* (14, 34). Cloning and sequencing studies of these genes revealed the identities of the *spo0H* (7) and *spo0K* (29, 35) genes as a sigma factor, σ^H, and the oligopeptide permease operon, respectively. The functions of the *spo0B* (9) and *spo0E* (30) genes were not readily determined from the primary amino acid sequence. The other sequences were only partially informative. The *spo0A* gene (10, 17) was found to code for a protein with homology to a class of transcription regulators which were eventually found to be part of a family of sensor-response regulator two-component regulatory systems (40).

The amino-terminal amino acid homology of the "response regulators" was also found in the Spo0F protein (49). This finding suggested that both Spo0A and Spo0F were parts of two-component regulatory systems, but response regulators were known to be the substrates of kinases that activated their function (26), and no proteins with homology to kinases were uncovered by the sequencing studies on *spo0* genes. Several questions remained: where were the kinases responsible for phosphorylation of Spo0A and Spo0F, and what roles did the phosphorylated forms of these proteins play in the initiation process?

A partial answer to these questions came from the sequence of a stage II gene, *spoIIJ*, which gave a deduced protein with homology to the kinases of the two-component regulatory class (1). The product of this gene, when purified, phosphorylated Spo0F readily, but Spo0A was a poor substrate (28). Thus, this kinase, KinA, phosphorylated Spo0F, whose function was unknown, whereas the kinase responsible for phosphorylating the suspected master transcription factor, Spo0A, was still a mystery. What was the role of Spo0F and how does Spo0A become activated? The solution to these problems was provided by the purification of the *spo0B* gene product. The Spo0B protein was revealed to be a heretofore undescribed enzyme type that phosphorylated Spo0A using Spo0F~P rather than ATP as a substrate (3). The function of Spo0F~P was that of an intermediate in the phosphorylation of Spo0A. This series of reactions was termed a phosphorelay (Fig. 1). Strains with mutations in the *spo0F* or *spo0B* genes are absolutely sporulation-deficient, indicating that the phosphorelay signal transduction pathway is the only normal physiological mechanism for activating the Spo0A transcription factor.

The phosphorelay is the signal transduction pathway interpreting signals to sporulate which are converted to phosphorylated Spo0A. Signal input is thought to originate from the environment, or from metabolic clues, which serve to activate the kinases KinA or KinB to phosphorylate Spo0F. KinA is a cytoplasmic enzyme whose deficiency slows the rate of sporulation by prolonging the initial stages (28). KinB mutations drop the frequency of sporulation to near zero, when present in a KinA-deficient strain (51). Thus, it is the combination of these two kinases that interprets environmental signals, and presumably they respond to different signals, although the nature of the signals remains a mystery. KinA activity is inhibited by *cis*-unsaturated fatty acids, which may be a metabolic signal linking the state of membrane or phospholipid synthesis or turnover to sporulation (42). KinB is an integral membrane protein which requires the function of a linked gene, *kapB*, coding for a small cytoplasmic protein for its activity (51). It is believed to phosphorylate Spo0F directly, but this conjecture is unproven. Again, nothing is known of the activators or inhib-

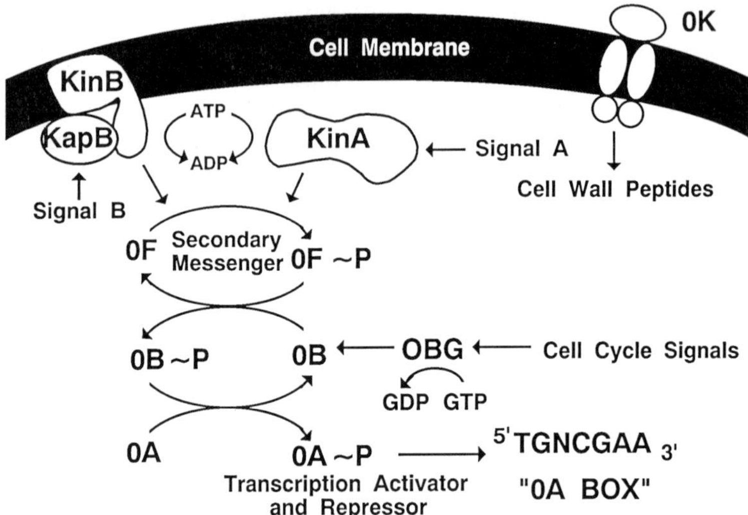

FIGURE 1. Phosphorelay signal transduction pathway. Signals of unknown origin activate either of the kinases to phosphorylate Spo0F. The Spo0F~P is a substrate for the Spo0B phosphotransferase which phosphorylates Spo0A. Spo0A is active in its phosphorylated form as a transcriptional activator and repressor recognizing the 0A box in promoters. The proposed roles of the *spo0K* and *obg* gene products are indicated.

itors of this enzyme. The identification of regulatory proteins with no information about the effectors controlling their activity is a recurring theme in sporulation.

Activation (or deinhibition) of the kinases leads to the formation of Spo0F~P, which may serve as a secondary messenger linking different environmental signals to the phosphorylation of Spo0A (3). The major role of Spo0F~P is as a substrate for the Spo0B-catalyzed phosphotransfer to Spo0A. This phosphotransferase activity is reminiscent of sensor kinases, and Spo0B only differs from such kinases in its choice of Spo0F~P rather than ATP as a source of phosphate. The *spo0B* gene is in an operon with another gene (*obg*), which codes for an essential GTP-binding protein (50). We have speculated that Obg may serve to link Spo0B and the phosphorelay to some cell cycle event, such as septation or DNA initiation (3). Inherent in this hypothesis is the control of Spo0B or phosphorelay activity by one or more of these events. No evidence exists to prove or disprove this notion, although the recent demonstration of the coupling of DNA synthesis to Spo0A~P formation (15) provides further evidence for the hypothesis of cell cycle dependency in the initiation of sporulation (21).

The end product of the phosphorelay is phosphorylated Spo0A, which serves as a multifunctional transcriptional repressor and activator of sporulation genes. Spo0A binds to a sequence, TGNCGAA, known as the "0A box," that resides in many promoters (46). Its transcriptional activities and promoter targets will be the subject of a later section of this review.

CONTROL OF SIGNAL TRANSDUCTION IN THE PHOSPHORELAY

Sporulation is an alternative to growth under unfavorable nutritional conditions. However, growth and division are the preferred life-style of bacteria, and as long as sufficient nutrients are available, sporulation is repressed. Therefore, it should not be surprising that complex controls on the activity of the phosphorelay have been found. The activity of the pathway is controlled by regulating phosphate flow to Spo0A, either by restricting the activity of its components or by repressing synthesis of several key components.

The major direct influence that the environment or metabolism has on the phosphorelay may be channeled through effector molecules that control the activity of KinA and KinB. Unfortunately, very little is known of such effector molecules other than the inhibition of KinA by *cis*-unsaturated fatty acids, which may indicate a regulatory role for phospholipid. KinB is an integral membrane protein with the kinase as a cytoplasmic domain. This molecular architecture may indicate that signal transduction occurs across the membrane, or the kinase might be involved in transport of some molecule into or out of the cell; however, the requirement for the small charged and presumably soluble KapB protein for KinB activity could be interpreted as evidence that the activating signal comes from within the cell (51). It seems likely that KinA and KinB could be the targets of complex regulatory pathways that monitor several key indicators of metabolism and the environment.

The phosphorelay is a phosphorylation-dephosphorylation cycle with some similarities to cell cycle control in eukaryotes (27). Negative regulation of phosphate flow in the phosphorelay is accomplished by the *spo0E* gene product (32). Overproduction of Spo0E results in sporulation inhibition, whereas a *spo0E* deletion mutation leads to a strain which is derepressed for sporulation. The Spo0E protein has been purified to homogeneity and the effect of adding it to the phosphorelay reactions has been determined (27a). Spo0E has two effects on the phosphorelay: it dephosphorylates the Spo0A~P protein but not Spo0F~P in a kinase-independent manner, and it stimulates KinA to phosphorylate Spo0F (Fig. 2). The phosphatase activity of Spo0E on Spo0A~P is entirely consis-

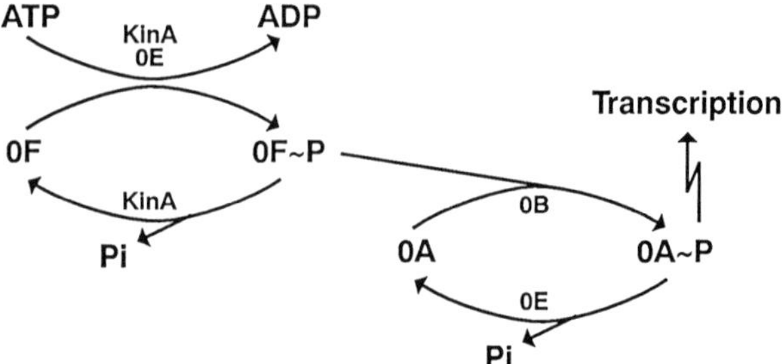

FIGURE 2. Phosphorylation-dephosphorylation reactions in the phosphorelay. The Spo0E protein is a phosphatase serving to deactivate Spo0A~P which also serves to speed up the rate of Spo0F phosphorylation by KinA. Spo0F~P is subject to the phosphatase activity of KinA.

tent with the phenotype of mutants overproducing the protein and with the deletion mutation (32). Spo0E stimulation of the phosphorylation of Spo0F by KinA has been interpreted to indicate that Spo0E complexes with KinA. KinA is known to have phosphatase activity toward Spo0F~P (14a). Our picture of phosphatase regulation of the phosphorelay is incomplete. If KinA and Spo0E form a complex, it seems possible that the phosphatase activities of these two proteins could be controlled by the same effector molecule or by the lack of an effector molecule. On the other hand, they could be controlled independently, forming two unique control sites for unknown effectors. Genetic studies have left little doubt that Spo0E plays an important role in the modulation of phosphate flux in the phosphorelay (32). This combination of kinase and phosphatase activities to control the phosphorylation level of key regulators occurs universally from bacteria to man, and as in sporulation, little is known of what regulates these activities.

TRANSCRIPTIONAL CONTROL OF THE PHOSPHORELAY

The transcriptional interactions among the components of the phosphorelay are schematically outlined in Fig. 3. Genes for two components of the phosphorelay, the *spo0A* gene and the *spo0F* gene, are subject to high-level control by transcription (55). Expression of the *spo0B* and *kinA* genes is minimally controlled, and no information is available about the regulation of the *kinB* operon. Both the *spo0A* and *spo0F* genes are transcribed from two promoters: a vegetative σ^A promoter and a sporulation σ^H promoter (4, 20, 54). It is thought that the vegetative σ^A promoter is a low-level promoter in both cases that produces a small defined quantity of both Spo0F and Spo0A during the exponential phase of growth. Induction of

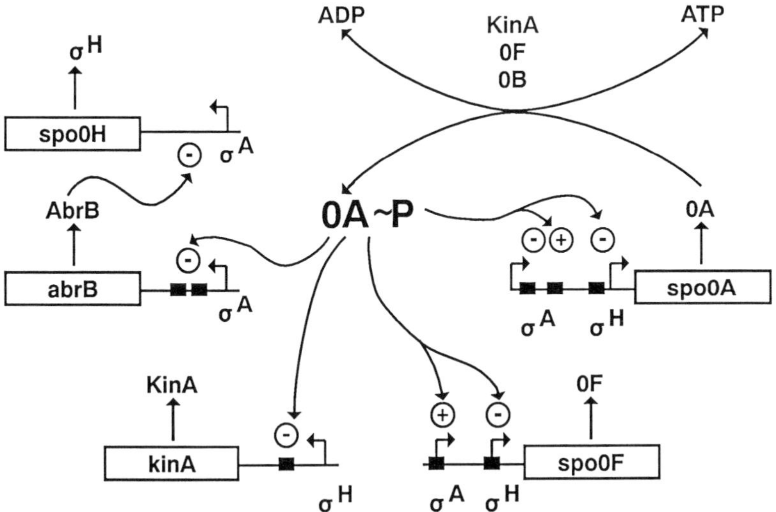

FIGURE 3. Transcriptional regulation of the genes for phosphorelay components. σ^H is required for transcription of the key components Spo0F and Spo0A. Its synthesis is regulated by AbrB, which is, in turn, regulated by Spo0A~P. In addition to σ^H, Spo0A~P is required as a positive activator of both *spo0F* and *spo0A*. Maintenance transcription levels of these genes are accomplished from σ^A promoters which are repressed by Spo0A~P. Both *spo0A* and *spo0F* promoters have 0A boxes within the RNA polymerase binding region which may serve as negative regulatory sites to limit Spo0A and Spo0F expression.

these genes occurs at the end of exponential growth and exclusively from the σ^H promoter (20, 54). Therefore, the control of σ^H expression has a direct bearing on the cells' ability to produce effective quantities of both Spo0F and Spo0A. Production of σ^H is partially under the control of the AbrB transition state regulator, which will be described in detail in a later section (53). Presumably, high levels of AbrB prevent the expression of the *spo0H* gene. These high levels of AbrB gene is repressed by the concentration of Spo0A~P in the cell, which under exponential growth conditions is very low. As the cell approaches the end of exponential growth, the accumulation of Spo0A~P represses transcription of the *abrB* gene, resulting in disinhibition of the expression of *spo0H* and *spo0E* genes, among others. In addition, the accumulation of Spo0A~P appears to inhibit transcription from the σ^A promoter of *spo0A* and activate transcription from the σ^H promoter of the same gene. Thus, Spo0A~P is not only a repressor of one promoter, but an activator of a second promoter, resulting in further production of Spo0A protein (47). A similar situation appears to occur with the *spo0F* gene; binding of Spo0A~P to a region upstream of the σ^H promoter results in activation of the synthesis of Spo0F. This situation leads to an autocatalytic positive feedback loop, which could drive the production of high levels of Spo0A~P in relatively short time spans (47). In addition, both the *spo0A* and *spo0F* promoters have an 0A box either within the σ^H promoter or just downstream, which may serve to modulate the expression of these promoters once sufficient Spo0A~P has accumulated in the cell. The promoter for the *kinA* gene has an 0A box just downstream of the start site of transcription that probably serves to shut off KinA production in response to Spo0A~P synthesis (51a).

This scheme of transcriptional regulation may be incomplete. There could be other regulatory proteins that control the transcription of either *spo0F* or *spo0A*, or both. The effects of certain transition state regulators, like the SinR regulator described below, could be ascribed to transcriptional effects of either *spo0F* or *spo0A* expression. In addition, other regulators might also function to regulate components of this pathway. For example, the *spo0B* gene might be controlled under certain conditions that have not been assayed at this time. The important lesson here with regard to the initiation of sporulation is that the control of phosphate flux through the phosphorelay can be controlled either by controlling the activity of the proteins producing Spo0A~P or by repressing certain key components of the pathway such that the pathway can only function at a minimal level as determined from the level of proteins produced from the constitutive vegetative promoters.

CATABOLITE REPRESSION OF SPORULATION

It has been known since the studies of Pierre Schaeffer almost 30 years ago that sporulation was subject to catabolite repression (38). Unfortunately, *B. subtilis* lacks cyclic AMP, and therefore the mechanism of catabolite repression so well studied in *Escherichia coli* does not function in this organism. Complicating this picture even further with regard to sporulation is the fact that mutations in many different genes have the ability to relieve catabolite repression of sporulation. A major target for catabolite repression has been defined by Kawamura and colleagues as the promoter switch from the vegetative to the sporulation promoter for the *spo0A* gene (4). Thus, conditions of catabolite repression prevent the switch to the sporulation σ^H promoter, which in turn prevents the synthesis of the high levels of Spo0A protein required for transcription activation of sporulation. This catabolite effect could be due to either a lack of σ^H or interference with the function of σ^H on the transcription from this promoter. One possibility for a regulatory protein that may be involved in the control of *spo0A* transcription is the putative regulatory protein that Weickert and Chambliss (52) suggest is responsible for recognition of a sequence common to promoters of catabolite repressed genes, including the *spo0A* gene. Until this protein is identified and subjected to mutational analysis, it is premature to conclude that transcription of the *spo0A* gene is the only target for catabolite repression of sporulation.

Mueller and Sonenshein (23, 24) have recently identified potentially important genes involved in catabolite repression by the isolation of two operons, *gsiA* and *gsiB*, susceptible to induction by glucose starvation. These operons are induced upon glucose starvation or transiently as the cells enter stationary phase in nutrient broth medium. Prolonged expression of these genes can be accomplished by mutation at another locus originally termed *gsiC*, which was subsequently identified as the *kinA* gene. This suggests that the absence of a repressor regulated by KinA, which could be phosphorylated Spo0A, results in elevated transcription of the *gsiA* operon during the early stationary phase. Interestingly, mutations in the *gsiA* gene relieve catabolite repression of sporulation, suggesting that the *gsiA* gene product functions to prevent sporulation in response to catabolites. Furthermore, the mutations in the *gsiA* gene suppress the sporulation defect of *kinA* mutants. This suggests that the *gsiA* mutation spares the requirement for Spo0A~P for sporulation or that the absence of GsiA activates the KinB pathway through which all Spo0A~P must now be formed.

Several additional proteins have been identified as being involved in catabolite repression of sporulation. The Hpr protein is known to code for a regulatory gene controlling both protease production and sporulation, and *hpr* mutants are catabolite-resistant for sporulation (16, 31). Hpr cannot be the hypothetical protein of Weickert and Chambliss (52), since *hpr* mutations do not result in catabolite resistance of amylase production. It has been reported that *degU*(Hy) mutations are catabolite-resistant for sporulation, suggesting that activation of DegU may be an important step that overcomes catabolite repression (19). The *spo0J* gene has been implicated in catabolite repression of sporulation (25). Finally, mutations in the *abrB* gene or in the *sin* gene partially relieve some of the catabolite repressive effects on sporulation (41a). Thus, catabolite repression of sporulation must play an important role in the determination of cell fate, but the actual mechanism by which catabolite repression functions is still a mystery.

OTHER GENES AFFECTING INITIATION

The *spo0K* locus was found to code for the oligopeptide permease system (29, 35). The *opp* operon of microorganisms, consisting of five genes, is known to be responsible for the permease system which transports short oligopeptides, up to about five amino acids in length. The OppA protein is located on the outside of the cellular membrane in *B. subtilis* as a lipoprotein (29) and in the periplasmic space of gram-negative organisms. This protein may determine the peptide specificity for transport through the system. Two membrane-spanning proteins, OppB and OppC, probably comprise the pore through which the peptide passes to the inside. On the cytoplasmic side of the membrane are two ATP-binding proteins, OppD and OppF, which provide the energy for peptide translocation through ATP hydrolysis. OppD and OppF are related to one another and the complete transport system is likely to consist of one molecule of each of the five proteins. The *B. subtilis* system differs somewhat from that found in organisms such as *Salmonella typhimurium* in that OppF does not appear to be required for all peptide transport. OppF mutants transport some peptides perfectly well and are normal for sporulation, but are blocked in competence (35). It seems reasonable to speculate that OppD and OppF have a role in determining specificity of peptide transport even though they are cytoplasmic or that OppF plays a dual role in peptide transport and in some competence pathway. The OppF requirement might be explained if this system also transported peptides out as well as in and outbound specificity was determined by the cytoplasmic components. The question remains as to the identity of the transported peptide that is required for the sporulation process. Furthermore, is it the lack (or excess) of the peptide within the cell that causes the sporulation defect or the accumulation of peptide outside the cell? Extracellular differentiation factors which might be peptide in nature have been postulated to be involved in cell density control in sporulation (13). Such factors might require internalization in order to elicit their effects. It is thought that the Opp system transports for recycling the peptides released from the cell wall during cell growth, and it seems possible that the level of recycling peptides may play some role in signaling internally the state of cell wall biosynthesis (29). Thus, turnover of cell wall peptides could play a role in control of growth or sporulation. At this point, the peptide responsible for the sporulation defect of opp mutants remains unidentified, and the target of its action is still a mystery.

Of the original *spo0* mutants identified by genetic analysis, the functions of the *spo0L* and *spo0J* loci are still unidentified. The *spo0L* locus is known to map between the *argC* and *metC* loci (32a). It has not yielded to cloning and sequence analysis at this point. The *spo0J* gene, on the other hand, has been cloned and sequenced, and revealed to be an operon of two genes with homology to the *korB-incC* genes of certain plasmids (22, 25). These genes are involved in the regulation of plasmid partition, and the obvious extrapolation is to suggest that the *spo0J* genes have a role in the segregation of the chromosome into the two compartments that ultimately become mother cell and forespore. It would be interesting if these genes did affect chromosome partition into the two compartments and if a defect in this partition led to the inability to express subsequent sporulation genes.

Pairs of genes with homology to *korB-incC* are also known to be involved in regulation of the expression of other genes. It is possible that the *spo0J* locus simply codes for regulatory proteins required for the transcription of certain genes necessary for the formation of stage II of sporulation. It will be of extreme interest to determine the role the *spo0J* locus plays in the control of subsequent sporulation gene expression.

REGULATION OF THE TRANSITION STATE

Sporulation is generally thought to begin at the end of exponential growth; however the actual hallmark of the initiation of sporulation is difficult to define. Certainly cells are capable of exiting exponential growth and entering stationary phase without initiating sporulation. This time interval existing between the end of exponential growth and the beginning of sporulation, as defined by some easily assayable property such as stage II gene activation, is the transition state. In typical sporulation medium, this period could last from 1 to 2 h, and it is characterized by production of several extracellular enzymes (e.g., proteases and amylase), as well as of antibiotics. Depending on the environment in which the organism finds itself, the transition state can be a staging period for sporulation, a period when the cell develops the competent state, or a period of very slow growth. Choosing between these states may involve the level of catabolizable carbohydrates in the media, since it has been found that high glucose levels and low free ammonia levels lead to hyperexpression of competence genes (18), a condition antithetical to high-level sporulation. Competence has recently been the subject of several comprehensive reviews (5, 6).

The regulatory proteins AbrB, Hpr, and SinR appear to affect directly the network of regulatory processes occurring during the transition state and, therefore, are loosely termed transition state regulators. The details of the control of each of these regulators have been recently reviewed, and for the purposes of this chapter only a conceptual framework will be constructed (39, 41, 43).

The AbrB protein is a classical transition state regulator, and its mechanism of action may be typical of this type of regulator. AbrB is a negative regulator of transcription of a fairly large number of unrelated genes that are normally thought to express and function during the transition state from exponential growth to stationary phase. Classical examples of such genes are those for proteases. AbrB prevents the expression of these genes in exponential growth by binding directly at the promoters for the genes and preventing their expression (45, 57). AbrB is not the main regulator of most of the genes that it controls, but instead it acts as a "preventer," impeding inadvertent expression during a growth period when these gene products either are not wanted or are deleterious to the growth of the cell. The repressive effects of AbrB appear to be a function of the level of AbrB protein in the cell, which is inversely proportional to the amount of Spo0A~P present in the cell (46). In early exponential growth when Spo0A is not phosphorylated, the *abrB* gene is maximally expressed and the high level of AbrB produced serves to prevent expression of these transition-state-regulated genes. As the cell approaches the onset of stationary phase, accumulation of Spo0A~P represses transcription of the *abrB* gene and the AbrB level within the cell falls, freeing these promoters for regulation by whatever normally regulates them (33, 44). Transcription of the *abrB* gene is tightly controlled by Spo0A~P, and this promoter is very sensitive to low levels of Spo0A~P in the cell (51). It is still unclear whether the AbrB protein is subject to any allosteric effector control on its activity. No effectors have been found and no evidence exists to point to effector molecules controlling its activity.

The AbrB protein was the first example of how the level of Spo0A~P in the cell can have wide-ranging effects on the regulation of large numbers of genes. AbrB serves to amplify the concentration effects of Spo0A~P by itself being responsive directly to the level of Spo0A~P in the cell. It is this control of other regulators by the Spo0A regulatory protein that complicated our understanding of its phenotype for so many years, but that also points to Spo0A as a master choreographer of postexponential events as well as sporulation.

An additional level of regulatory control by Spo0A~P is afforded by the regulation of the transcription of other transition state regulators by the AbrB protein. The *hpr* gene codes for a protein that is known to be a negative regulator of the synthesis of proteases, as well as being involved in catabolite repression of sporulation (16, 31). Overproduction of the AbrB protein in response to low levels of Spo0A~P appears to induce the transcription of *hpr* (Fig. 4). Hpr controls transcription of the major protease genes by negatively regulating their transcription and presumably has effects on other genes since overproduction of the Hpr protein causes a sporulation-defective phenotype (31). Transcription of some of the genes that Hpr controls is also prevented by the AbrB protein. Again, there is no evidence for effector molecules controlling the activity of Hpr protein, although the present data cannot rule out this possibility.

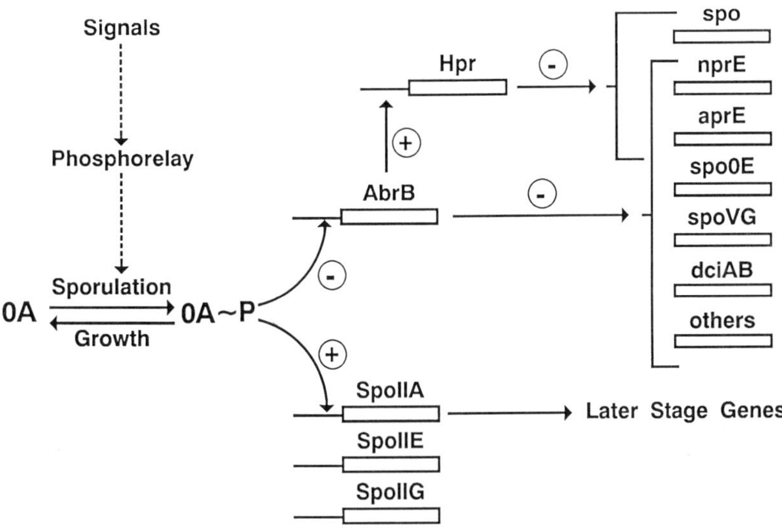

FIGURE 4. Central role of AbrB as a transition state regulator. Growth decreases the level of Spo0A~P, a situation which leads to high-level expression of AbrB. This regulator activates the synthesis of Hpr, which, with AbrB, represses the transcription of many genes associated with the onset of stationary phase.

The complex control pattern of the *sinR* gene is an example of how many different regulators can converge on the synthesis and control of another transition state regulator. This gene codes for a regulator termed SinR, for sporulation inhibition, and the overproduction of this regulatory protein results in inhibition of sporulation (11). The *sinR* gene appears to be constitutively transcribed and codes for a DNA binding protein (12). The repressive function of the SinR protein can be negated by the production of an inhibitor protein SinI, which is the product of a gene just upstream of the *sinR* locus (2) (Fig. 5). The expression of the *sinI* gene is controlled by the cellular environment. The promoter for the *sinI* gene has binding sites in vitro for Hpr, AbrB, and Spo0A (41b). Under conditions of exponential growth, it is expected that SinI transcription would be repressed since both AbrB and Hpr are known to be active negative regulators during this time. The consequence of this situation is that SinR would be an effective negative regulator of sporulation since its inhibitor is not present. As the cells progress toward the end of exponential growth and stationary phase, the production of both AbrB and Hpr is known to fall, thus freeing the promoter of *sinI* for transcription. Additionally, an Spo0A~P binding site is located upstream of the *sinI* promoter, suggesting that Spo0A~P accumulation positively regulates the transcription of the *sinI* gene (41a). As a

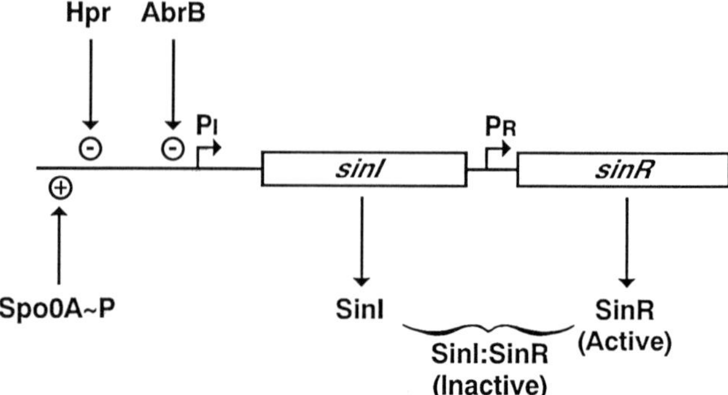

FIGURE 5. Complex regulation of the sporulation inhibitor SinR. SinR is a negative regulator of sporulation whose activity is neutralized by interaction with SinI. During growth, SinI is repressed by both Hpr and AbrB, resulting in active SinR. The onset of sporulation raises the Spo0A~P level, which may act as a positive regulator of SinI transcription while decreasing the repressive activity of both AbrB and Hpr.

consequence, the production of SinI should result in the inhibition of SinR activity and thus relieve from repression those genes negatively regulated by SinR.

These examples probably only provide a glimpse of the complexity of regulatory interactions in the rapidly changing period that we term the transition state. For example, AbrB is known to have effects on competence, and it seems likely that unraveling these networks and attempting to isolate the effects of a given regulator may consume our energies for the next few years. As mentioned before, the genes involved in the regulation appear to be yielding to molecular genetic analyses, but the role of metabolic and environmental effector molecules in this process or in any other transition state process still remains a mystery. Perhaps we are fast approaching the limitations of molecular biology, and it may be necessary to revive the lost art of biochemistry.

REGULATORY PROPERTIES OF THE Spo0A TRANSCRIPTION FACTOR

The end result of the action of the transition state regulators and the phosphorelay is to phosphorylate the Spo0A transcription factor. It is clear from mutation studies that phosphorylation is required for both the repression and activation properties of Spo0A (48). The level of Spo0A~P in the cell is controlled by both transcription of the *spo0A* gene and control of the flow of phosphate to Spo0A. These two factors cooperate to produce different levels of Spo0A~P at different times in the life cycle of the organism. It is thought, but has not been proven, that the level of phosphorylated Spo0A is very low in exponential growth, and as the culture approaches the end of exponential growth, there is an accumulation of a moderate level of Spo0A~P. It is believed that the major function of this Spo0A~P is to repress the AbrB promoter and any other promoter that might have high affinity for Spo0A~P. The AbrB promoter is unique in that it contains tandemly arrayed 0A boxes separated by one helical turn of the DNA (46). This arrangement may lead to an especially high-affinity site for Spo0A~P, since it is possible that two molecules of Spo0A~P can bind to this site and stabilize through protein-protein interactions as well as protein-DNA interactions. Regardless of the actual mechanism, the AbrB promoter seems to be the most sensitive of the Spo0A-controlled promoters to Spo0A~P. The consequence of this sensitivity is that the level of AbrB protein within the cell falls, allowing transcription of many of the genes characteristic of the transition state. In a *spo0A* mutant that is unable to repress *abrB*, the AbrB concentration continues to increase during this time period and none of these AbrB-sensitive genes are transcribed, resulting in a cell which appears to be locked in exponential growth phase transcription properties.

The other major role of Spo0A~P is to act as an activator of the transcription of the stage II genes *spoIIA*, *spoIIE*, and *spoIIG*, and perhaps others that have yet to be identified (37, 48, 56). This activation is known to occur at some time later than the turning on of AbrB-controlled functions, and it is believed that activation of these promoters requires much higher concentrations of Spo0A~P than were required for repression of the *abrB* gene. Thus, the concept of a concentration barrier to stage II gene expression may be applicable. Stage II promoters need the phosphorylated form of Spo0A in order to be recognized as promoters by the transcription complex (48). Spo0A footprints over large regions of the stage II promoters, suggesting that more than one molecule of Spo0A~P binds to these upstream regions (37, 48, 56). These results may indicate that several molecules of Spo0A~P are required for transcription to initiate from these promoters. Whether this process involves Spo0A-Spo0A interaction or involves some higher-order protein-DNA interaction has yet to be determined.

The present picture of how Spo0A~P controls transcription is thought to reflect the level of Spo0A~P in the cell, coupled with the differential affinity of the various promoters for Spo0A~P. This view fits the available evidence but certainly does not rule out levels of control other than concentration. For example, several eukaryotic transcription factors are controlled by phosphorylation, and by phosphorylation at several different sites brought about by different protein kinases. Thus, it might be possible that the function of other protein kinases or modifying enzymes are required for Spo0A~P to act as a transcription activator of the stage II genes, but not, for example, as a repressor of the *abrB* gene. Several other possible alterations could be envisioned, such as increased or decreased supercoiling of the template that could play a role in the ability of Spo0A~P to activate promoters.

PERSPECTIVES

The study of sporulation in *B. subtilis* has not only given us a glimpse of the mechanisms of cellular differentiation, but also opened our eyes to the complex regulatory interactions that occur under conditions of limited growth in stationary phase. To put sporulation into perspective, it is the last resort of the cell that would rather grow and divide if it had the choice. Under natural conditions, the cell must be forced to assess continually its environment and metabolic state in order to decide whether to initiate another round of DNA replication and cell division or enter stationary phase. Our ignorance of the signals being monitored by kinases A and B, transition state regulators, and the rest of the regulatory network directing growth and sporulation certainly must be counted as one of the great failures of this research. We have only a rudimentary knowledge of the cellular conditions that direct these decisions. Why is this so? In the case of the kinases the duplication of pathways precluded the isolation of mutants in the signaling network to any individual kinase. Our preconceived idea that such mutants should have a Spo0 phenotype was wrong. Now that the phenotype of such mutants is known, there should be rapid progress toward uncovering the mechanism of activation of the kinases.

We know more about the transcriptional control of the early events than about the regulatory controls on preformed pathways. Transcriptional events are easier to detect with molecular genetic techniques than protein-effector molecule interactions. Yet protein-effector interactions are at the heart of sporulation regulation and are at least of equal importance to transcriptional events. One need only look at the surfeit of regulatory proteins such as Hpr, AbrB, Sin, GsiA, and the entire competence cascade for which we have no clue as to effector molecules to realize that there is a serious imbalance in our knowledge. New techniques and probably fresh minds are needed to look at this problem from a protein chemistry perspective.

We have a fragmentary picture of the extremely complicated network of regulatory interactions occurring at the onset of stationary phase and absolute ignorance about the molecules directing this network. The formation of a forespore is a complicated process of membrane growth and differentiation which may be one of the most interesting problems in the developmental biology of membranes. We have knowledge of the genes that block this process, yet the biochemical attack on this problem has been virtually nonexistent. This is a time of great change within the cell, and the opportunity to study unknown mechanisms of basic importance has never been greater. We know so much, yet we know so little.

The writing of this chapter was supported, in part, by grant GM19416-22 from the National Institute of General Medical Sciences, National Institutes of Health, United States Public Health Service. This is manuscript 8028-MEM from the Department of Molecular and Experimental Medicine.

REFERENCES

1. **Antoniewski, C., B. Savelli, and P. Stragier.** 1990. The *spoIIJ* gene, which regulates early developmental steps in *Bacillus subtilis,* belongs to a class of environmentally responsive genes. *J. Bacteriol.* **172:**86–93.
2. **Bai, U., I. Mandic-Mulec, and I. Smith.** 1993. I-sin modulates the activity of Sin, a developmental switch protein of *Bacillus subtilis,* by protein-protein interaction. *Genes Dev.* **7:**139–148.
3. **Burbulys, D., K. A. Trach, and J. A. Hoch.** 1991. The initiation of sporulation in *Bacillus subtilis* is controlled by a multicomponent phosphorelay. *Cell* **64:**545–552.
4. **Chibazakura, T., F. Kawamura, and H. Takahashi.** 1991. Differential regulation of *spo0A* transcription in *Bacillus subtilis:* Glucose represses promoter switching at the initiation of sporulation. *J. Bacteriol.* **173:**2625–2632.
5. **Dubnau, D.** 1991. The regulation of genetic competence in *Bacillus subtilis. Mol. Microbiol.* **5:**11–18.
6. **Dubnau, D.** 1991. Genetic competence in *Bacillus subtilis. Microbiol. Rev.* **55:**395–424.
7. **Dubnau, E., J. Weir, G. Nair, L. Carter, III, C. Moran, Jr., and I. Smith.** 1988. *Bacillus* sporulation gene *spo0H* codes for sigma-30 (sigma-H). *J. Bacteriol.* **170:**1054–1062.
8. **Errington, J.** 1993. Sporulation in *Bacillus subtilis:* Regulation of gene expression and control of morphogenesis. *Microbiol. Rev.* **57:**1–33.
9. **Ferrari, F. A., K. Trach, and J. A. Hoch.** 1985. Sequence analysis of the *spo0B* locus reveals a polycistronic transcription unit. *J. Bacteriol.* **161:**556–562.
10. **Ferrari, F. A., K. Trach, D. LeCoq, J. Spence, E. Ferrari, and J. A. Hoch.** 1985. Characterization of the *spo0A* locus and its deduced product. *Proc. Natl. Acad. Sci. USA* **82:**2647–2651.
11. **Gaur, N. K., E. Dubnau, and I. Smith.** 1986. Characterization of a cloned *Bacillus subtilis* gene that inhibits sporulation in multiple copies. *J. Bacteriol.* **168:**860–869.
12. **Gaur, N. K., J. Oppenheim, and I. Smith.** 1991. The *Bacillus subtilis sin* gene, a regulator of alternate developmental processes, codes for a DNA-binding protein. *J. Bacteriol.* **173:**678–686.

13. **Grossman, A. D., and R. Losick.** 1988. Extracellular control of spore formation in *Bacillus subtilis. Proc. Natl. Acad. Sci. USA* **85:**4369–4373.
14. **Hoch, J. A.** 1976. Genetics of bacterial sporulation. *Adv. Genet.* **18:**69–99.
14a. **Hoch, J. A.** Unpublished data.
15. **Ireton, K., and A. D. Grossman.** 1992. Coupling between gene expression and DNA synthesis early during development in *Bacillus subtilis. Proc. Natl. Acad. Sci. USA* **89:**8808–8812.
16. **Ito, J., and J. Spizizen.** 1973. Genetic studies of catabolite repression insensitive sporulation mutants of *Bacillus subtilis. Colloq. Int. CNRS* **227:**81–82.
17. **Kudoh, J., T. Ikeuchi, and K. Kurahashi.** 1985. Nucleotide sequences of the sporulation gene *spo0A* and its mutant genes of *Bacillus subtilis. Proc. Natl. Acad. Sci. USA* **82:**2665–2668.
18. **Kunst, F., T. Msadek, and G. Rapoport.** Signal transduction network controlling degradative enzyme synthesis and competence in *Bacillus subtilis. Mol. Microbiol.*, in press.
19. **Lepesant, J. -A., F. Kunst, M. Pascal, J. Kejzlarova-Lepesant, M. Steinmetz, and R. Dedonder.** 1976. Specific and pleiotropic regulatory mechanisms in the sucrose system of *Bacillus subtilis* 168, p. 58–69. *In* D. Schlessinger (ed.), *Microbiology—1976.* American Society for Microbiology, Washington, D.C.
20. **Lewandoski, M., E. Dubnau, and I. Smith.** 1986. Transcriptional regulation of the *spo0F* gene of *Bacillus subtilis. J. Bacteriol.* **168:**870–877.
21. **Mandelstam, J., and S. A. Higgs.** 1974. Induction of sporulation during synchronized chromosome replication in *Bacillus subtilis. J. Bacteriol.* **120:**38–42.
22 **Moriya, S., T. Atlung, F. G. Hansen, H. Yoshikawa, and N. Ogasawara.** 1992. Cloning of an autonomously replicating sequence (*ars*) from the *Bacillus subtilis* chromosome. *Mol. Microbiol.* **6:**309–315.
23. **Mueller, J. P., G. Bukusoglu, and A. L. Sonenshein.** 1992. Transcriptional regulation of *Bacillus subtilis* glucose starvation inducible genes: control of *gsiA* by the Comp-ComA signal transduction system. *J. Bacteriol.* **174:**4361–4373.
24. **Mueller, J. P., and A. L. Sonenshein.** 1992. Role of the *Bacillus subtilis gsiA* gene in regulation of early sporulation gene expression. *J. Bacteriol.* **174:**4374–4383.
25. **Mysliwiec, T. H., Errington, A. B. Vaidya, and M. G. Bramucci.** 1991. The *Bacillus subtilis spo0J* gene: evidence for involvement in catabolite repression of sporulation. *J. Bacteriol.* **173:**1911–1919.
26. **Ninfa, A. J., and B. Magasanik.** 1986. Covalent modification of the *glnG* product, NRI, by the *glnL* product, NRII, regulates the transcription of the *glnALG* operon in *Escherichia coli. Proc. Natl. Acad. Sci. USA* **83:**5909–5913.
27. **Nurse, P.** 1990. Universal control mechanism regulating onset of M-phase. *Nature* (London) **344:**503–508.
27a. **Ohlsen, K., and J. Hoch.** Unpublished data.
28. **Perego, M., S. P. Cole, D. Burbulys, K. Trach, and J. A. Hoch.** 1989. Characterization of the gene for a protein kinase which phosphorylates the sporulation-regulatory proteins Spo0A and Spo0F of *Bacillus subtilis. J. Bacteriol.* **171:** 6187–6196.
29. **Perego, M., C. F. Higgins, S. R. Pearce, M. P. Gallagher, and J. A. Hoch.** 1991. The oligopeptide transport system of *Bacillus subtilis* plays a role in the initiation of sporulation. *Mol. Microbiol.* **5:**173–185.
30. **Perego, M., and J. A. Hoch.** 1987. Isolation and sequence of the *spo0E* gene: its role in initiation of sporulation in *Bacillus subtilis. Mol. Microbiol.* **1:**125–132.

31. **Perego, M., and J. A. Hoch.** 1988. Sequence analysis and regulation of the *hpr* locus, a regulatory gene for protease production and sporulation in *Bacillus subtilis*. *J. Bacteriol.* **170:**2560–2567.
32. **Perego, M., and J. A. Hoch.** 1991. Negative regulation of *Bacillus subtilis* sporulation by the *spo0E* gene product. *J. Bacteriol.* **173:**2514–2520.
32a. **Perego, M., and J. A. Hoch.** Unpublished data.
33. **Perego, M., G. B. Spiegelman, and J. A. Hoch.** 1988. Structure of the gene for the transition state regulator, *abrB:* regulator synthesis is controlled by the *spo0A* sporulation gene in *Bacillus subtilis*. *Mol. Microbiol.* **2:**689–699.
34. **Piggot, P. J., and J. G. Coote.** 1976. Genetic aspects of bacterial endospore formation. *Bacteriol. Rev.* **40:**908–962.
35. **Rudner, D. Z., J. R. Ladeaux, K. Breton, and A. D. Grossman.** 1991. The *spo0K* locus of *Bacillus subtilis* is homologous to the oligopeptide permease locus and is required for sporulation and competence. *J. Bacteriol.* **173:**1388–1398.
36. **Ryter, A.** 1965. Étude morphologique de la sporulation de *Bacillus subtilis*. *Ann. Inst. Pasteur* **108:**40–60.
37. **Satola, S. W., J. M. Baldus, and C. P. Moran, Jr.** 1992. Binding of Spo0A stimulates *spoIIG* promoter activity in *Bacillus subtilis*. *J. Bacteriol.* **174:**1448–1453.
38. **Schaeffer, P., J. Millet, and J. Aubert.** 1965. Catabolic repression of bacterial sporulation. *Proc. Natl. Acad. Sci. USA* **54:**701–711.
39. **Smith, I.** 1993. Regulatory proteins that control late growth development, p. 785–800. *In* A. L. Sonenshein, J. A. Hoch, and R. Losick (ed.), *Bacillus subtilis and Other Gram-Positive Bacteria: Biochemistry, Physiology, and Molecular Genetics*. American Society for Microbiology, Washington, D.C.
40. **Stock, J. B., A. J. Ninfa, and A. M. Stock.** 1989. Protein phosphorylation and regulation of adaptive response in bacteria. *Microbiol. Rev.* **53:**450–490.
41. **Strauch, M. A.** 1993. AbrB, a transition state regulator, p. 757–764. *In* A. L. Sonenshein, J. A. Hoch, and R. Losick (ed.), *Bacillus subtilis and Other Gram-Positive Bacteria: Biochemistry, Physiology and Molecular Genetics*. American Society for Microbiology, Washington, D.C.
41a. **Strauch, M. A.** Unpublished data.
41b. **Strauch, M. A.** Personal communication.
42. **Strauch, M. A., D. de Mendoza, and J. A. Hoch.** 1992. *cis*-Unsaturated fatty acids specifically inhibit a signal-transducing protein kinase required for initiation of sporulation in *Bacillus subtilis*. *Mol. Microbiol.* **6:**2909–2917.
43. **Strauch, M. A., and J. A. Hoch.** 1992. Transition state regulators: sentinels of *Bacillus subtilis* post-exponential gene expression. *Mol. Microbiol.* **7:**337–342.
44. **Strauch, M. A., M. Perego, D. Burbulys, and J. A. Hoch.** 1989. The transition state transcription regulator AbrB of *Bacillus subtilis* is autoregulated during vegetative growth. *Mol. Microbiol.* **3:**1203–1209.
45. **Strauch, M. A., G. B. Spiegelman, M. Perego, W. C. Johnson, D. Burbulys, and J. A. Hoch.** 1989. The transition state transcription regulator *abrB* of *Bacillus subtilis* is a DNA binding protein. *EMBO J.* **8:**1615–1621.
46. **Strauch, M., V. Webb, G. Spiegelman, and J. A. Hoch.** 1990. The Spo0A protein of *Bacillus subtilis* is a repressor of the *abrB* gene. *Proc Natl. Acad. Sci. USA* **87:**1801–1805.
47. **Strauch, M. A., J. -J. Wu, R. H. Jonas, and J. A. Hoch.** 1992. A positive feedback loop controls transcription of the *spo0F* gene, a component of the sporulation phosphorelay in *Bacillus subtilis*. *Mol. Microbiol.* **7:**967–974.

48. **Trach, K., D. Burbulys, M. Strauch, J. -J. Wu, N. Dhillon, R. Jonas, C. Hanstein, P. Kallio, M. Perego, T. Bird, G. Spiegelman, C. Fogher, and J. A. Hoch.** 1991. Control of the initiation of sporulation in *Bacillus subtilis* by a phosphorelay. *Res. Microbiol.* **142:**815–823.
49. **Trach, K., J. W. Chapman, P. J. Piggot, and J. A. Hoch.** 1985. Deduced product of the stage 0 sporulation gene *spo0F* shares homology with the Spo0A, OmpR and SfrA proteins. *Proc. Natl. Acad. Sci. USA* **82:**7260–7264.
50. **Trach, K., and J. A. Hoch.** 1989. The *Bacillus subtilis spo0B* stage 0 sporulation operon encodes an essential GTP-binding protein. *J. Bacteriol.* **171:**1362–1371.
51. **Trach, K. A., and J. A. Hoch.** 1993. Multisensory activation of the phosphorelay initiating sporulation in *Bacillus subtilis:* identification and sequence of the protein kinase of the alternate pathway. *Mol. Microbiol.* **8:**69–79.
51a. **Trach, K. A., M. Strauch, and J. A. Hoch.** Unpublished data.
52. **Weickert, M. J., and G. H. Chambliss.** 1990. Site-directed mutagenesis of a catabolite repression operator sequence in *Bacillus subtilis. Proc. Natl. Acad. Sci. USA* **87:**6238–6242.
53. **Weir, J., M. Predich, E. Dubnau, G. Nair, and I. Smith.** 1991. Regulation of *spo0H,* a gene coding for the *Bacillus subtilis* σ^H factor. *J. Bacteriol.* **173:**521–529.
54. **Yamashita, S., F. Kawamura, H. Yoshikawa, H. Takahashi, Y. Kobayashi, and H. Saito.** 1989. Dissection of the expression signals of the *spo0A* gene of *Bacillus subtilis:* glucose represses sporulation-specific expression. *J. Gen. Microbiol.* **135:**1335–1345.
55. **Yamashita, S., H. Yoshikawa, F. Kawamura, H. Takahashi, T. Yamamoto, Y. Kobayashi, and H. Saito.** 1986. The effect of *spo0* mutations on the expression of *spo0A*- and *spo0F-lacZ* fusions. *Mol. Gen. Genet.* **205:**28–33.
56. **York, K., T. J. Kenney, S. Satola, C. P. Moran, Jr., H. Poth, and P. Youngman.** 1992. Spo0A controls the σ^A-dependent activation of *Bacillus subtilis* sporulation-specific transcription unit *spoIIE. J. Bacteriol.* **174:**2648–2658.
57. **Zuber, P., and R. Losick.** 1987. Role of AbrB in Spo0A- and Spo0B-dependent utilization of a sporulation promoter in *Bacillus subtilis. J. Bacteriol.* **169:**2223–2230.

Regulation of Bacterial Differentiation
Edited by P. Piggot et al.

Chapter 4

Regulation and Integration of Antibiotic Production and Morphological Differentiation in *Streptomyces* spp.

Wendy C. Champness and Keith F. Chater

The streptomycetes are common filamentous gram-positive soil bacteria with a morphological complexity unusual among prokaryotes. They are well-known for their capacity to synthesize a vast repertoire of secondary metabolites, including many useful antibiotics and other products such as the antitumor drug adriamycin; ivermectin, an agent used to combat African river blindness; the immunosuppressants cyclosporin, FK-506, and rapamycin; and the herbicide bialaphos (phosphinothricin).

Besides their commercial importance, streptomycetes present a fascinating example of a primitive multicellular developmental cycle that includes true cellular differentiation. Growth is by hyphal extension and branching, forming a matted substrate mycelium. After a period of growth, typically 1 to 3 days, depending on laboratory conditions, vertically directed aerial hyphae develop and secondary metabolism commences. Sometimes the secondary metabolites are pigments, and the synchrony with which these two processes occur is particularly obvious. Each aerial hypha grows as a multigenomic filament which eventually subdivides into perhaps 50 or more haploid spores. Substantial portions of the substrate mycelium are lysed to provide nutrients for the developing aerial mycelium. On plate cultures, the colony can function for several weeks as a differentiated, multicellular organism: growth continues at the colony edges; sporulating aerial hyphae continually grow out from the substrate mycelium; and certain cells (we do not know which or how many) produce antibiotics.

Wendy C. Champness, Department of Microbiology, Michigan State University, East Lansing, Michigan 48824. ***Keith F. Chater,*** John Innes Institute, John Innes Centre, Colney Lane, Norwich NR4 7UH, United Kingdom.

In this chapter we briefly review the earlier stages in colony formation, which have yet to be subjected to genetic analysis, and then consider in more detail the ensuing morphological and physiological differentiation.

VEGETATIVE GROWTH OF STREPTOMYCETES OBLIGATORILY INVOLVES AT LEAST TWO CELL TYPES

In appropriate conditions, a *Streptomyces* spp. spore germinates (59). Germ tube emergence is followed by a period of extension growth, during which rounds of DNA replication are initiated synchronously at intervals of approximately 30 (110) to 47 (89) min. Each round of replication takes about 90 min in *Streptomyces antibioticus* (110), implying that there are multiple replication forks. This is about twice the replication time of *Escherichia coli,* as might be expected based on the evidence from pulsed field gel analysis that the chromosomes of *Streptomyces* spp. are nearly twice as long as that of *E. coli* (85, 96), and assuming a single replication origin—an assumption partially borne out by the isolation of unique *oriC*-like DNA fragments from *Streptomyces coelicolor* and *Streptomyces lividans* (22, 140), although the existence of other replication origins with different characteristics is not ruled out. The rate of germ tube elongation doubles with each successive round of replication and may exceed 40 µm/h (91). It has been proposed that each new replication fork stimulates the synthesis of a new site of peptidoglycan synthesis at the growing tip (most cell wall synthesis is located within 10 µm of the tip) (49, 110). A model of the organization of these sites in relation to the extending cell wall has been proposed (110). After the initial period of rapid extension, the rate of elongation becomes constant (it can be more than 20 µm/h) (5, 89). This observation may reflect the formation of septa cutting off the growing tip from the influence of chromosomes beyond the new septum, and an equilibrium between establishment and inactivation of sites of wall synthesis (110). At rapid growth rates, it seems likely that a position for septation is somehow marked in the center of a hyphal tip cell that is about 25 µm long (90). A morphologically obvious septum develops more than 30 min later, by which time the tip has moved by several micrometers; as a result, the new septum is closer to the preceding septum than to the tip (90).

Clearly implied in these considerations is the generation, as a result of septation, of two different cell types: the apical cell continues to extend, and normal nucleoid segregation takes place, while the interseptal cell does not elongate, even though DNA replication continues (93). This unbalanced situation in the interseptal cell places spatial constraints on nucleoid segregation, and indeed it seems that nucleoids increase in size rather than separate. The implicit increase in the DNA/cytoplasm ratio may be partially balanced by an increase in hyphal diameter. However, the most obvious escape from the imbalance is through branching. In *Streptomyces granaticolor,* nearly every subapical cell develops a branch (92), which becomes populated by properly segregating nucleoids apparently derived from one of the enlarged nucleoids of the parental cell (88).

OTHER HYPHAL CELL TYPES OCCUR AS THE MYCELIUM DEVELOPS

This pattern of primary—and further subsidiary—branching inevitably leads to hyphal crowding. This crowding might be sensed in any of several ways: by some kind of internal counting of cell cycles or branching order; by the occurrence of direct contact between hyphae; by an increased concentration of extracellular signaling molecules; or by an outstripping of nutrient supply by the increasing demands of growth, i.e., starvation. Of these possibilities, only the last two have received experimental attention (see below). In any case, physiological changes can be detected as the vegetative mycelium becomes more dense and the overall growth rate falls. Secondary metabolism begins, some hyphae accumulate intracellular glycogen granules (14), and some undergo autolysis (137). It is by no means clear whether these three physiological processes always occur in different cells, or successively or simultaneously in one and the same cell. It is typical for any one *Streptomyces* sp. to produce several different secondary metabolites. Since the environmental regulation of each pathway and the metabolic origins of the precursors are to some extent specific, different hyphal compartments may perhaps synthesize different metabolites. Thus, the proportions of physiologically different cell types could well differ in different growth conditions, in different locations within the colony, or at different times during colony development.

As these changes take place in the substrate mycelium, aerial branches grow away from the nutrient source, apparently by apical extension as during vegetative growth (109). This aerial growth follows a transitory cessation of macromolecular synthesis (48). The further development of aerial hyphae and the formation of spores are considered in later sections.

STREPTOMYCES COELICOLOR A3(2): A MODEL ORGANISM

Streptomyces research over the years has been diffusely spread over many *Streptomyces* species and strains, because of their production of important natural products. However, to analyze the fundamental biology of streptomycetes, molecular geneticists have focused on *S. coelicolor* A3(2), which has well-developed genetics (36, 63). *S. coelicolor* produces at least four antibiotics (actinorhodin, undecylprodigiosin, methylenomycin, and the Ca^{2+}-dependent antibiotic, CDA). Interest in actinorhodin has been especially high because it is a polyketide, as are many medically and commercially important antibiotics (64, 78). Also, actinorhodin is blue or red and undecylprodigiosin is red or yellow, depending on pH, so color phenotypes can be used easily to dissect antibiotic biosynthesis and regulation. On plate-grown cultures, the formation of fluffy white aerial hyphae coincides with production of the antibiotic pigments, and the aerial mycelium subsequently becomes gray-brown as mature spores form. These attributes present tempting visual phenotypes for mutant isolation.

In liquid culture, *S. coelicolor* produces antibiotics, but does not show morphological differentiation. This characteristic hinders physiological and biochemical studies on sporulation. A recent report (41) that calcium addition facilitates formation of spore-like structures in *S. coelicolor* may prove useful. Some strains of another streptomycete, *Streptomyces griseus,* do sporulate in response to defined nutritional limitations or to nutritional downshift (80, 94) and have therefore been investigated in some detail.

ANTIBIOTICS AND OTHER *STREPTOMYCES* NATURAL PRODUCTS ARE GENERALLY GROWTH-PHASE-REGULATED

Antibiotics (and other secondary metabolites) are generally produced only at low growth rate or during stationary phase (103). The mycelial nature of *Streptomyces* spp. growth complicates distinctions between growth and stationary phases, since the hyphae within a mycelial clump may be physiologically heterogeneous and individual cell compartments may experience different degrees of growth limitation. Nevertheless, exponential biomass accumulation can be achieved in batch culture for a few (five to six) doublings even in defined or partially defined liquid medium (59, 131). In *Streptomyces hygroscopicus* grown in a complex medium, a transient growth pause preceded entry into stationary phase when bialaphos production commenced. Expression of the bialaphos genes was correlated with the pause period (60). A similar pause has also been reported in complex medium for *S. coelicolor* (99). Whether this pause reflects a particular aspect of vegetative growth, such as cessation of branch formation, is not known.

Although antibiotic production in *S. coelicolor* is usually associated with stationary phase (47, 51, 58, 113, 133), it can occur during vegetative growth under certain conditions (57). Some investigators have noted a correlation between ppGpp accumulation and antibiotic biosynthesis in various streptomycetes (60, 79, 114). Nevertheless, a causal relationship has not been established: ppGpp accumulation in response to nutritional shiftdown or serine hydroxamate treatment is not sufficient to trigger antibiotic production (10, 133). Rather, the suggestion has been made that sensing of growth rate or growth cessation may be critical (133).

CLUSTERS OF GENES FOR ANTIBIOTIC BIOSYNTHESIS

A detailed picture of the genetic organization and regulation of antibiotic biosynthetic genes has emerged from extensive studies of cloned DNA from a range of *Streptomyces* strains (for recent reviews, see references 28, 30, 77, 104, and 126). The *act* genes, for actinorhodin synthesis, serve as a prototype (reviewed in reference 35). Early genetic analysis of a large collection of *act* mutants (121) established the general principle of clustering of the entire set of genes involved in synthesis of a particular antibiotic. Subsequent cloning by complementation of the Act phenotype led to isolation of a 26-kb fragment which complemented all of the *act* mutants (100), and could confer actinorhodin production on nonproducing *Streptomyces* spp. Twenty-three open reading frames are closely spaced within the *act* cluster (101). More than five *act* transcripts have been identified, some being monocistronic, some encoding many polypeptides. Many of the early biosynthetic enzymes are encoded by one large transcript, whereas the middle of the cluster is expressed as several shorter transcripts encoding additional biosynthetic, regulatory, and resistance/export functions. Complete *S. coelicolor* gene sets have also been cloned that permit surrogate streptomycete hosts to synthesize undecylprodigiosin (the *red* genes [102]) and methylenomycin (the *mmy* genes [28]). Like the *act* genes, these clusters occupy 20 to 30 kb of DNA. It is now a general principle that antibiotic biosynthesis is genetically determined by large gene clusters (Fig. 1) that also contain specific resistance and regulatory genes (30).

EXPRESSION OF AN ANTIBIOTIC'S BIOSYNTHETIC GENES DEPENDS ON ONE OR MORE PATHWAY-SPECIFIC REGULATORS

Regulation by pathway-specific regulators is an emerging general paradigm for antibiotic regulation (30). For example, one centrally located gene in the actinorhodin cluster, *actII-ORF4*, encodes a positive regulator of many or all of the *act* biosynthetic genes (reviewed in reference 35). *actII-ORF4* mutations prevent actinorhodin cosynthesis with all other *act* mu-

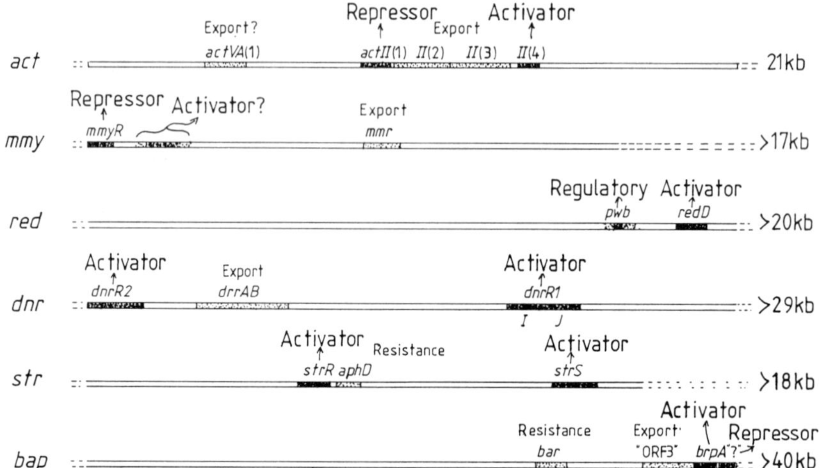

FIGURE 1. Gene clusters encoding biosynthesis of various antibiotics. Known or suspected regulatory, resistance, and export genes are emphasized by stippling (heavier for regulatory genes). The extent of the known relevant DNA is indicated by solid lines. Regions indicated by broken lines may be unrelated to the gene clusters. The *act* (actinorhodin [44, 100]), *mmy* (methylenomycin [30, 33]), and *red* (undecylprodigiosin [102, 113]) clusters are found in *S. coelicolor.* The *dnr* (daunorubicin [132]) cluster is in *Streptomyces peucetius; str* (streptomycin [42]) is in *S. griseus* and *Streptomyces glaucescens;* and *bap* (bialaphos [6, 60, 119]) is in *Streptomyces hygroscopicus.* The pathway-specific regulator genes are discussed in the text.

tant classes by preventing accumulation of *act* transcripts. Interestingly, addition of only one or two extra copies of *actII-ORF4* on a low-copy-number plasmid can cause enormous actinorhodin overproduction. Similar observations define *redD* as a putative pathway-specific activator of red biosynthetic genes (113). Remarkably, the products (44, 113) of *actII-ORF4* and *redD* share considerable amino acid similarity throughout almost their entire lengths, so they are likely to have similar modes of action (Fig. 2). Although a potential DNA-binding domain was suggested near the RedD N terminus (113), recent work makes it likely that the correct N terminus of RedD does not extend so far upstream (11). Thus the amino acid sequences of ActII ORF4 and RedD have not yet helped in prediction of their precise functions. Interestingly, DnrI, the product of the *dnrI* activator gene for the daunorubicin biosynthetic genes of *S. peucetius,* is very similar in amino acid sequence to ActII ORF4 and RedD, and can even restore some actinorhodin production to an *S. coelicolor actII-ORF4* mutant (132). Likewise, introduction of *actII-ORF4* into *S. peucetius* can stimulate daunorubicin overproduction. The functional equivalence of DnrI and ActII

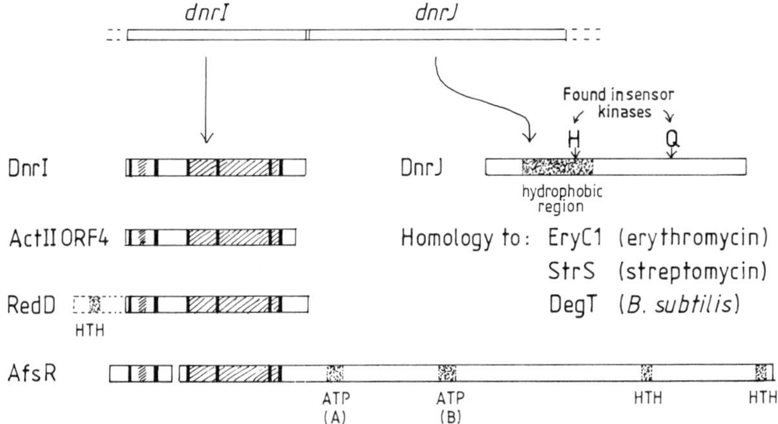

FIGURE 2. Families of regulators involved in secondary metabolism. Adjacent genes in the *dnr* (daunorubicin) cluster of *S. peucetius* encode regulators of families otherwise found in isolation from each other. Density of shading in Dnr, ActII ORF4, RedD, and AfsR indicates the degree of conservation among them (44, 132). The dotted extension of RedD indicates a segment originally considered from DNA sequence analysis to be present (113), but more recent evidence suggests that the N terminus may align with that of ActII ORF4 (11). ATP(A) and ATP(B) indicate potential ATP-binding sites, and HTH indicates possible helix-turn-helix DNA-binding motifs. The members of the DnrJ family possess histidine and glutamine residues in positions equivalent to those of sensor kinases (132).

ORF4 may be related to the fact that daunorubicin and actinorhodin are structurally related, both being aromatic polyketides. Clearly not all polyketide antibiotics are regulated by a member of an ActII ORF4 family, since regulation of the macrolide polyketide spiromycin in *Streptomyces ambofaciens* involves a gene, *srmR,* whose predicted product is not similar in sequence to other data base proteins (46).

Other well-characterized antibiotic gene clusters, including those producing streptomycin in *S. griseus* and the herbicide bialaphos in *S. hygroscopicus,* employ the activator genes *strR/strS* (reviewed in reference 42) and *brpA* (119), respectively (Fig. 2), whereas two further pathway activator elements, *dnrJ* and R_2, have been found in the *dnr* cluster (132). Further description of the relatedness of pathway-specific activators within and across species lines and with respect to the antibiotic structural classes will be of great practical and evolutionary interest.

Some repressor genes have also been found in clusters of antibiotic biosynthetic genes. The *actII-ORF1* gene product represses the *actII-ORF2,3* transcription unit involved in actinorhodin export (21, 44), and disruption of the *mmyR* gene, at one end of the gene cluster for methylenomycin production, causes methylenomycin overproduction (33). Interestingly, both gene products resemble repressors of tetracycline resistance genes in gram-negative bacteria (18, 44).

GROWTH-PHASE-REGULATED EXPRESSION OF PATHWAY-SPECIFIC REGULATORS

The *actII-ORF4* gene is expressed as a monocistronic transcript from a single transcription start point (47). In a defined medium liquid culture system, this transcript is barely detectable during exponential phase but increases dramatically in abundance when the culture enters stationary phase, shortly before the *act* biosynthetic gene transcripts appear (47) Similar patterns of expression have been reported for *redD* (133) and the *brpA* activator gene (119). In these conditions, accumulation of a threshold quantity of ActII ORF4 or RedD appears to be sufficient to initiate actinorhodin or undecylprodigiosin production. If *actII-ORF4* is introduced as a multicopy clone, high levels of *actII-ORF4* transcript appear in early log phase, followed soon after by biosynthetic gene transcription and actinorhodin production (47). Again, similar results were obtained for undecylprodigiosin when multiple copies of *redD* were present (133). These experiments suggest either that the ActII ORF4 or RedD proteins are themselves sufficient to activate transcription of the biosynthetic genes or that any other gene products required are not growth-phase-limited and are already present in exponential growth. Alternatively, overproduction of ActII ORF4 or RedD bypasses or substitutes for any other requirements. Besides growth phase transcriptional regulation, an additional requirement for *actII-ORF4* expression involves translational dependence on the tRNA product of the *bldA* gene (see below).

HOW ARE PATHWAY-SPECIFIC REGULATORS TRANSCRIPTIONALLY REGULATED? A POSSIBLE COORDINATE CONTROL MECHANISM FOR ANTIBIOTIC REGULATION

Does expression of a pathway-specific regulator occur as an individual response to growth limitation, or does the common expression pattern of the various regulators reflect the operation of a global or coordinate control mechanism? Genetic evidence for coordinate control comes from mutants which are pleiotropically blocked in antibiotic synthesis. One class, the *bld* mutants, are so named because they form "bald" colonies that lack aerial mycelium in at least some growth conditions (see below). Several *bld* loci have been identified in *S. coelicolor* (23, 108, 125, 139; reviewed in references 27 and 59). Most *bld* mutants are affected in production of all four of the *S. coelicolor* antibiotics (23, 108). In contrast, mutants carrying mutations in the *absA* (3), *absB* (1), *abaA* (45), and *afsB* (54) loci are pleiotropically defective in secondary metabolism but have relatively normal morphological development (see below). There is limited evidence to suggest that at least some of the affected genes may be involved in regulation of the *S. coelicolor* pathway-specific antibiotic regulators. The map locations of the pleiotropic genes are shown in Fig. 3.

Virtually complete loss of production of all four known antibiotics, with retention of sporulation, characterizes mutants of the Abs$^-$ phenotypic class. Ten Abs$^-$ mutants resulted from an extensive visual screen for mutants that lacked the pigments actinorhodin and undecylprodigiosin (the Act$^-$ Red$^-$ phenotype), among sporulating survivors of UV or *N*-methyl-*N'*-nitro-*N*-nitrosoguanidine mutagenesis. They also proved to be defective in synthesis of methylenomycin and CDA (the Mmy$^-$ CDA$^-$ phenotype). Genetic analysis sorted the *abs* mutations into two groups—one identifying the *absA* locus at 10 o'clock (3) and the other, the *absB* locus at 5 o'clock (1). Hara et al. (54) had previously isolated another, less severely affected, class of Act$^-$ Red$^-$ mutants (*afsB*) during screening for inability to make the extracellular hormone-like butyrolactone, A-factor (see below).

The *abaA* locus (45) was discovered as a clone from an *S. coelicolor* multicopy library that stimulated actinorhodin production in *S. lividans*, a close relative of *S. coelicolor* that normally produces actinorhodin at only very low levels. An *abaA* mutant allele was then generated in *S. coelicolor* by gene disruption, causing reduced production of actinorhodin, undecylprodigiosin, and CDA without an effect on methylenomycin or morphology. This suggests coregulation of a subset of pathways by *abaA*. No data base relationships are evident for either of two open reading frames of the *abaA* locus.

The phenotypes of the *absA*, *absB*, *abaA*, and *afsB* mutants suggest the existence of a global regulatory mechanism for antibiotic regulation that is, at least in part, distinct from sporulation regulation. These mutants' characteristics also extend the observations that mutants singly defective in *act*, *red*, *cda*, or *mmy* biosynthetic genes are capable of normal morphological development (65, 86, 121, 122), tending to rule out a general role for antibiotics in morphological development.

Do the *abs*, *aba*, and *afsB* genes regulate antibiotic gene expression? Northern (RNA) blots show that the *afsB* mutant accumulates very little *act*

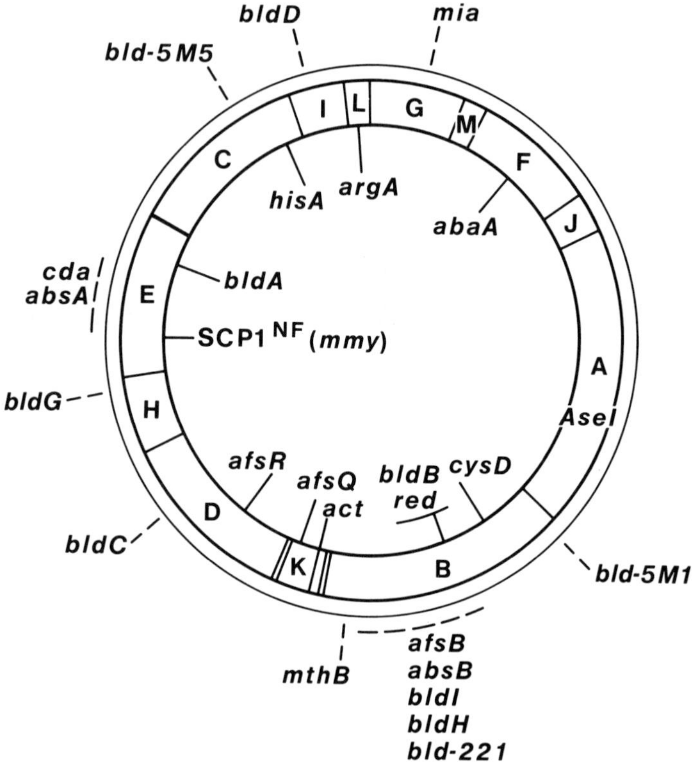

FIGURE 3. Locations in the *S. coelicolor* chromosome of genes involved in antibiotic synthesis and regulation. References are given in the text and in Table 1. The genes outside the circle have been located by genetic mapping. Those inside the circle have been located by hybridization to *Ase*I fragments, which have been mapped (85); many of the latter genes have also been genetically mapped. Some nutritional genes have been included for orientation. Preliminary evidence indicates that the *Ase*I A/J junction may be the ends of a linear chromosome (84). Map locations for genes involved in morphological differentiation (*whi* and *sap* genes) are given in reference 31.

mRNA, at least in some growth conditions (73), and indirect evidence that the *abs* genes play a role in transcription of antibiotic genes comes from the observation that introduction of multiple copies of *actII-ORF4* or *redD* into *absA* and *absB* mutants elicits copious production of the respective antibiotics (1, 2, 24). This effect would not be expected if a biosynthetic or metabolic limitation were responsible for the *abs* antibiotic production defects. Perhaps the only limitation to actinorhodin or undecylprodigiosin synthesis in *abs* strains is failure to produce sufficient active ActII ORF4 or

TABLE 1. Genes involved in streptomycete antibiotic regulation

Gene	Comments, reference(s)
Pathway-specific regulators	
actII-ORF4	Mutants cause loss of actinorhodin production and fail to cosynthesize with other mutant classes (92). Accumulation of *act* transcripts reduced in mutants (44). Multiple copies of the cloned gene restore actinorhodin production to *abs* (1, 24) and many *bld* mutants (116). Contains TTA codon (44).
redD	Mutants cause loss of undecylprodigiosin production and fail to cosynthesize with other mutant classes (122). Accumulation of some *red* transcripts reduced in mutant (113). Gene product related to ActII ORF4 (44).
mmyR	Mutant overproduces methylenomycin (33). Product resembles ActII ORF1 and various repressors of tetracycline resistance genes in transposons and plasmids (30).
dnrI	*S. peucetius* mutant blocked in daunorubicin production (139). Product similar to ActII ORF4 and RedD (139).
dnrJ	Phenotype of a potentially polar insertion mutation in upstream gene (*dnrI*) suggests role as activator of daunorubicin production. Product resembles StrS, EryC1, and DegT (139).
brpA	*S. hygroscopicus* mutant blocked in bialaphos production and in accumulation of most *bap* transcripts (6). Abundance of the *brpA* transcript increases just before stationary phase (119). Similarity to a family of "two-component" transcriptional regulators (119). Contains TTA codon (119).
strR	Required for expression of at least one *str* gene in *S. griseus.* Also found in *Streptomyces glaucescens str* cluster (42). Contains TTA codon.
strS	Product resembles DnrJ, EryC1, DegT (42, 139).
srmR	*S. ambofaciens* mutant blocked in spiramycin production and cosynthesis and in accumulation of *srm* transcripts (46). No similarities in data bases. Contains TTA codon (46).
Genes putatively involved in general antibiotic regulation	
abaA	Multicopy clone, containing five open reading frames, enhances actinorhodin synthesis in *S. coelicolor* and *S. lividans.* Disruption of ORFB abolishes actinorhodin production and strongly reduces undecylprodigiosin and CDA; sporulation not affected. No significant homology in data bases (45).
absA	Mutants produce none of *S. coelicolor*'s four antibiotics; sporulate well (3).

(*Continued*)

TABLE 1. *Continued.*

Gene	Comments, reference(s)
absB	Mutants produce none of *S. coelicolor*'s four antibiotics; sporulate well. Phenotype is leakier than *absA* mutants (1).
afsB	Mutants somewhat defective in production of actinorhodin, undecylprodigiosin, and A-factor; sporulation is unaffected (1, 54).
afsR	Cloned alleles suppress the *afsB* phenotype (70) and also restore actinorhodin and undecylprodigiosin to *abs* mutants (4, 24). Phosphorylated protein (61, 69). Chromosomal disruptions show reduced and delayed actinorhodin production (71). N-terminal similarity of AfsR to ActII ORF4, RedD, and DnrI (44, 139).
afsK	Product membrane-bound and responsible for AfsR phosphorylation; gene near *afsR* (38, 50).
afsQ1/afsQ2	Cloned alleles suppress the *afsB* phenotype and restore actinorhodin and undecylprodigiosin production to an *absA* mutant (but not to *absB*) (76). Gene product homologous to response-regulator pairs (76).

RedD protein. Alternatively, another as yet undescribed gene product may function with ActII ORF4 or RedD in antibiotic transcription, and the *abs* loci could provide or be required to express such a factor; overproduction of ActII ORF4 or RedD might bypass the *abs* requirement.

Clones of a sequence named *mia*, for multicopy inhibition of antibiotics, were isolated in a screen for cloned sequences capable of causing a severe Abs$^-$ effect when introduced into wild-type *S. coelicolor* (120). With the caveat that the *mia* effect on methylenomycin is not yet known, *mia* appears to define an additional genetic element involved in global antibiotic regulation. Whether the effect of *mia* involves expression of an inhibitory gene product or sequestering of an activator remains to be established.

ANOTHER LEVEL OF GENETIC CONTROL—AUXILIARY SENSORS?

The *afsQ1-afsQ2* and *afsR-afsK* gene pairs add an additional layer of complexity to antibiotic gene regulation. Like *abaA*, *afsQ1-afsQ2* and *afsR* were discovered as cloned *S. coelicolor* sequences that stimulated actinorhodin production in *S. lividans* (70, 76). Little has been published on their effects on production of other *S. coelicolor* antibiotics, although extra copies of *afsR* are known to stimulate production of undecylprodigiosin (67) but not of methylenomycin or CDA (4).

DNA sequence analysis suggests that *afsQ1* and *afsQ2* specify regulator and sensor proteins, respectively, in a typical prokaryotic two-component regulatory system (76). Mutational disruption of either gene causes no antibiotic-deficient phenotype. Perhaps the *afsQ1* and *afsQ2* functions are redundant to other antibiotic regulators or function to elicit antibiotic production in response to a specific, as yet undefined, growth condition. It is interesting to note that cloned *afsQ1* can restore actinorhodin and undecylprodigiosin to an *absA* mutant (76).

Phosphorylation cascades have been implicated in regulating the onset of sporulation in *Bacillus subtilis* (20) and the yeast *Saccharomyces cerevisiae* (105). The *afsR* gene product, AfsR, which may function as a transcriptional regulator of antibiotic genes, is phosphorylated, by a membrane-bound kinase specified by the nearby *afsK* gene (61, 66). Unlike the *afsQ1-Q2* gene pair, neither *afsR* nor *afsK* would specify proteins resembling known two-component systems (69). Interestingly, the AfsR N terminus shows amino acid similarity to the family of pathway-specific activators, including ActII ORF4, RedD, and DnrI (44, 132), discussed above (Fig. 2). The mechanistic significance of the similarities is not yet known, but they suggest the possibility of interactions among the proteins (44). Despite its similarity to ActII ORF4, AfsR apparently cannot substitute for the actinorhodin regulator in activating *act* expression (4). Mutational disruption of *afsR* caused reduced and delayed actinorhodin production, although effects on other antibiotics were not reported (71). Because the disruptions did not delete most of the *afsR* gene, the degree to which *afsR* is required for antibiotic regulation is not yet clear.

Interestingly, the pathway-specific regulator of the bialaphos genes, BrpA, weakly resembles response regulators (119), although the relationship is obscured by lack of either a conserved phosphorylation motif or a cognate kinase gene adjacent to the *brpA* gene. It is also noteworthy that various inhibitors of eukaryotic protein kinases inhibit both secondary metabolism and aerial mycelium development in *S. griseus,* and the same agents elicit different patterns of inhibition of protein phosphorylation in vitro (62). Taken together, these results suggest that the onset of antibiotic production may be triggered by a variety of stimuli (either internal or external), each giving rise to an activated phosphoryl group that is transmitted by specific kinases to regulators like AfsQ1 or AfsR. In turn these somehow increase the activity of pathway-specific activators such as ActII ORF4 or RedD. Thus, the various antibiotic gene clusters in a particular streptomycete may be subject to multiple levels of control, some operating on individual antibiotic pathways and some exerting global control. The level of antibiotic we see in optimal laboratory conditions may reflect an additive response of numerous control mechanisms.

GENETIC COUPLING OF ANTIBIOTIC BIOSYNTHESIS AND SPORULATION

As discussed above, many *bld* mutants have been isolated from *S. coelicolor*. Of the *S. coelicolor* mutants, genetic and phenotypic characterization has been documented for loci named *bldA, bldB, bldC, bldD* (108), *bldG, bldH,* and *bldI* (23, 55) and for single *bld* alleles named *bld-5M5, bld-5M1* (125), and *bld-221* (139). These mutant strains provide genetic evidence that common genetic controls underlie the visually apparent coupling of morphological and physiological differentiation, since almost all were found to be severely or completely deficient in antibiotic production. Especially in the cases of *bldA, bldB,* and *bldG* mutants, it is clear that a single mutation causes pleiotropic loss of aerial hyphae, actinorhodin, undecylprodigiosin, methylenomycin, and CDA (4, 23, 65, 81, 108). This phenotype, with its early sporulation block and pleiotropic effect on antibiotic synthesis, is reminiscent of the pleiotropic phenotype of the early *B. subtilis spo0A, spo0B,* and *spo0F* mutants. Whether any *S. coelicolor bld* genes are involved in a *spo0A, 0B, 0F*-like signal transduction system (20) is not yet known: only two *bld* genes—*bldA* and *bldB*—have been cloned and sequenced, and neither of these shows features connecting them with phosphorylation cascades (55, 95, 117).

THE *bldA* GENE IMPOSES A TRANSLATIONAL REQUIREMENT ON SOME SPORULATION AND ANTIBIOTIC GENES

A number of observations circumstantially implicate translational dependence of key sporulation and antibiotic genes on the *bldA*-encoded $tRNA^{Leu}_{UUA}$ as an aspect of *Streptomyces* spp. developmental regulation. Although it is the only UUA-decoding tRNA, the *bldA* gene product is nonessential for vegetative growth, as a *bldA* deletion mutant grows normally (99) and no primary metabolism gene yet sequenced has any TTA codons (reviewed in reference 97). The existence of phenotypically similar *bldA* mutants in *S. lividans* and *S. griseus* suggests that this may be a general phenomenon among *Streptomyces* spp. The TTA codon has, however, been found in a variety of antibiotic resistance and regulatory genes, in other genes involved in morphological and physiological differentiation, and in a few other genes (Fig. 4) (97). With regard to antibiotic synthesis, representative *act, red,* and *mmy* genes tested were transcriptionally inactive in an *S. coelicolor bldA* mutant (19, 51, 136). This is explained for *act* by the discovery of a TTA codon in the *act* pathway-specific activator gene, *actII-*

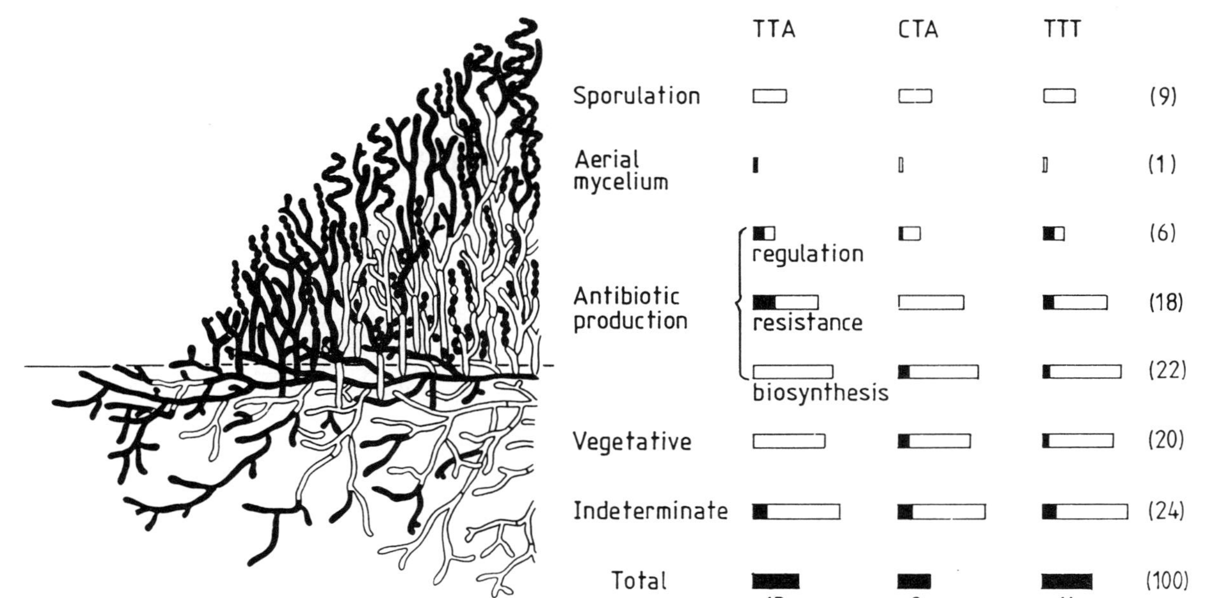

FIGURE 4. Among the three rarest codons in *Streptomyces* spp. genes, only TTA shows a specialized distribution. A total of 100 well-established DNA sequences from diverse genes in different *Streptomyces* spp. have been classified according to their developmental role. The proportion of each of three rare codons (TTA, CTA, TTT) is indicated by the black areas in the boxes. The numbers of genes in each category are shown in brackets. Each category of genes is most likely to be expressed in the colony in positions indicated by alignment with the diagrammatic colony section. Modified from reference 137.

orf4 (44). The only other TTA codon in the 20-kb *act* gene cluster lies in an actinorhodin export gene, *actII-ORF2* (44). Curiously, despite sequence homology to *actII-ORF4,* the *redD* pathway-specific activator gene lacks any TTA codon (113). Perhaps *bldA* is involved in expression of an additional regulatory gene required for *redD* transcription. Mutations restoring undecylprodigiosin production to a *bldA* mutant (named *pwb,* for pigmented while bald) have been tentatively mapped to a different part of the *red* cluster (52): these may help to identify the *bldA*-sensitive component of the *red* regulatory system. How *bldA* is required for methylenomycin and CDA production is not yet known. Like *S. coelicolor bldA* mutants, *S. griseus bldA* mutants are antibiotic-negative, producing no streptomycin (106). As in the actinorhodin gene cluster, a TTA codon occurs in *strR,* the pathway-specific activator gene for streptomycin biosynthesis (reviewed in reference 42).

It is tempting to speculate that these observations reflect a regulatory role for *bldA.* Evidence for temporal regulation of either *bldA*'s expression or the translatability of UUA codons would support the hypothesis of a regulatory role. In a study addressing these questions, a single major transcription start for *bldA* was identified by S1 mapping and in vitro transcription (99). The 5′ end of this transcript (which is subsequently removed in production of the mature tRNA) is readily detectable only in young cultures, in a variety of growth conditions (47, 99): the opposite of what is expected if *bldA* expression is important for regulating translation of UUA-containing mRNAs for antibiotic regulators. On the other hand, the mature tRNA increased in abundance late in growth, in contrast to a major lysyl-tRNA, as assessed by S1 mapping or Northern blotting (99). (The magnitude of the increase in the mature *bldA* tRNA was much less in a different report [47].) It is possible that the relative rates of primary transcription and RNA processing change as cultures age, perhaps involving interactions of the primary transcript with an antisense RNA that has been detected by promoter probing and in vitro transcription (99). Tests of the crucial question of whether UUA-containing mRNAs become more translatable when growth slows down have also given confusing results. Leskiw et al. (98) first reported that the TTA-containing *carB* gene of *Streptomyces thermotolerans* (a lincomycin resistance gene) did not confer lincomycin resistance on germinating spores of *S. coelicolor* unless its two TTA codons were replaced by alternative leucine codons. Later studies compared levels of UUA-containing mRNAs with levels of translated gene product. In the case of the *ampC* mRNA (with seven UUA codons), the transcript accumulated markedly earlier than the *ampC*-specific β-lactamase enzyme (99), whereas an *actII-ORF4::ermE* fusion mRNA (with one UUA codon) was well translated even in young cultures (47). In the latter case, eliminating the UUA codon or adding two more had no clear effect on translation at different growth stages. These different experiments used different genotypes, culture conditions, reporter genes, and protocols for quantifying mRNA, perhaps accounting for some of the apparent disparities. At least it was clear that translatability of UUA codons did not play a significant part in regulating the onset of actinorhodin synthesis in the experimental conditions used by Gramajo et al. (47).

Another comparable case involving specialized use of a rare codon is found in growth-phase-regulated production of butanol and acetone by *Clostridium acetobutylicum,* a gram-positive organism that, in contrast to streptomycetes, has low G+C in its DNA. In this organism, a Tn*916* insertion in the $tRNA^{thr}_{ACG}$ caused a failure to produce acetone and butanol. The ACG codon has been found only in *C. acetobutylicum* genes related to sporulation, low-growth-rate-associated solvent formation and uptake, and metabolism of minor carbon and nitrogen substrates (124). With these parallel examples of incorporation of rare codons into late-growth-stage genes, in *C. acetobutylicum* and in various streptomycetes, the intriguing possibility that rare codon distribution serves some regulatory purpose remains, although firm evidence is elusive.

MOLECULAR ANALYSIS OF THE *bldB* LOCUS

The only *S. coelicolor bld* locus other than *bldA* to have been sequenced (55) and studied in detail is *bldB,* which encodes a negatively charged 11-kDa protein and does not appear to be transcriptionally regulated during the developmental cycle (117). Surprisingly, *bldB* DNA fails to hybridize to DNA of any other of the strains that have been examined, including *S. lividans,* although antibodies against BldB protein react with an 11-kDa protein from *S. lividans* (117). Sequence similarity searches have proven uninformative and the developmental role of *bldB* remains mysterious.

ROLES OF *bld* GENES IN MORPHOLOGICAL DIFFERENTIATION

Most of the known *bld* mutants were selected for their Bld phenotype on minimal media containing glucose as the carbon source or on complex sporulation medium. Surprisingly, all of the well-characterized classes except *bldB* and *bldI* produce a sporulating aerial mycelium when grown on poorer carbon sources such as galactose, maltose, or mannitol (23, 108; reviewed in reference 27). The carbon sources that rescue sporulation restore full antibiotic production only to *bldH* mutants (23). Thus, on maltose media, colonies of *abs* and, for example, *bldA* mutants appear very similar. (However, antibiotic production [but not sporulation] in *bldA* mutants is responsive to phosphate concentration, since low-phosphate media allow production of at least undecylprodigiosin [51]. The *bldA* requirement in *actII-ORF4* translation presumably imposes a block to actinorhodin production that low phosphate concentration cannot bypass.) These observations suggest a complex network of regulatory interactions among the *Streptomyces* spp. developmental genes. Alternative pathways, one of which appears to be glucose-repressible, may govern early morphological differentiation. These pathways appear to overlap partially with the antibiotic regulatory mechanisms.

When observed on plate-grown cultures, the *bldA* morphological phenotype is somewhat misleading. Although the colonies visually lack the characteristic "fuzzy" white aerial hyphae (108), closer examination by transmission electron microscopy reveals prostrate hyphae with frequent crosswalls resembling sporulation septa (37). The sporulation-related targets of *bldA* have not yet been defined, although a candidate is the *S. coelicolor* homolog of an *S. griseus bld* gene, ORF1590 (8, 9). Both the *S. coelicolor* and *S. griseus* genes contain a TTA codon (106). The *S. coelicolor* ORF1590 mutant phenotype has not yet been determined, but in *S. griseus bldA* and ORF1590 mutants share similar phenotypes (reviewed in reference 106). In *S. griseus*, in conditions inducing submerged sporulation of the wild type, both mutants show unusually early sporulation septation and wall thickening, and fail to accumulate two sporulation-specific proteins (106).

Many *bld* mutant strains produce aerial hyphae when grown near sporulating cultures. The best-characterized example of this phenomenon occurs in *S. griseus* and involves a diffusible compound called A-factor; A-factor is reviewed in more detail below. The early *S. coelicolor bld* mutant collection (108) included one mutant strain, *bldC*, that sporulated in response to an undefined diffusible factor (reviewed in reference 27). Recent work has more fully explored an example of extracellular complementation in *S. coelicolor*, involving the spore-associated protein SapB (139), an abundant 18-amino-acid protein which can readily be washed from aerial hyphae and spores (50). SapB production is temporally associated with production of aerial hyphae. It is absent from all *bld* mutants tested, but it is present in *abs* and *whi* mutants (the latter, which are described in detail below, produce aerial hyphae but are blocked in spore development). Growth of a SapB-producing strain near a *bld*, SapB-nonproducing strain results in formation of aerial hyphae on the *bld* strain close to the SapB producer. The area of aerial hyphal stimulation correlates with the SapB diffusion zone, which is detectable using anti-SapB antiserum. Furthermore, application of purified SapB also stimulates the formation of aerial hyphae in *bld* mutants. These phenomena were first reported for *bld-221* (139), but recent work extends these observations to all *bld* mutants tested (138). In contrast to its effect on morphological development, the addition of SapB does not restore antibiotic production to *bld* mutants. These observations implicate SapB as a morphogenetic protein involved in early morphological differentiation; coating of aerial hyphae to facilitate their aerial growth is a possible role for SapB that has parallels in the hydrophobins that cover aerial hyphae of many fungi (29, 139).

In the course of these experiments, an intriguing observation was made: one Bld$^-$, SapB nonproducer stimulated another Bld$^-$ SapB nonproducer to produce a sporulating aerial mycelium (139). Thus, *S. coelicolor* differentiation involves at least one extracellular signal other than SapB. Further studies have indicated a more elaborate series of sporulation-inducing interactions among different *bld* mutants that suggests that an exchange of as many as four distinct signals may be necessary for aerial growth to occur (138). These findings parallel the discoveries of extracellular developmental signaling molecules in the Myxobacteria and in *B. subtilis* (Chapter 8, this volume).

The observations of putative alternative morphogenetic pathways discussed above are reiterated in the SapB story. The experiments with SapB all used cultures grown on complex sporulation medium. SapB is not detectable in cultures grown on minimal media containing either glucose or mannitol as carbon source (139). A SapB-independent pathway is presumably responsible for aerial mycelium formation in these growth conditions.

AN AUTOREGULATOR INVOLVED IN *STREPTOMYCES GRISEUS* DEVELOPMENT

A-factor, a butyrolactone compound, plays a critical role in differentiation in at least one streptomycete, *S. griseus*. First discovered as a factor in culture broth that induced streptomycin production in an *S. griseus* mutant, A-factor is essential for both sporulation and streptomycin production in *S. griseus*. A genetic analysis of A-factor's synthesis, regulation, and developmental role has led to the following general model, which has been reviewed recently (68, 69).

A-factor is produced just prior to the onset of streptomycin production. A putative biosynthetic gene for A-factor, *afsA*, has been cloned from *S. coelicolor* and sequenced (72, 75). *S. griseus* mutants defective in A-factor production fail to sporulate or produce streptomycin, but application of purified A-factor overcomes these defects (53). A-factor is proposed to exert its effect on streptomycin biosynthesis by relieving negative regulation of the streptomycin activator, *strR* (112). Genetic evidence for a repressor protein led to identification of a cytoplasmic A-factor-binding protein (111), which is proposed to repress *strR* transcription, perhaps indirectly. Interaction of A-factor with the binding protein would result in release of the repressor from the promoter of *strR*.

Many other streptomycetes produce A-factor analogs (68). Some of these may also function in antibiotic and developmental regulation. Although *S. coelicolor* produces A-factor, it does not seem to be important for *S. coelicolor* itself. *S. coelicolor* mutants deficient in A-factor have been isolated (54): one class (*afsA*) was unaffected in morphology or secondary metabolism, and the other class (*afsB*), which produced only low levels of antibiotic pigments and sporulated normally, was not restored to the wild-type phenotype by adding extracellular A-factor. *S. coelicolor* lacks A-factor binding protein (111), the putative negative regulator of antibiotic gene expression. Lacking the repressor, *S. coelicolor* would not require A-factor as an inducer of antibiotics. Perhaps *S. coelicolor* could be thought of as a natural mutant variant of the A-factor regulatory cascade. *S. coelicolor* adds a further twist to the A-factor story: the *afsR* gene, discussed previously because of its role in actinorhodin and undecylprodigiosin production, restores A-factor production to *afsB* mutants (70, 74). AfsB and AfsR are proposed to be involved in A-factor regulation, perhaps by controlling *afsA* expression. *S. griseus*, however, lacks an *afsR* homolog (68), so it must have another mechanism of regulating A-factor synthesis.

STORAGE COMPOUNDS PRODUCED IN SUBSTRATE HYPHAE

Most bacteria accumulate intracellular storage compounds such as glycogen, poly-β-hydroxybutyrate, and polyphosphate when they are growth-limited for nutrients other than the source of the storage compound (40). There is evidence from electron microscopy and biochemical studies that polyphosphate and fatty or oily substances may form as electron-dense and electron-transparent bodies, respectively, when colonies are approaching secondary metabolism and morphological differentiation (115, 118a); the disaccharide trehalose, which probably protects hyphae against osmotic stress and damaging effects of dehydration (14), increases from 2% of the dry weight in younger hyphae to 5% in aerial hyphae; and glycogen, which can be visualized as small dark clusters by a silver-staining technique, also accumulates in the central parts of aging colonies (14). Recently, direct evidence showing that poly-β-hydroxybutyrate is synthesized under nutrient-limiting conditions has been obtained, and a putative poly-β-hydroxybutyrate synthase gene has been partially characterized by T. Elwing and D. H. Sherman (43). This, and the recent cloning of the apparent glycogen branching enzyme genes from *S. coelicolor* (18) and *S. aureofaciens* (87), should provide the first opportunity to investigate the genetic regulation of storage metabolism in streptomycetes and, by gene disruption, to learn about the roles of storage compounds. For example, it has been proposed that the balance between synthesis and degradation of storage polymers may be a means of controlling the turgor presumed to be needed to drive aerial hyphal extension (27). It is of some interest that *bldA* mutants growing on excess glucose accumulate no detectable glycogen, but electron-transparent bodies thought to be fatty deposits are particularly abundant instead (118). We speculate that glycogen biosynthesis may be activated in a *bldA*-dependent manner, and that the fatty or oily deposits may be *degraded* by a glucose-repressible route. In a *bldA* mutant carbon reserves might then be channeled into a metabolic cul-de-sac that would impair turgor control and, as a consequence, aerial growth. On other carbon sources, such as mannitol, glucose repression of fat degradation would be relieved, and normal turgor control and morphogenesis restored. We believe the possible interplay of storage metabolism and morphogenesis to be an important area for investigation. Moreover, this statement may equally well apply to some *Bacillus* spp., in which genes encoding glycogen branching enzyme metabolic steps have promoters recognized by a sporulation-associated form of RNA polymerase (82, 83), and in which glycogen synthesis and subsequent degradation have been shown to occur during the course of sporulation (127).

FROM AERIAL HYPHAE TO SPORES

With the possible help of SapB, other Sap proteins (such as SapA, C, D, and E [50]), and storage compounds, aerial branches emerge from the colony surface after about 2 days. They may grow to be many tens of micrometers in length before ceasing extension and initiating sporulation. This is manifested as the subdivision of the long, aseptate aerial hyphal tip into numerous unigenomic compartments, by the rapid, regular, and synchronous ingrowth of morphologically distinctive sporulation septa. The cylindrical prespore compartments so formed usually contain abundant glycogen (which otherwise appears to be absent from aerial hyphae). A shape change ensues, from cylindrical to ovoid, during which the developing spores start to separate from each other. Finally, the spore wall thickens and becomes pigmented. Glycogen disappears again as the spores mature, while trehalose reaches its highest concentration (12%) in the mature spore (14). As in the earlier phase of storage compound deposition, it will be interesting to investigate the regulation and physiological and morphogenetic roles of these deposits during sporulation.

Because spore pigmentation is a late developmental marker, mutants blocked at various stages of sporulation give unpigmented aerial mycelium, thus identifying a set of at least seven *whi* genes (or gene clusters) that play important roles in sporulation but have no apparent role in vegetative growth or normal secondary metabolism. Mutations in the *whiE* gene cluster for biosynthesis of the pigment itself were also isolated in this mutant hunt. Genetic analysis of *whi* mutants (reviewed in reference 26) has more recently led to cloning and molecular studies of some *whi* genes.

A REGULATORY NETWORK THAT UNDERPINS SPORULATION

Although the morphological deficiencies of *bldA* mutants of *S. coelicolor* are conditional (see above), their inability to translate UUA codons is not. This indicates that TTA codons are absent from the *whiA, B, G, H,* and *I* sporulation genes, since these genes are needed for the physiologically induced restoration of normal sporulation to a *bldA* mutant (as shown by the phenotypes of relevant *bldA whi* double mutants [32]). Indeed, no TTA codon is found in the sequences of *whiG* and *whiB* genes from *S. coelicolor* or two other streptomycetes (27, 39, 87, 130), nor in any of the known genes in the spore pigment clusters of *S. coelicolor* or *Streptomyces halstedii* which are presumably expressed preferentially in sporulating cells. This absence of TTA codons from sporulation genes suggests that the presence of the codon might be disadvantageous—perhaps the *bldA*-specified tRNA is absent from aerial hyphae, thereby preventing inappropriate expression of genes for secondary metabolite biosynthesis.

Mutations in *whiA, B, G, H,* or *I* prevent the occurrence of regularly spaced sporulation septa (25, 107). At least *whiA, B, G,* and *H* are likely to play regulatory roles, because the corresponding mutants all show deficiences in the transcription of sporulation-associated genes (see below). Only *whiB* and *whiG* have been sequenced, and their sequences do indeed suggest regulatory roles.

The clearest case is that of *whiG,* which specifies a deduced protein extensively similar to sigma factors σ^D of *B. subtilis* and σ^F of *Salmonella typhimurium* and *Pseudomonas aeruginosa* (27). These sigma factors direct RNA polymerase to promoters of many genes associated with motility

(56). Two cloned *S. coelicolor* promoters, P_{TH4} and P_{TH270}, have been described that are dependent on *whiG* (135). Both contain appropriately located sequences resembling the consensus sequences of σ^D- and σ^F-dependent promoters of other bacteria. The promoters are activated in surface-grown cultures when aerial hyphae become visible. Their function is unknown, although analysis of the surrounding sequence indicates that each of them may cause a sporulation-specific increase in transcription of genes internal to a transcription unit that can be expressed as a polycistronic mRNA in some other undefined circumstances. At a high copy number, these promoters and a σ^D-dependent promoter of *B. subtilis* (34) are capable of causing a sporulation deficiency, probably by a partial sequestering of the σ^{WhiG} form of RNA polymerase, which is thought to be present in amounts that limit the initiation of sporulation. A complementary manifestation of this limitation is the finding that early, excessive, and spatially inappropriate sporulation occurs when additional copies of *whiG* are introduced into wild-type *S. coelicolor* (34).

Studies of the transcription of *whiG* itself in *S. coelicolor* have identified a single transcription start site (16). Insertion of a fragment containing the promoter in a high-copy-number promoter-probe plasmid, containing the *xylE* reporter gene, has been used to investigate the temporal pattern and genetic dependence of *whiG* expression. In young surface cultures, *xylE* expression is very low until the onset of aerial mycelium formation. The increased expression detectable during differentiation is sharply reduced in representative *whiA, B,* or *H* mutants, whereas it is unimpaired in *whiI* and *bldA* mutants.

This finding reveals a paradox, since *whiA* and *B* are apparently needed for *whiG* expression but not for the expression of the *whiG*-dependent promoters P_{TH4} and P_{TH270} (134, 135). To explain this observation, it is proposed that the latter promoters are expressed during an initial *whiA*- and *whiB*-independent period of low-level expression of *whiG,* which has so far escaped direct detection.

Of the three putative activator genes for *whiG* transcription, *whiA, B,* and *H,* only *whiB* has been studied in detail (39, 128), *whiA*- and *whiH*-complementing clones having only recently been isolated (123). The deduced product of *whiB* is an unusual small protein with a high proportion of charged residues (Fig. 5). Although it is not homologous to any proteins of known function, it has a basic, potentially α-helical C terminus suggestive of interactions with DNA, and an acidic, potentially α-helical N terminus that might interact with other proteins. The gene can be deleted without any obvious effects on vegetative growth, giving the same phenotype (long, spiral, aseptate aerial hyphae) as the point mutation shown in Fig. 5. A close homolog of *whiB* was found in all streptomycetes tested, as well as

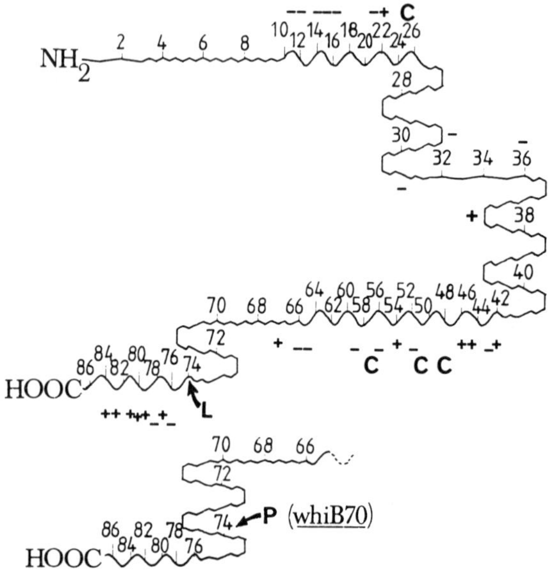

FIGURE 5. A small, highly charged protein with potentially transcription-factor-like structure is encoded by *whiB*. The diagram shows that most of the charged residues and cysteines are in potential α helices (sine waves). The lower part of the figure shows that the L74P change in the *whiB70* mutant protein is predicted to distort the C-terminal basic α helix. Reprinted from reference 39 with permission. Copyright © 1992 Springer-Verlag.

in each of a representative collection of ten actinomycete genera, including some—such as *Mycobacterium tuberculosis* BCG—that do not make aerial mycelium or spores. Possibly *whiB* may be involved in kinds of fragmentation other than just aerial sporulation, in contrast to *whiG*, homologs of which could not be detected in actinomycetes that do not undergo aerial sporulation (130). Two apparent promoters have been defined for *whiB*. The more upstream, *whiB*P1, is very weak and apparently constitutive. The other, *whiB*P2, is strongly expressed in surface culture only when aerial mycelium is forming. Neither promoter shows a clear-cut dependence on *whiA, B, G,* or *H* or on *bldA,* and both are utilized in vitro by RNA polymerase purified from liquid-grown cultures (128).

These observations suggest a developmental regulatory network in which *whiB* (perhaps together with *whiA* and *whiH*) is expressed early in aerial hyphal development, and its product is involved in activating various executor genes for the late stages of sporulation, as well as increasing transcription of another regulatory gene, *whiG*. Certain genes, such as those controlled by P_{TH4} and P_{TH270}, appear to be transcribed during an initial *whiB*-independent phase of low-level *whiG* expression. These early genes may determine important functions such as shutting off continued extension growth. It is attractive to think that the *whiB* gene product is activated as a result of this round of gene expression, thus leading to increased *whiG* activity and efficient expression of a further set of genes, perhaps encoding, inter alia, aspects of glycogen metabolism.

GENETIC DETERMINATION OF SPORE PIGMENT SYNTHESIS

At least eight genes involved in spore pigmentation are arranged in similar clusters called *whiE* in *S. coelicolor* and *sch* in *Streptomyces halstedii* (12, 13, 15, 38). Southern blotting indicates that similar clusters are present in about half of known streptomycetes (13). Among the derived *whiE*/*sch* proteins are several with highly significant similarity to the key enzymes of biosynthesis of aromatic polyketide antibiotics such as actinorhodin (64), indicating that spore pigment is synthesized by the polyketide route (13, 38). Several DNA fragments from the *whiE* and *sch* clusters show apparent promoter activity, which depends on *whiA*, *B*, and *H* but not on *whiG*; but only one transcription start point has been accurately determined, corresponding to *whiE*P1 (12, 15). Interestingly this promoter shows some similarity to the *whiG* promoter, which has the same dependence pattern.

Since *whiE* promoters are expressed in *whiG* mutants, why do *whiG* mutants not produce pigment in their aerial mycelium? One possibility is that *whiG* may influence the supply of metabolic precursors through its putative effects on glycogen metabolism (see above).

CONCLUDING REMARKS

The study of development in *Streptomyces* spp. is poised at an exciting stage. Over the next few years we expect to see progress toward understanding how the various intracellular and extracellular signals that influence the onset of secondary metabolism are perceived; how the information is transmitted to pathway-specific genes; how SapB production is regulated; whether storage metabolism is indeed significant in development and morphogenesis; the molecular basis for the regulatory interactions that underpin sporulation; and the nature of the genes that carry out the morphogenetic program controlled by the *whi* genes.

It is already clear that sporulation in *Streptomyces* spp. has evolved independently of sporulation in *Bacillus* spp., although there are signs of interesting analogies. An obvious example is the involvement of specialized sigma factors, a theme now also well-established in the developmental systems of *Caulobacter cresentus* (17) and *Myxococcus xanthus* (7). A second common feature may be small regulatory proteins such as *whiB*, which are reminiscent of the products of the *sinR* and *spoIIID* genes of *B. subtilis* (Chapter 8, this volume). A third parallel is sporulation-associated storage metabolism, which, although apparently absent from *B. subtilis*, is present in many other species. This observation emphasizes that sporulation in both genera probably evolved from aspects of stationary-phase metabolism in nonsporulating ancestors. There are also contrasts. For example, secondary metabolism in *Bacillus* spp. has usually been considered to be sporulation-associated, whereas in *Streptomyces* spp. it seems more likely that sporulation and antibiotic production are mutually exclusive at the cellular level: thus, multiple copies of *whiB* repress—by an unknown mechanism—the transcription of some genes for actinorhodin synthesis (129). It remains to be seen whether some secondary metabolites of *Bacillus* spp. may also be produced only by nonsporulating cells.

We thank M. J. Bibb, G. Blanco, T. Elwing, D. Hopwood, S. Horinouchi, J. Kormanec, F. Malpartida, E. Miguélez, N. Packter, J. Piret, D. Sherman, and J. Willey for communicating results prior to publication. Work in our laboratories was supported by grants (DMB8811338 and MCB9206068) from the National Science Foundation to W.C.C. and from the Agriculture and Food Research Council, the John Innes Foundation, and the European Economic Community BRIDGE program to K.F.C.

REFERENCES

1. **Adamidis, T., and W. Champness.** 1992. Genetic analysis of *absB*, a *Streptomyces coelicolor* locus involved in global antibiotic regulation. *J. Bacteriol.* **174:**4622–4628.
2. **Adamidis, T., and W. Champness.** Unpublished data.
3. **Adamidis, T., P. Riggle, and W. Champness.** 1990. Mutations in a new *Streptomyces coelicolor* locus which globally block antibiotic biosynthesis but not sporulation. *J. Bacteriol.* **172:**2962–2969.
4. **Adamidis, T., P. Riggle, and W. Champness.** Unpublished data.
5. **Allen, E. J., and J. I. Prosser.** 1985. A kinetic study of the colony growth of *Streptomyces coelicolor* A3(2) and J802 on solid medium. *J. Gen. Microbiol.* **131:**2521–2532.
6. **Anzai, H., T. Murakami, S. Imai, A. Satoh, K. Nagaoka, and C. J. Thompson.** 1987. Transcriptional regulation of bialaphos biosynthesis in *Streptomyces hygroscopicus*. *J. Bacteriol.* **169:**3482–3488.
7. **Apelian, D., and S. Inouye.** 1990. Development-specific σ-factor essential for late-stage differentiation of *Myxococcus xanthus*. *Genes Dev.* **4:**1396–1403.
8. **Babcock, M. J., and K. E. Kendrick.** 1988. Cloning of DNA involved in sporulation of *Streptomyces griseus*. *J. Bacteriol.* **170:**2802–2808.

9. **Babcock, M. J., and K. E. Kendrick.** 1990. Transcriptional and translational features of a sporulation gene of *Streptomyces griseus. Gene* **95:**57–63.
10. **Bascaran, V., L. Sanchez, C. Hardisson, and A. F. Brana.** 1991. Stringent response and initiation of secondary metabolism in *Streptomyces clavuligerus. J. Gen. Microbiol.* **137:**1625–1634.
11. **Bibb, M. J.** Personal communication.
12. **Blanco, G.** Personal communication.
13. **Blanco, G., P. Brian, A. Perida, C. Mendez, J. A. Salas, and K. F. Chater.** 1993. Hybridization and DNA sequence analyses suggest an early evolutionary divergence of related biosynthetic gene sets for polypeptide antibiotics and spore pigments in *Streptomyces* spp. *Gene* **30:**107–116.
14. **Brana, A. F., C. Mendez, L. A. Diaz, M. B. Manzanal, and C. Hardisson.** 1986. Glycogen and trehalose accumulation during colony development in *Streptomyces antibioticus. J. Gen. Microbiol.* **132:**1319–1326.
15. **Brian, P.** 1992. A developmentally regulated spore pigment locus from *Streptomyces coelicolor* A3(2). Ph.D. thesis. University of East Anglia, Norwich, United Kingdom.
16. **Brown, G. L., and K. F. Chater.** Unpublished data.
17. **Brun, Y. V., and L. Shapiro.** 1992. A temporally controlled σ-factor is required for polar morphogenesis and normal cell division in Caulobacter. *Genes Dev.* **6:**2395–2408.
18. **Bruton, C. J., and K. F. Chater.** Unpublished data.
19. **Bruton, C. J., E. P. Guthrie, and K. F. Chater.** 1991. Phage vectors that allow monitoring of secondary metabolism genes in *Streptomyces. Bio/Technology* **9:**652–656.
20. **Burbulys, D., K. A. Trach, and J. A. Hoch.** 1991. Initiation of sporulation in *B. subtilis* is controlled by a multicomponent phosphorelay. *Cell* **64:**545–552.
21. **Caballero, J. L., F. Malpartida, and D. A. Hopwood.** 1991. Transcriptional organization and regulation of an antibiotic export complex in the producing *Streptomyces* cultures. *Mol. Gen. Genet.* **228:**372–380.
22. **Calcutt, M. J., and F. J. Schmidt.** 1992. Conserved gene arrangement in the origin region of the *Streptomyces coelicolor* chromosome. *J. Bacteriol.* **174:**3220–3226.
23. **Champness, W.** 1988. New loci required for *Streptomyces coelicolor* morphological and physiological differentiation. *J. Bacteriol.* **170:**1168–1174.
24. **Champness, W., P. Riggle, T. Adamidis, and P. VanderVere.** 1992. Identification of *Streptomyces coelicolor* genes involved in regulation of antibiotic synthesis. *Gene* **115:**55–60.
25. **Chater, K. F.** 1972. A morphological and genetic mapping study of white colony mutants of *Streptomyces coelicolor. J. Gen. Microbiol.* **72:**9–28.
26. **Chater, K. F.** 1984. Morphological and physiological differentiation in *Streptomyces*, p. 89–115. *In* R. Losick and L. Shapiro (ed.), *Microbial Development.* Cold Spring Harbor Laboratory Press, Cold Spring Harbor, N.Y.
27. **Chater, K. F.** 1989. Sporulation in *Streptomyces,* p. 277–299. *In* I. Smith, R. A. Slepecky, and P. Setlow (ed.), *Regulation of Procaryotic Development.* American Society for Microbiology, Washington, D.C.
28. **Chater, K. F.** 1990. The improving prospects for yield increase by genetic engineering in antibiotic-producing streptomycetes. *Bio/Technology* **8:**115–121.
29. **Chater, K. F.** 1991. Saps, hydrophobins and aerial growth. *Curr. Biol.* **1:**318–320.

30. **Chater, K. F.** 1992. Genetic regulation of secondary metabolic pathways in *Streptomyces,* p. 144–162. *In* D. J. Chadwick and J. Whelan (ed.), *Secondary Metabolites: Their Function and Evolution.* Ciba Foundation Symposium 171. John Wiley & Sons, Chichester, United Kingdom.
31. **Chater, K. F.** 1993. Genetics of differentiation in *Streptomyces. Annu. Rev. Microbiol.* **47:**685–713.
32. **Chater, K. F.** Unpublished data.
33. **Chater, K. F., and C. J. Bruton.** 1985. Resistance, regulatory and production genes for the antibiotic methylenomycin are clustered. *EMBO J.* **4:** 1893–1897.
34. **Chater, K. F., C. J. Bruton, K. A. Plaskitt, M. J. Buttner, C. Mendez, and J. Helmann.** 1989. The developmental fate of *Streptomyces coelicolor* hyphae depends crucially on a gene product homologous with the motility sigma factor of *Bacillus subtilis. Cell* **59:**133–143.
35. **Chater, K. F., and D. A. Hopwood.** 1989. Antibiotic biosynthesis in *Streptomyces,* p. 129–151. *In* D. A. Hopwood and K. F. Chater (ed.), *Genetics of Bacterial Diversity.* Academic Press Ltd., London.
36. **Chater, K. F., and D. A. Hopwood.** 1993. *Streptomyces,* p. 83–99. *In* A. L. Sonenshein, J. A. Hoch, and R. Losick (ed.), *Bacillus subtilis and Other Gram-Positive Bacteria: Biochemistry, Physiology, and Molecular Genetics.* American Society for Microbiology, Washington, D.C.
37. **Chater, K. F., and M. J. Merrick.** 1979. *Streptomyces,* p. 93–114. *In* J. H. Parish (ed.), *Developmental Biology of Prokaryotes.* University of California Press, Berkeley and Los Angeles, Calif.
38. **Davis, N. K., and K. F. Chater.** 1990. Spore colour in *Streptomyces coelicolor* A3(2) involves the developmentally regulated synthesis of a compound biosynthetically related to polyketide antibiotics. *Mol. Microbiol.* **4:**1679–1691.
39. **Davis, N. K., and K. F. Chater.** 1992. The *Streptomyces coelicolor whiB* gene encodes a small transcription factor-like protein dispensable for growth but essential for sporulation. *Mol. Gen. Genet.* **232:**351–358.
40. **Dawes, E. A.** 1992. Storage polymers in prokaryotes, p. 81–122. *In* S. Mohan, C. Dow, and J. A. Cole (ed.), *Prokaryotic Structure and Function: A New Perspective.* Society for General Microbiology Symposium 47. Cambridge University Press, Cambridge.
41. **Daza, A., J. F. Martin, A. Dominguez, and J. A. Gil.** 1989. Sporulation of several species of *Streptomyces* in submerged cultures after nutritional downshift. *J. Gen. Microbiol.* **135:**2483–2491.
42. **Distler, J., K. Mansouri, G. Mayer, M. Stockmann, and W. Piepersberg.** 1992. Streptomycin biosynthesis and its regulation in streptomycetes. *Gene* **115:**105–111.
43. **Elwing, T., and D. H. Sherman.** Personal communication.
44. **Fernandez-Moreno, M. A., J. L. Caballero, D. A. Hopwood, and F. Malpartida.** 1991. The *act* gene cluster contains regulatory and antibiotic export genes, direct targets for translational control by the *bldA* tRNA gene of *Streptomyces coelicolor. Cell* **66:**769–780.
45. **Fernandez-Moreno, M. A., A. J. Martin-Triana, E. Martinez, J. Niemi, H. M. Kieser, D. A. Hopwood, and F. Malpartida.** 1992. *abaA,* a new pleiotropic regulatory locus for antibiotic production in *Streptomyces coelicolor. J. Bacteriol.* **174:**2958–2967.

46. **Geistlich, M., R. Losick, J. R. Turner, and R. N. Rao.** 1992. Characterization of a novel regulatory gene governing the expression of a polyketide synthase gene in *Streptomyces ambofaciens*. *Mol. Microbiol.* **6:**2019–2029.
47. **Gramajo, H. C., E. Takano, and M. J. Bibb.** 1993. Stationary phase production of the antibiotic actinorhodin in *Streptomyces coelicolor* A3(2) is transcriptionally regulated. *Mol. Microbiol.* **7:**837–845.
48. **Granozzi, C., R. Billeta, R. Passantino, M. Sollazzo, and A. M. Puglia.** 1990. A breakdown in macromolecular synthesis preceeding differentiation in *Streptomyces coelicolor* A3(2). *J. Gen. Microbiol.* **136:**713–718.
49. **Gray, D. I.,, G. W. Gooday, and J. I. Prosser.** 1990. Apical hyphal extension in *Streptomyces coelicolor* A3(2). *J. Gen. Microbiol.* **136:**1077–1084.
50. **Guijarro, J., R. Santamaria, A. Schauer, and R. Losick.** 1988. Promoter determining the timing and spatial localization of transcription of a cloned *Streptomyces coelicolor* gene encoding a spore-associated polypeptide. *J. Bacteriol.* **170:**1895–1901.
51. **Guthrie, E. P., and K. F. Chater.** 1990. The level of a transcript required for production of a *Streptomyces coelicolor* antibiotic is conditionally dependent on a tRNA gene. *J. Bacteriol.* **172:**6189–6193.
52. **Guthrie, E. P., and K. F. Chater.** Unpublished data.
53. **Hara, O., and T. Beppu.** 1982. Mutants blocked in streptomycin production in *Streptomyces griseus*—the role of A factor. *J. Antibiot.* **35:**349–358.
54. **Hara, O. S., T. Horinouchi, T. Uozumi, and T. Beppu.** 1983. Genetic analysis of A-factor synthesis in *Streptomyces coelicolor* A3(2) and *Streptomyces griseus*. *J. Gen. Microbiol.* **129:**2939–2944.
55. **Harasym, M., L.-H. Zhang, K. F. Chater, and J. M. Piret.** 1990. The *Streptomyces coelicolor* A3(2) *bldB* region contains at least two genes involved in morphological development. *J. Gen. Microbiol.* **136:**1543–1550.
56. **Helmann, J. D.** 1991. Alternative sigma factors and the control of flagellar gene expression. *Mol. Microbiol.* **5:**2875–2882.
57. **Hobbs, G., C. M. Frazer, D. C. J. Gardner, J. A. Cullum, and S. G. Oliver.** 1990. Pigmented antibiotic production by *Streptomyces coelicolor* A3(2): kinetics and the influence of nutrients. *J. Gen. Microbiol.* **136:**2291–2296.
58. **Hobbs, G., A. I. C. Obanye, J. Petty, J. C. Mason, E. Barratt, D. C. J. Gardner, F. Flett, C. P. Smith, P. Broda, and S. G. Oliver.** 1992. An integrated approach to studying regulation of production of the antibiotic methylenomycin by *Streptomyces coelicolor* A3(2). *J. Bacteriol.* **174:**1487–1494.
59. **Hodgson, D. A.** 1992. Differentiation in actinomycetes, p. 407–440. *In* S. Mohan, C. Dow, and J. A. Cole (ed.), *Prokaryotic Structure and Function: A New Perspective*. Society for General Microbiology Symposium 47. Cambridge University Press, Cambridge.
60. **Holt, T. G., C. Chang, C. Laurent-Winter, T. Murakami, J. I. Barrels, J. E. Davies, and C. J. Thompson.** 1992. Global changes in gene expression related to antibiotic synthesis in *Streptomyces hygroscopicus*. *Mol. Microbiol.* **6:**969–980.
61. **Hong, S.-K., M. Kito, T. Beppu, and S. Horinouchi.** 1991. Phosphorylation of the *afsR* product, a global regulatory protein for secondary metabolite formation in *Streptomyces coelicolor* A3(2). *J. Bacteriol.* **173:**2311–2318.
62. **Hong, S.-K., A. Matsumoto, S. Horinouchi, and T. Beppu.** 1993. Effects of protein kinase inhibitors on *in vitro* protein phosphorylation and cellular differentiation of *Streptomyces griseus*. *Mol. Gen. Genet.* **236:**347–354.

63. **Hopwood, D. A., M. J. Bibb, K. F. Chater, T. Kieser, C. J. Bruton, H. M. Kieser, D. J. Lydiate, C. P. Smith, J. M. Ward, and H. Schrempf.** 1985. *Genetic Manipulation of Streptomyces: A Laboratory Manual.* John Innes Foundation, Norwich, United Kingdom.
64. **Hopwood, D. A., and D. H. Sherman.** 1990. Molecular genetics of polyketides and its comparison to fatty acid biosynthesis. *Annu. Rev. Genet.* **24:**37–66.
65. **Hopwood, D. A., and H. M. Wright.** 1983. CDA is a new chromosomally-determined antibiotic from *Streptomyces coelicolor* A3(2). *J. Gen. Microbiol.* **129:** 3575–3579.
66. **Horinouchi, S.** Personal communication.
67. **Horinouchi, S., and T. Beppu.** 1984. Production in large quantities of actinorhodin and undecylprodigiosin induced by *afsB* in *Streptomyces lividans. Agric. Biol. Chem.* **48:**2131–2133.
68. **Horinouchi, S., and T. Beppu.** 1992. Autoregulatory factors and communication in actinomycetes. *Annu. Rev. Microbiol.* **46:**377–398.
69. **Horinouchi, S., and T. Beppu.** 1992. Regulation of secondary metabolism and cell differentiation in *Streptomyces:* A-factor as a microbial hormone and the AfsR protein as a component of a two-component regulatory system. *Gene* **115:**167–172.
70. **Horinouchi, S., O. Hara, and T. Beppu.** 1983. Cloning of a pleiotropic gene that positively controls biosynthesis of A-factor, actinorhodin, and prodigiosin in *Streptomyces coelicolor* A3(2) and *Streptomyces lividans. J. Bacteriol.* **155:**1238–1248.
71. **Horinouchi, S., M. Kito, M. Nishiyama, K. Furuya, S.-K. Hong, K. Miyake, and T. Beppu.** 1990. Primary structure of AfsR, a global regulatory protein for secondary metabolite formation in *Streptomyces coelicolor* A3(2). *Gene* **95:**49–56.
72. **Horinouchi, S., Y. Kumada, and T. Beppu.** 1984. Unstable genetic determinant of A-factor biosynthesis in streptomycin producing microorganisms: cloning and characterization. *J. Bacteriol.* **158:**481–487.
73. **Horinouchi, S., F. Malpartida, D. A. Hopwood, and T. Beppu.** 1989. *afsB* stimulates transcription of the actinorhodin biosynthetic pathway in *Streptomyces coelicolor* A3(2) and *Streptomyces lividans. Mol. Gen. Genet.* **215:** 355–357.
74. **Horinouchi, S., H. Suzuki, and T. Beppu.** 1986. Nucleotide sequence of *afsB,* a pleiotropic gene involved in secondary metabolism in *Streptomyces coelicolor* A3(2) and *Streptomyces lividans. J. Bacteriol.* **168:**257–269.
75. **Horinouchi, S., H. Suzuki, M. Nishiyama, and T. Beppu.** 1989. Nucleotide sequence and transcriptional analysis of the *Streptomyces griseus* gene (*afsA*) responsible for A-factor biosynthesis. *J. Bacteriol.* **171:**1206–1210.
76. **Ishizuka, H., S. Horinouchi, H. M. Kieser, D. A. Hopwood, and T. Beppu.** 1992. A putative two-component regulatory system involved in secondary metabolism in *Streptomyces* spp. *J. Bacteriol.* **174:**7585–7594.
77. **Jones, G. H.** 1989. Cloning of streptomycete genes involved in antibiotic synthesis and its regulation, p. 49–73. *In* S. Shapiro (ed.), *Regulation of Secondary Metabolism in Actinomycetes.* CRC Press, Inc., Boca Raton, Fla.
78. **Katz, L., and S. Donadio.** Polyketide synthesis: prospects for hybrid antibiotics. *Annu. Rev. Microbiol.,* in press.

79. **Kelly, K. S., K. Ochi, and G. H. Jones.** 1991. Pleiotropic effects of a *relC* mutation in *Streptomyces antibioticus*. *J. Bacteriol.* **173:**2297–2300.
80. **Kendrick, K. E., and J. C. Ensign.** 1983. Sporulation of *S. griseus* in submerged culture. *J. Bacteriol.* **155:**357–366.
81. **Kenney, B., and W. Champness.** Unpublished data.
82. **Kiel, J. A. K. W.** 1990. A genetic analysis of bacterial glycogen branching enzymes. Ph.D. thesis. Rijksuniversiteit Groningen, The Netherlands.
83. **Kiel, J. A. K. W., J. M. Boels, G. Beldman, and G. Venema.** 1991. Molecular cloning and nucleotide sequence of the glycogen branching enzyme gene (*glgB*) from *Bacillus stearothermophilus* and expression in *Escherichia coli* and *Bacillus subtilis*. *Mol. Gen. Genet.* **230:**136–144.
84. **Kieser, H. M., and D. A. Hopwood.** Personal communication.
85. **Kieser, H. M., T. Kieser, and D. Hopwood.** 1992. A combined genetic and physical map of the chromosome of *Streptomyces coelicolor* A3(2). *J. Bacteriol.* **174:**5496–5507.
86. **Kirby, R., and D. Hopwood.** 1977. Genetic determination of methylenomycin synthesis by the SCP1 plasmid of *Streptomyces coelicolor* A3(2). *J. Gen. Microbiol.* **98:**239–252.
87. **Kormanec, J.** Personal communication.
88. **Kretschmer, S.** 1987. Nucleoid segregation pattern during branching in *Streptomyces granaticolor* mycelia. *J. Basic Microbiol.* **27:**203–206.
89. **Kretschmer, S.** 1988. Stepwise increase of elongation rate in individual hyphae of *Streptomyces granaticolor* during outgrowth. *J. Basic Microbiol.* **28:**1–2, 35–43.
90. **Kretschmer, S.** 1989. Septation behavior of the apical cell in *Streptomyces granaticolor* mycelia. *J. Basic Microbiol.* **29:**587–595.
91. **Kretschmer, S.** 1991. Correlation between branching and elongation in germ tubes of *Streptomyces granaticolor*. *J. Basic Microbiol.* **31:**259–264.
92. **Kretschmer, S.** 1992. Fate of the subapical cell in *Streptomyces granaticolor* mycelia. *J. Basic Microbiol.* **32:**355–359.
93. **Kretschmer, S., and C. Kummer.** 1987. Increase of nucleoid size with increasing age of hyphal region in vegetative mycelia of *Streptomyces granaticolor*. *J. Basic Microbiol.* **27:**23–27.
94. **Kroening, T. A., and K. Kendrick.** 1987. In vivo regulation of histidine ammonia-lyase activity from *Streptomyces griseus*. *J. Bacteriol.* **169:**823–829.
95. **Lawlor, E. J., H. A. Baylis, and K. F. Chater.** 1988. Pleiotropic morphological and antibiotic deficiencies result from mutations in a gene encoding a tRNA-like product in *Streptomyces coelicolor* A3(2). *Genes Dev.* **1:**1305–1310.
96. **Leblond, P., F. X. Francou, J.-M. Simonet, and B. Decaris.** 1990. Pulsed-field gel electrophoresis analysis of the genome of *Streptomyces ambofaciens* strains. *FEMS Microbiol. Lett.* **72:**79–88.
97. **Leskiw, B. K., M. J. Bibb, and K. F. Chater.** 1991. The use of a rare codon specifically during development? *Mol. Microbiol.* **5:**2861–2867.
98. **Leskiw, B. K., E. J. Lawlor, J. M. Fernandez-Abalos, and K. F. Chater.** 1991. TTA codons in some genes prevent their expression in a class of developmental, antibiotic-negative *Streptomyces* mutants. *Proc. Natl. Acad. Sci. USA* **88:**2461–2465.
99. **Leskiw, B. K., R. Mah, E. J. Lawlor, and K. F. Chater.** 1993. Accumulation of the *bldA*-specified tRNA is temporally regulated in *Streptomyces coelicolor* A3(2). *J. Bacteriol.* **175:**1995–2005.

100. **Malpartida, F., and D. A. Hopwood.** 1984. Molecular cloning of the whole biosynthetic pathway of a *Streptomyces* antibiotic and its expression in a heterologous host. *Nature* (London) **309:**462–464.
101. **Malpartida, F., and D. A. Hopwood.** Personal communication.
102. **Malpartida, F., J. Niemi, R. Navarrete, and D. A. Hopwood.** 1990. Cloning and expression in a heterologous host of the complete set of genes for biosynthesis of the *Streptomyces coelicolor* antibiotic undecyclprodigiosin. *Gene* **93:**91–99.
103. **Martin, J. F., and A. L. Demain.** 1980. Control of antibiotic biosynthesis. *Microbiol. Rev.* **44:**230–251.
104. **Martin, J. F., and P. Liras.** 1989. Organization and expression of genes involved in the biosynthesis of antibiotics and other secondary metabolites. *Annu. Rev. Microbiol.* **43:**173–206.
105. **Matsuura, A., M. Treinin, H. Mitsuzawa, Y. Kassir, I. Uno, and G. Simchen.** 1990. The adenylate cyclase/protein kinase cascade regulates entry into meiosis in *Saccharomyces cerevisiae* through the gene IME1. *EMBO J.* **9:**3225–3232.
106. **McCue, L. A., J. Kwak, M. J. Babcock, and K. E. Kendrick.** 1992. Molecular analysis of sporulation in *Streptomyces griseus*. *Gene* **115:**173–179.
107. **McVittie, A. M.** 1974. Ultrastructural studies on sporulation in wild-type and white colony mutants of *Streptomyces coelicolor*. *J. Gen. Microbiol.* **81:**291–302.
108. **Merrick, M. J.** 1976. A morphological and genetic mapping study of bald colony mutants of *Streptomyces coelicolor* A3(2). *J. Gen. Microbiol.* **96:**299–315.
109. **Miguélez, E. M.** Personal communication.
110. **Miguélez, E. M., C. Martin, M. B. Manzanal, and C. Hardisson.** 1992. Growth and morphogenesis in *Streptomyces*. *FEMS Microbiol. Lett.* **100:**357–360.
111. **Miyake, K., S. Horinouchi, M. Yoshida, N. Chiba, K. Mori, N. Nogawa, N. Morikawa, and T. Beppu.** 1989. Detection and properties of A-factor-binding protein from *Streptomyces griseus*. *J. Bacteriol.* **171:**4298–4302.
112. **Miyake, K., T. Kuzuyama, S. Horinouchi, and T. Beppu.** 1990. The A factor-binding protein of *Streptomyces griseus* negatively controls streptomycin production and sporulation. *J. Bacteriol.* **172:**3003–3008.
113. **Narva, K. E., and J. S. Feitelson.** 1990. Nucleotide sequence and transcriptional analysis of the *redD* locus of *Streptomyces coelicolor* A3(2). *J. Bacteriol.* **172:**326–333.
114. **Ochi, K.** 1990. A relaxed (rel) mutant of *Streptomyces coelicolor* A3(2) with a missing ribosomal protein lacks the ability to accumulate ppGpp, A-factor and prodigiosin. *J. Gen. Microbiol.* **136:**2405–2412.
115. **Olukoshi, E. R., and N. M. Pachter.** Personal communication.
116. **Passantino, R., A.-M. Puglia, and K. Chater.** 1991. Additional copies of the *actII* regulatory gene induce actinorhodin production in pleiotropic *bld* mutants of *Streptomyces coelicolor* A3(2). *J. Gen. Microbiol.* **137:**2059–2064.
117. **Piret, J.** Personal communication.
118. **Plaskitt, K. A., and K. F. Chater.** Unpublished data.
118a. **Plaskitt, K. A., R. Gowing, and K. F. Chater.** Unpublished data.
119. **Raibaud, A., M. Zalacain, T. G. Holt, R. Tizard, and C. J. Thompson.** 1991. Nucleotide sequence analysis reveals linked N-acetyl hydrolase, thioesterase, transport and regulatory genes encoded by the bialaphos biosynthetic gene cluster of *Streptomyces hygroscopicus*. *J. Bacteriol.* **173:**4454–4463.
120. **Riggle, P., and W. Champness.** Unpublished data.

121. **Rudd, B. A. M., and D. A. Hopwood.** 1979. Genetics of actinorhodin biosynthesis by *Streptomyces coelicolor* A3(2). *J. Gen. Microbiol.* **114:**35–43.
122. **Rudd, B. A. M., and D. A. Hopwood.** 1980. A pigmented mycelial antibiotic in *Streptomyces coelicolor:* control by a chromosomal gene cluster. *J. Gen. Microbiol.* **119:**333–340.
123. **Ryding, N. J., and K. F. Chater.** Unpublished data.
124. **Sauer, U., and P. Durre.** 1992. Possible function of $tRNA^{Thr}_{ACG}$ in regulation of solvent formation in *Clostridium acetobutylicum. FEMS Microbiol. Lett.* **100:** 147–154.
125. **Schauer, A., A. Nelson, and J. Daniel.** 1991. Tn4563 transposition in *Streptomyces coelicolor* and its application to isolation of new morphological mutants. *J. Bacteriol.* **173:**5060–5067.
126. **Seno, E. T., and R. H. Baltz.** 1989. Structural organization and regulation of antibiotic biosynthesis and resistance genes in Actinomycetes, p. 1–48. *In* S. Shapiro (ed.), *Regulation of Secondary Metabolism in Actinomycetes.* CRC Press, Inc., Boca Raton, Fla.
127. **Slock, J. A., and D. P. Stahly.** 1974. Polysaccharide that may serve as a carbon and energy storage compound for sporulation in *Bacillus cereus. J. Bacteriol.* **120:**399–406.
128. **Soliveri, J., K. L. Brown, M. J. Buttner, and K. F. Chater.** 1992. Two promoters for the *whiB* sporulation gene of *Streptomyces coelicolor* A3(2) and their activities in relation to development. *J. Bacteriol.* **174:**6215–6220.
129. **Soliveri, J., and K. F. Chater.** Unpublished data.
130. **Soliveri, J., C. Granozzi, and K. F. Chater.** Unpublished data.
131. **Strauch, E., E. Takano, and M. J. Bibb.** 1991. The stringent response in *Streptomyces coelicolor* A3(2). *Mol. Microbiol.* **5:**289–298.
132. **Stutzman-Engwall, K. J., S. L. Otten, and C. Richard Hutchinson.** 1992. Regulation of secondary metabolism in *Streptomyces* spp. and the overproduction of daunorubicin in *Streptomyces peucetius. J. Bacteriol.* **174:**144–154.
133. **Takano, E., H. C. Gramajo, E. Strauch, N. Andres, J. White, and M. J. Bibb.** 1992. Transcriptional regulation of the *redD* transcriptional activator gene accounts for growth-phase-dependent production of the antibiotic undecylprodigiosin in *Streptomyces coelicolor* A3(2). *Mol. Microbiol.* **6:**2797–2804.
134. **Tan, H.** 1991. Molecular genetics of developmentally regulated promoters in *Streptomyces coelicolor* A3(2). Ph.D. thesis. University of East Anglia, Norwich, United Kingdom.
135. **Tan, H., and K. F. Chater.** 1993. Two developmentally controlled promoters of *Streptomyces coelicolor* A3(2) that resemble the major class of motility-related promoters in other bacteria. *J. Bacteriol.* **175:**933–940.
136. **Wietzorrek, A., and K. F. Chater.** Unpublished data.
137. **Wildermuth, H.** 1970. Development and organization of the aerial mycelium in *Streptomyces coelicolor. J. Gen. Microbiol.* **60:**43–50.
138. **Willey, J.** Personal communication.
139. **Willey, J., R. Santamaria, J. Guijarro, M. Geistlich, and R. Losick.** 1991. Extracellular complementation of a developmental mutation implicates a small sporulation protein in aerial mycelium formation. *Cell* **65:**641–650.
140. **Zakrzewska-Czerwinska, J., and H. Schrempf.** 1992. Characterization of an autonomously replicating region from the *Streptomyces lividans* chromosome. *J. Bacteriol.* **174:**2688–2693.

Regulation of Bacterial Differentiation
Edited by P. Piggot et al.

Chapter 5

Asymmetric Septation in *Bacillus subtilis*

Joe Lutkenhaus

In *Bacillus subtilis* the generation of two cells with different developmental fates is preceded by an asymmetric division. This asymmetric division or septation event occurs during sporulation and involves placement of the septum near one of the cell poles. It is the key morphological step in the formation of the two cells, one destined to become the spore and the other the mother cell. A full understanding of the generation of these two different cell types will undoubtedly require an understanding of the biogenesis of the asymmetric septum and probably what distinguishes it from the vegetative septum. Morphologically the asymmetric septum can be readily distinguished from the vegetative septum because of its decreased content of peptidoglycan. This difference suggests that if asymmetric septation is a modified form of vegetative septation a sporulation product(s) interacts with the septation machinery, modifying it such that this unique sporulation septum is synthesized. This situation offers an opportunity to the investigator since such a product should provide direct access to the septation machinery. The study of asymmetric septation during sporulation also offers a unique and accessible example of developmental regulation of the positioning of the division site in bacteria and offers a unique opportunity to investigate a septation event that is not essential to the survival of the organism. In addition, the study of septation in *B. subtilis,* both vegetative and asymmetric, should complement studies in progress with other bacteria, especially *Escherichia coli.* Studies of septation in these two different species should reveal the conserved elements of the division machinery in eubacteria.

MORPHOLOGY OF SEPTATION IN *B. SUBTILIS*

Electron microscopic studies of vegetative and sporulating cells have revealed the similarities and differences of the septa formed. The vegeta-

---

Joe Lutkenhaus, Department of Microbiology, Molecular Genetics, and Immunology, University of Kansas Medical Center, Kansas City, Kansas 66103.

tive septum is formed at midcell between apparently well-separated nucleoids (52). The septum is characterized by the presence of a thick peptidoglycan layer that starts to split as septation is completed. The sporulation or asymmetric septum is formed 1 to 2 h after the initiation of sporulation (57). It is located very near one of the cell poles and is characterized by a thin layer of peptidoglycan that is subsequently removed by hydrolysis. Based upon the similarities in these two septation events it was suggested that asymmetric septation was a modified form of vegetative cell division (34). Although our knowledge of cell division is still rather rudimentary it appears that this suggestion is correct (see below).

As with vegetative cell division the asymmetric septation event must be well coordinated with chromosome segregation to ensure successful separation of the two chromosomes. Early during sporulation the chromosome destined for the spore migrates to a cell pole and undergoes condensation (61). This process occurs at about the same time that the asymmetric septum is formed. It raises a number of questions, including which event is initiated first, how these two events are coordinated, what determines the location of the septum, and, if septum localization is restricted to the cell poles, how one of the two poles of the cell is selected.

GENES INVOLVED IN SEPTATION

Genes involved in vegetative septation have been identified following the isolation of conditional lethal mutations and screening for filamentous morphology at the nonpermissive temperature. The results of a number of early studies resulted in the identification of a number of potential cell division loci (Table 1). However, the morphological criterion used for screening is not specific, and mutations in genes not directly involved in cell division can lead to filamentous growth. For example the *div-341* mutation maps in the *secA* gene (59). In addition, some mutants were defective in DNA synthesis, for example, *div-526* (49).

In *E. coli* four high-molecular-weight penicillin binding proteins (PBPs) carry out the final stages of peptidoglycan biosynthesis. These PBPs have distinct functions affecting the morphology of the cell, and one of them, PBP3, is dedicated to septum biosynthesis (63). *B. subtilis* also contains numerous PBPs, although their physiological roles have not been elucidated (62). However, the recent cloning of several of these genes should lead to an elaboration of their function and the determination of whether or not one of them is dedicated to septal biosynthesis (26).

In another approach to the study of cell division genes in *B. subtilis,* we isolated the *ftsZ* homolog (3). This study was undertaken in recognition of

TABLE 1. Loci affecting cell division in *B. subtilis*

Mutation	Phenotype	Gene	Map position	Reference(s)
ts1	Filamentation	*ftsZ*	134	3, 53
ts12, tms12	Filamentation	*dds(divIB)*	134	4, 13, 31
ts341(div341)	Filamentation	*secA*	312	49, 59
ts31	Filamentation	?	134	49
spo279(Ts)	Temperature-sensitive sporulation defect	*ftsA(spoIIN)*	134	39, 44, 70
divIVB1	Minicell formation	*minD*	242	41, 56, 67
spoIIE20,21,48	Thick asymmetric septum	*spoIIE*	10	35

the key role *ftsZ* plays in cell division in *E. coli* (45) and the knowledge that *B. subtilis,* along with a diverse group of eubacteria, contains a protein that cross-reacts with *E. coli* FtsZ antisera (15). The *B. subtilis ftsZ* gene encodes a protein that has considerable homology to its *E. coli* counterpart: 50% identity at the amino acid level (3). It was gratifying to find that the *ts1* mutation, which is a well-characterized cell division mutation (14), mapped in the *ftsZ* gene (3, 31). Construction of a strain that conditionally expressed the *ftsZ* gene confirmed that it was essential for vegetative cell division at all temperatures (5). Immediately upstream of the *ftsZ* gene is a gene that is homologous to the *ftsA* gene of *E. coli* with 35% amino acid identity. Interestingly, a *spoII* mutation, *spo-279*(Ts) (70), mapped to the *ftsA* (*spoIIN*) gene (39). In addition to a defect in sporulation this mutation causes filamentous growth at high temperature. The *ftsA* gene is not absolutely essential, although mutants lacking this gene are extremely filamentous and grow poorly (6). Other previously isolated mutations, *tms12* and *ts12,* mapped to a gene upstream of *ftsA* which was designated *dds* or *divIB* (4, 31). This gene is also not essential; however, cells lacking this gene are extremely filamentous and temperature-sensitive. Although this gene has no known homolog in *E. coli* it apparently has a similar topology to a number of cell division gene products in *E. coli.* These gene products are all transmembrane proteins with a large extracytoplasmic domain connected to a short amino-terminal domain through a hydrophobic segment (18). Such proteins would be ideally suited to transmit information in the cytoplasm across the cytoplasmic membrane to the peptidoglycan synthetic machinery.

The availability of the temperature-sensitive mutations and knockout mutations, as well as a strain in which *ftsZ* is conditionally expressed, has allowed researchers to determine if these genes, isolated for their role in

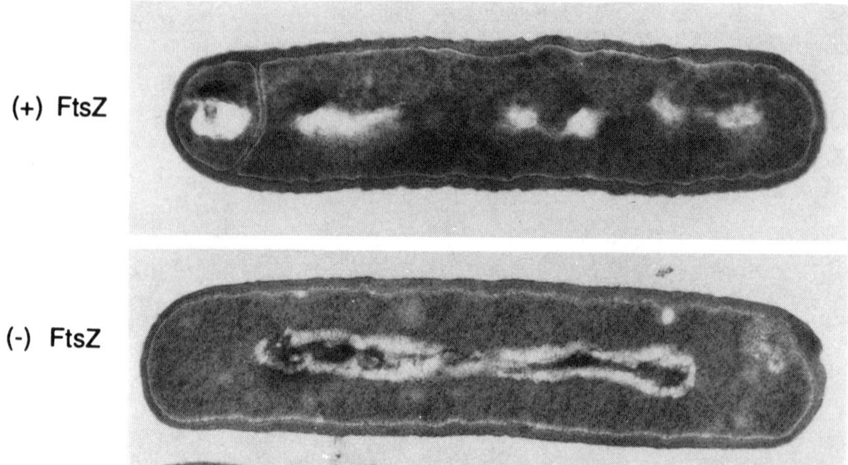

FIGURE 1. FtsZ is required for asymmetric septation. Typical cells from a culture induced to sporulate in the absence or presence of *ftsZ* expression. Sporulation was induced in a *B. subtilis* strain in which the *ftsZ* gene is under an inducible (*spac*) promoter. Reprinted from reference 5 with permission. Copyright © 1991 Cold Spring Harbor Laboratory Press.

vegetative septation, had a role in sporulation, specifically in asymmetric septation. The answer is yes. The *ftsZ1*(Ts) mutation reduces sporulation approximately 1,000-fold, and restricting expression of *ftsZ* as cells undergo nutrient exhaustion reduces sporulation more than 10,000-fold (5). Electron microscopic examination of cells in this latter case revealed no observable septa, indicating that *ftsZ* is also required for this septation event (Fig. 1). In addition, strains deleted for *ftsA* or *dds* show reduced efficiency of sporulation (4, 6) and the *ts31* mutation also results in a sporulation deficiency at the nonpermissive temperature (58). In these cases cells have not been examined by electron microscopy, although the pattern of gene expression for the *ftsA* null mutant is consistent with a block in asymmetric septation (6) (see below). These results support the proposal that asymmetric septation is a modified form of vegetative septation and uses the same basic machinery.

THE ROLE OF *ftsZ* IN SEPTATION

In *E. coli ftsZ* appears to play a pivotal role in cell division (reviewed in reference 45). It acts earlier than other well-studied *fts* genes (7) and appears to be the target of several division inhibitors, including SulA, a component of the SOS response, and MinCD, thought to play a role in selection of the division site (8, 9). The concentration of FtsZ is critical as either an increase or a decrease in the level of FtsZ prevents cell division (16, 17). Significantly, FtsZ has been localized in a ring structure at the division site (10). This ring structure is formed at the division site before there is visible invagination and remains at the leading edge of the septum throughout septation. As septation is completed FtsZ disassociates and is not associated with the new cell pole. It was postulated that the FtsZ ring forms through self-assembly and functions to mark the division site and activate the division machinery. Significantly, inhibitors of cell division, SulA and MinCD, prevent localization of FtsZ into a ring when they are overexpressed (12).

The observed dynamic behavior of FtsZ invites comparisons to eukaryotic cytoskeletal proteins. In addition, the presence of a short amino acid segment in FtsZ (GGGTGTG) that is homologous to a highly conserved segment in tubulin (GGGTGSG), which is thought to be part of the GTP binding site, led to a search for an interaction between FtsZ and GTP. We and two other groups independently determined that FtsZ is a GTP binding protein with a GTPase activity, leading to speculation that FtsZ may utilize GTP to assemble into a structure (21, 50, 55). Significantly, a lethal allele of *ftsZ*, *ftsZ3*(Rsa), results in a protein that has the first T in the homologous segment changed to A and displays dramatically reduced GTP binding and GTPase activity (50). In addition, the temperature-sensitive *ftsZ84* allele results in a change in the first G to S and a protein that displays dramatically reduced interaction with GTP (21, 55).

In *B. subtilis* FtsZ is also localized to the leading edge of the invaginating vegetative septum (68). The purified protein has a GTPase activity, and the specific activity is dependent upon the FtsZ concentration, suggesting that the protein must oligomerize to express the GTPase activity (68). The question of whether FtsZ is also associated with the asymmetric septum requires further work, but the genetic evidence shows that it is required (5).

The available evidence is consistent with FtsZ forming a cytoskeletal structure at the division site. One possibility is that a nucleation site is formed at midcell under cell cycle control and that its formation triggers the self-assembly of the FtsZ ring (45a). Once formed the FtsZ ring would function to coordinate the circumferential invagination of the septum and activate septal peptidoglycan biosynthetic machinery. This machinery might consist of other cell division gene products, including FtsA, FtsL, FtsN, FtsQ, and FtsI (PBP3) (18, 51). The idea that the FtsZ might direct septal peptidoglycan biosynthesis is consistent with the altered polar morphology induced by several *ftsZ* mutations (11). The altered polar morphology appears to arise from an altered geometry of the FtsZ ring, suggesting that the FtsZ ring may direct septal peptidoglycan biosynthesis. This model is quite speculative and further work is necessary to confirm or disprove it.

EXPRESSION OF THE *ftsAZ* OPERON

The *ftsA* and *ftsZ* genes are arranged in an operon located at 135°. Recent examination of this operon by two groups, that of Piggot and that of Stragier, reveals that the regulation of this operon is complex (29, 30). The operon is expressed from three promoters located just upstream of *ftsA* (Fig. 2). Two of these promoters (P1 and P3) are dependent on the main vegetative sigma factor (σ^A), and the third (P2) is dependent upon σ^H, the activity of which is known to increase as cells exit exponential growth and enter stationary phase (32). Both groups have shown that there is a burst of activity from P2 at the end of exponential growth and that that activity is dependent upon σ^H. One group has found that this burst is also dependent upon functional *spo0A* (30); however, the other has not (29).

What are the physiological roles of these promoters, especially the role of the P2 promoter in adjustment to stationary phase and in sporulation? The two groups disagree. One of the major differences in these two studies is that Piggot's group was able to construct a strain that grew well vegetatively with just P1 driving *ftsAZ* expression (29), whereas Stragier's group found that such a strain was very filamentous and unstable (30). We also observed this latter result (45b). With respect to sporulation, Stragier's group found that in the absence of P2 sporulation efficiency was reduced by 70%. Piggot's group found that in the absence of P3 and P2 sporulation was abolished. It is difficult to reconcile the two studies; the differences must be due to the strategies employed in constructing the various strains. Further work is necessary to clear up the discrepancies.

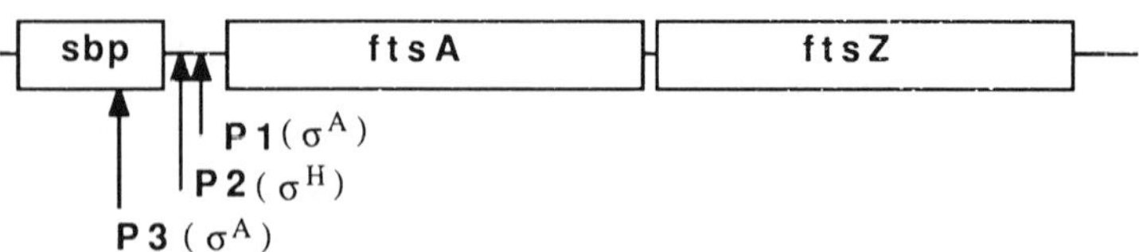

FIGURE 2. The *ftsAZ* operon. The *ftsA* and *ftsZ* genes are arranged in an operon at 135° on the *B. subtilis* genetic map. The operon is preceded by three promoters, two of which (P1 and P3) are σ^A-dependent and a third of which (P2) is σ^H-dependent.

EFFECT OF *spo* MUTATIONS ON SEPTATION

Mutations that specifically block sporulation relatively early in development either block at stage 0 (terminal phenotype resembles vegetative cells) or just after asymmetric septation but before engulfment (stage II) (Fig. 3). The corresponding mutations are designated *spo0* and *spoII*, respectively (43, 54). As noted above, limiting the expression of *ftsZ* as cells reached the end of exponential growth prevented cells from initiating asymmetric septation (5). In addition, the DNA appeared to be in an axial filament and there was no sign of condensation of the DNA at the cell poles, suggesting that this process was blocked or was reversible (Fig. 1). There are several possible explanations. One is that FtsZ is required directly for the polar migration and condensation of the DNA. Another is that these two separate events, asymmetric septation and DNA migration with the accompanying condensation of the DNA, have to occur concurrently. It is also possible that the initiation of septation has to precede the polar migration of the DNA and condensation. Further work will be required to determine which of these possibilities is correct. In any event, a deficiency in FtsZ blocks sporulation later into the developmental program than *spo0* mutations (as assayed by *spo-lacZ* fusions, see below) but earlier than *spoII* mutations. The resultant phenotype is similar to the postulated stage I of sporulation (54, 57). The existence of this stage is in doubt since no mutations are known that block at this stage, and the morphology, axial filament formation, may not be specific to early sporulation.

Although phenotypically all *spo0* mutants are grouped together and all *spoII* mutants are grouped together, closer scrutiny of their terminal phenotype reveals some differences (Fig. 3). Many *spoII* mutants are terminally disporic, including *spoIIAA, spoIIAC, spoIIGA,* and *spoIIGB* mutants (35, 54). With these mutants the asymmetric septum formed at each end of the cell has the morphology of a typical sporulation septum. A *spoIIB spoVG* double mutant also forms a typical asymmetric septum but is not disporic (48). In contrast *spoIIE* mutants, which are also not disporic, form an asymmetric septum that is thicker, similar to a vegetative septum (35). This suggests that the *spoIIE* gene product may function to limit the peptidoglycan content of the asymmetric septum, making it a candidate for a sporulation gene product that interacts directly with the septation machinery.

The terminal disporic phenotype of the above-mentioned *spoII* mutants results from the sequential appearance of the asymmetric septa (26). This observation suggests that in wild-type cells formation of the second asymmetric septum is blocked by an inhibitor activated after formation of the first asymmetric septum. It has been suggested that this inhibitor is under the control of σ^E (35). Such an inhibitor would not be required to have

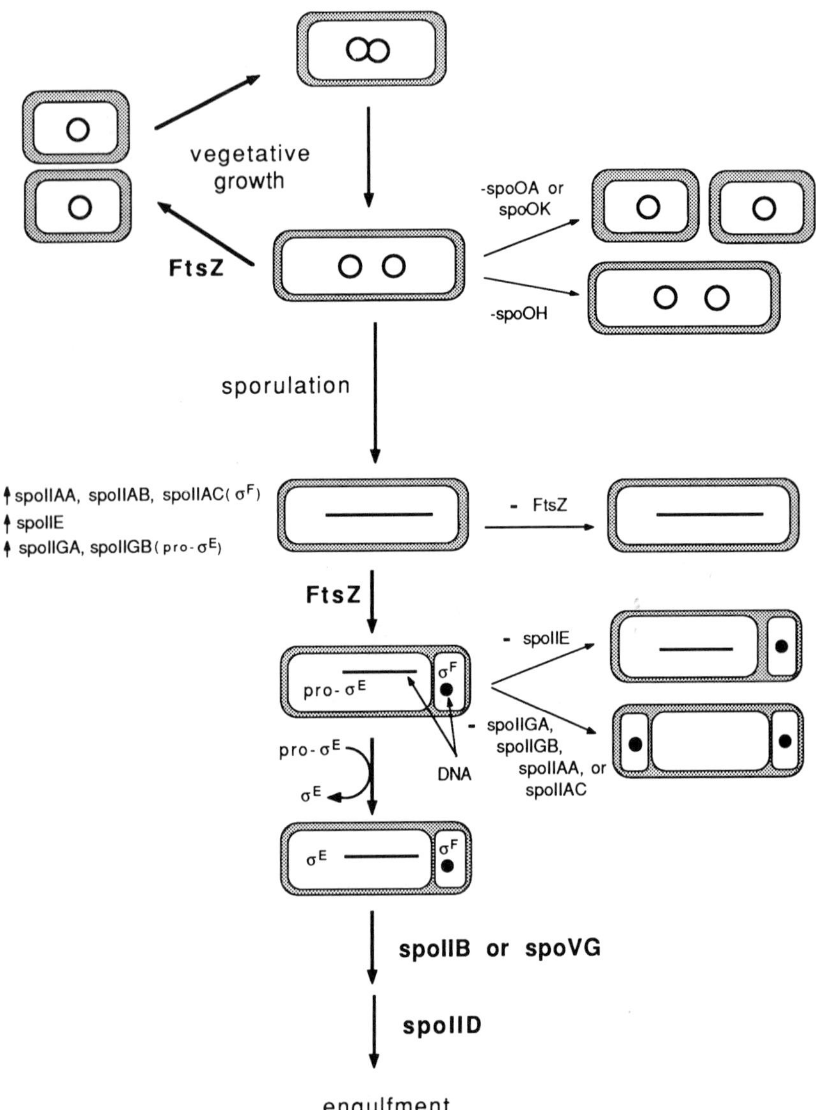

FIGURE 3. Asymmetric septation and development. A signal to sporulate is generated in response to nutrient depletion before the final round of DNA replication is completed. This leads to a sequence of early events dependent upon the *spo0* gene products that includes expression of the early *spoII* genes and formation of the asymmetric septum, which results in activation of σ^F in the prespore and processing of pro-σ^E in the mother cell. Absence of functional *spo0* gene products halts development at stage 0. Absence of *spo0A* or *spo0K* results in a final symmetric division that is not observed in an *spo0H* mutant. In the absence of FtsZ asymmetric

topological specificity but need only be a generalized inhibitor of the septation machinery, like SulA in *E. coli* (45). It is also possible, for example, that the failure of disporic mutants to progress on the sporulation pathway leads to excess expression of the *ftsAZ* operon and formation of the second asymmetric septum. With such a model no specific inhibitor of septation would be required. Nonetheless, the appearance of the disporic phenotype in some *spoII* mutants suggests that a discrete site exists at each cell pole since septation does not occur randomly along the cell length. It is also noteworthy that in these disporic mutants each pole is associated with a condensed chromosome, indicating that both poles are functionally equivalent (61).

Once the asymmetric septum is formed the peptidoglycan is removed by hydrolysis starting from the center of the septum, and the prespore is engulfed to form the forespore. Based upon the morphology of several *spo* mutants Illing and Errington (35) have separated this process into several discrete stages. Mutations that prevent activation of σ^E prevent peptidoglycan hydrolysis, indicating that this process is carried out in part by genes under control of this sigma factor. In addition, the *spoIIB* and *spoVG* genes, not under σ^E control, code for redundant functions necessary to initiate peptidoglycan hydrolysis (48). Mutations at *spoIID* allow the peptidoglycan hydrolysis to initiate at the center of the septum but not to reach the sidewall (35, 54). In addition, Higgins and Piggot (33) have suggested that the two membranes formed during asymmetric septation fuse once the peptidoglycan is removed.

Dunn et al. (24) raised the issue of whether a final symmetric division is actively blocked in cells entering sporulation as a prelude to formation of the asymmetric septum (reviewed in reference 25). If the midcell site was active it would probably compete with the polar, asymmetric sites for the septation machinery and interfere with sporulation by producing cells with only one chromosome. Some *spo0* mutants (Fig. 3), *spo0A* and *spo0K*, appear one-half the size of wild-type cells and have apparently undergone an extra symmetric division at the end of exponential growth (24). In

---

septation is prevented; however, the early *spoII* gene products are still expressed, but activation of σ^F and processing of pro-σ^E are blocked. In the absence of *spoIIE* an abnormal asymmetric septum is formed and σ^F activation is blocked. Most mutations in the *spoIIG* and *spoIIA* operons lead to a terminal disporic phenotype; however, mutations in *spoIIG* do not prevent σ^F activation (47). In an *spoIIB spoVG* double mutant a typical asymmetric septum is formed and σ^F and σ^E are activated, but hydrolysis of septal peptidoglycan is blocked and further development is prevented. In an *spoIID* mutant hydrolysis of the septal peptidoglycan is initiated but not completed.

contrast, cells of at least one *spo0H* mutant are the same length as wild-type cells at the end of exponential growth and do not undergo this extra division (29). Interestingly, in a strain in which the P2 and P3 promoters were removed from the front of the *ftsAZ* operon cells are even longer at the end of exponential growth, suggesting that postexponential expression of this operon is necessary for the decrease in cell size (29). A more careful comparison of the phenotype of all *spo0* mutants is necessary.

Although from the above discussion it would appear that the midcell site must be blocked during sporulation, it is also possible that the midcell site is not formed in cells in which sporulation has been induced. In such a model it would not be necessary to have an inhibitor of cell division that would show topological specificity. The answer will only be known when more is known about what constitutes a division site.

Work from Mandelstam's laboratory indicates that the initiation of sporulation is coupled to the cell cycle, particularly to the DNA replication cycle (19, 46). Cells reach their maximum potential for sporulation when the DNA is half replicated. These studies are complicated by the observation that inhibition of DNA replication prevents activation of Spo0A, which may be due to the generation of an inhibitory signal generated when DNA replication is blocked, perhaps as part of the SOS response (36).

EFFECT OF ASYMMETRIC SEPTATION ON THE TEMPORAL PROGRAM OF GENE EXPRESSION

Formation of the asymmetric septum is the first morphological feature of sporulation, but how is this event connected to the temporal program of gene expression and the establishment of cell-specific gene expression? Stragier et al. (64) proposed a model in which formation of the asymmetric septum was coupled to the processing of pro-σ^E to its active form (40). It was suggested that the formation of this unique septum activated the protease responsible for the proteolytic activation of pro-σ^E. The availability of a strain in which asymmetric septation could be specifically blocked allowed the first part of the model to be addressed (5). Blocking asymmetric septation by restricting the expression of *ftsZ* did not prevent expression of *spoIIA, spoIIE,* or *spoIIG,* confirming earlier evidence (28) that they are expressed in the predivisional cell (Fig. 3). However, it did block expression of *spoIID*. Since *spoIID* expression requires processed pro-σ^E, the result is consistent with Stragier's proposal. Direct examination of pro-σ^E using Haldenwang's monoclonal antibody (40) confirmed that blocking septation blocked processing (5).

Other approaches have also been used to try to examine the effect of blocking septation on processing of pro-σ^E. One approach involved the addition of penicillin, which had the complication of preventing synthesis of pro-σ^E (38). Another involved the *spo-279*(Ts) (*ftsA279*) mutation. This mutation, however, also prevents the synthesis of pro-σ^E, indicating that the induction of sporulation might be sensitive to alterations in cell wall metabolism (37, 44). In contrast, a deletion mutant of *ftsA,* which has an extremely filamentous phenotype, appears blocked in processing but not synthesis of pro-σ^E (6). Among the approaches used to block asymmetric septation, the one involving restricting *ftsZ* expression seems to offer the most specific and least pleiotropic way to block septation.

Studies by Losick's group demonstrated that the activity of σ^F, encoded by the *spoIIA* operon and expressed in the predivisional cell (5), is restricted to the prespore (47). Furthermore, when asymmetric septation is blocked by restricting expression of *ftsZ* σ^F is not activated (41) (Fig. 3). This result indicates that asymmetric septation resulting in the formation of two unequally sized cells has a role in this activation. How formation of the asymmetric septum could activate σ^F is not known. It is known that the activity of σ^F is regulated by two additional gene products from the *spoIIA* operon, SpoIIAA and SpoIIAB (60). SpoIIAB is an antagonist of σ^F and SpoIIAA is an antagonist of SpoIIAB. In the predivisional and mother cells the activity of SpoIIAB must be dominant, whereas in the prespore the activity of SpoIIAA must predominate. Presumably these two proteins are differentially segregated into the prespore or their activity is differentially regulated. In addition, σ^F activation requires a functional *spoIIE* (47), the gene required to limit the amount of peptidoglycan in the septum (35), suggesting that SpoIIE has a role in setting up this asymmetry in σ^F activity. Furthermore, the processing of σ^E, which is restricted to the mother cell (22), depends upon activation of σ^F in the prespore, suggesting that asymmetric septation may only be needed indirectly to activate σ^E (reviewed in references 27 and 42). Of course the asymmetric septum could still play an additional, more direct, role in σ^F activation. Together these results suggest that the critical step in establishing differential gene expression is formation of an asymmetric septum with the accompanying activation of σ^F in the prespore. Furthermore, results with *spoIIE* mutants argue that this asymmetric septum has to have the correct morphology and also argue that formation of two cells of unequal size, the smaller with a condensed chromosome, is not sufficient to activate σ^F. Preventing asymmetric septation, or forming an abnormal asymmetric septum, blocks the developmental program by preventing σ^F activation, which in turn prevents σ^E activation.

LOCATION OF THE ASYMMETRIC SEPTUM

How is the septum positioned near the poles during sporulation? In one model it was suggested that cells contain a pair of replicating chromosomes upon entry into the sporulation pathway and that asymmetric septation results from septation taking place between the daughter chromosomes of the first of the pair to complete replication (25). This model does not appear to be correct, since several *spoII* mutants with a disporic phenotype have a chromosome in each prespore and none in the mother cell (61). This phenotype of disporic mutants suggests a much more active chromosome segregation process than the passive process implied by the model. In fact, the migration of a chromosome into the prespore is a dramatic example of an active segregation in prokaryotes. Below I discuss a model that was proposed previously (5) based on the study of *ftsZ* and *min* in *E. coli*.

E. coli and *B. subtilis min* mutants have been isolated which result in the frequent polar localization of the division site, resulting in minicells (1, 56, 66). In *E. coli* minicell formation can also result from overproduction of FtsZ (69). It has been postulated that the function of *min* is to mask old division sites, the cell poles (65). More recently this suggestion has been questioned because *min* mutants have a defect in DNA segregation, suggesting that the effect of *min* on polar septation may not be direct (2). In *E. coli* the *min* locus consists of three genes; two of these encode a division inhibitor, MinCD, and the third, *minE*, encodes a topological specificity factor (20). Cloning of one of the *min* loci in *B. subtilis*, *divIVB*, revealed that it contained the *minCD* homologs but lacked a *minE* equivalent (41, 67). Other *min* loci have been identified in *B. subtilis* but are not well-characterized (66). Because of the similarity between minicell formation and asymmetric septation the question of a possible role of *min* in sporulation arises, as does the question of whether the study of minicell formation can provide useful information on how the asymmetric septum is localized. It must be emphasized, however, that *min* mutants sporulate fairly efficiently, indicating that *min* has no essential role in asymmetric septum formation or the accompanying DNA segregation (41).

In a previous model for asymmetric septation during sporulation it was proposed that *min* function is inactivated early during sporulation, unmasking both polar sites (5). This unmasking must be under *spo0* control and could occur through induction of a *minE*-like homolog or indirectly through DNA condensation. The induction of sporulation must also block the midcell site or prevent its formation. When the level of FtsZ is sufficient nucleation of assembly occurs at one of the poles and an FtsZ ring is formed, resulting in initiation of asymmetric septation. The nucleation of the FtsZ ring, which could occur at random at either pole, could be the event that dictates at which pole the prespore will form. It does appear that under some conditions the selection of the pole is random, but this depends upon the medium (23). Perhaps this observation is a reflection of a differential unmasking of the polar sites depending upon growth rate. Alternatively, DNA segregation could be initiated toward one pole, which would then dictate where the FtsZ ring is to form. After the FtsZ ring is formed and asymmetric septation is initiated other sporulation products then modify the normal segregation machinery to ensure DNA segregation and condensation in the forming prespore. This modified segregation along with DNA condensation is probably unique to sporulation and would explain why minicell formation during vegetative growth is not accompanied by DNA segregation into the minicell. The model accounts for the lack of an effect of *min* mutations on sporulation; *min* only has a passive role. In *min* mutants the poles are already unmasked and therefore available to the septation machinery. The model is also consistent with the disporic phenotype of *spoII* mutants and would explain why septation occurs only at the poles and not elsewhere along the length of the cell; it is the poles that contain old sites that can nucleate the formation of the FtsZ ring when unmasked. The second asymmetric septum would form in disporic mutants due to continued synthesis of FtsZ, causing nucleation of an FtsZ ring at the second pole.

SUMMARY

B. subtilis can undergo two distinct septation events: a symmetric septation event during vegetative growth, resulting in the formation of two cells with the same developmental fate, or an asymmetric septation event during sporulation, yielding two cells with different developmental fates. These two septation events are carried out by the same division machinery involving FtsZ. Restricting *ftsZ* expression during sporulation prevents asymmetric septation and blocks development between stage 0 and stage II, perhaps at the elusive stage I. In the absence of FtsZ the early *spoII* genes are expressed, but their gene products, the cell-specific sigma factors, σ^F and σ^E, are not activated, implying a key role for asymmetric septation in their activation. During asymmetric septation the division machinery is probably modified by SpoIIE, resulting in the morphologically distinct septum and activation of σ^F in the prespore. This appears to be the key event that establishes cell-specific gene expression in the prespore and leads to processing of pro-σ^E in the mother cell and thus cell-specific gene expression in this cell. We have presented a model for asymmetric septation that suggests that during sporulation polar division sites are unmasked, allowing FtsZ to assemble at one of these sites, chosen at random. Formation of an FtsZ ring at the pole initiates septation, and additional sporulation products modify the cell's segregation machinery to coordinate DNA segregation and condensation into the prespore.

I am grateful to Jeff Errington for providing his review before publication. I am also grateful to members of my laboratory for discussions and reading of this manuscript. Work in my laboratory was supported by Public Health Service grant GM29764 and a grant from the Kansas Health Foundation.

REFERENCES

1. **Adler, H. I., W. D. Fisher, A. Cohen, and A. A. Hardigree.** 1967. Miniature *Escherichia coli* cells deficient in DNA. *Proc. Natl. Acad. Sci. USA* **57:**321–326.
2. **Akerlund, T., R. Bernander, and K. Nordstrom.** 1992. Cell division in *Escherichia coli minB* mutants. *Mol. Microbiol.* **6:**2073–2083.
3. **Beall, B., M. Lowe, and J. Lutkenhaus.** 1988. Cloning and characterization of *Bacillus subtilis* mutant homologs of *Escherichia coli* cell division genes *ftsZ* and *ftsA*. *J. Bacteriol.* **170:**4855–4864.
4. **Beall, B., and J. Lutkenhaus.** 1989. Nucleotide sequence and insertional inactivation of a *Bacillus subtilis* gene that affects cell division, sporulation and temperature sensitivity. *J. Bacteriol.* **171:**6621–6834.
5. **Beall, B., and J. Lutkenhaus.** 1991. FtsZ in *Bacillus subtilis* is required for vegetative septation and asymmetric septation during sporulation. *Genes Dev.* **5:**447–455.
6. **Beall, B., and J. Lutkenhaus.** 1992. Impaired cell division and sporulation of a *Bacillus subtilis* strain with the *ftsA* gene deleted. *J. Bacteriol.* **174:**2398–2403.
7. **Begg, K. J., and W. D. Donachie.** 1985. Cell shape and division in *Escherichia coli:* experiments with shape and division mutants. *J. Bacteriol.* **163:**615–622.
8. **Bi, E., and J. Lutkenhaus.** 1990. Analysis of *ftsZ* mutations that confer resistance to the cell division inhibitor SulA (SfiA). *J. Bacteriol.* **172:**5602–5609.
9. **Bi, E., and J. Lutkenhaus.** 1990. Interaction between the *min* locus and *ftsZ*. *J. Bacteriol.* **172:**5610–5616.
10. **Bi, E., and J. Lutkenhaus.** 1991. FtsZ ring structure associated with division in *Escherichia coli*. *Nature* (London) **354:**161–164.
11. **Bi, E., and J. Lutkenhaus.** 1992. Isolation and characterization of *ftsZ* alleles that affect septal morphology. *J. Bacteriol.* **174:**5414–5423.
12. **Bi, E., and J. Lutkenhaus.** 1993. Cell division inhibitors, SulA and MinCD, prevent localization of FtsZ. *J. Bacteriol.* **175:**1118–1125.
13. **Breakfield, X. O., and O. E. Landman.** 1973. Temperature-sensitive divisionless mutant of *Bacillus subtilis* defective in the initiation of septation. *J. Bacteriol.* **113:**985–998.
14. **Callister, H., and R. G. Wake.** 1981. Characterization and mapping of temperature-sensitive division initiation mutations of *Bacillus subtilis*. *J. Bacteriol.* **145:**1042–1051.
15. **Corton, J. C., J. E. Ward, Jr., and J. Lutkenhaus.** 1987. Analysis of cell division gene *ftsZ* (*sulB*) from gram-negative and gram-positive bacteria. *J. Bacteriol.* **169:**1–7.

16. **Dai, K., and J. Lutkenhaus.** 1991. *ftsZ* is an essential cell division gene in *Escherichia coli. J. Bacteriol.* **173:**3500–3506.
17. **Dai, K., and J. Lutkenhaus.** 1992. The proper ratio of FtsZ to FtsA is required for cell division to occur in *Escherichia coli. J. Bacteriol.* **174:**6145–6151.
18. **Dai, K., Y. Xu, and J. Lutkenhaus.** 1993. Cloning and characterization of *ftsN,* an essential cell division gene in *Escherichia coli* isolated as a multicopy suppressor of *ftsA12* (Ts). *J. Bacteriol.* **175:**3790–3797.
19. **Dawes, I. W., D. Kay, and J. Mandelstam.** 1971. Determining the effect of growth medium on the shape and position of daughter chromosomes and on sporulation in *Bacillus subtilis. Nature* (London) **230:**567–569.
20. **de Boer, P., R. Crossley, and L. Rothfield.** 1989. A division inhibitor and a topological specificity factor coded for by the minicell locus determine proper placement of the division septum in *Escherichia coli. Cell* **56:**641–649.
21. **de Boer, P., R. Crossley, and L. Rothfield.** 1992. The essential bacterial cell division protein FtsZ is a GTPase. *Nature* (London) **359:**254–256.
22. **Driks, A., and R. Losick.** 1991. Compartmentalized expression of a gene under the control of sporulation transcription factor σ^E in *Bacillus subtilis. Proc. Natl. Acad. Sci. USA* **88:**9934–9938.
23. **Dunn, G., and J. Mandelstam.** 1977. Cell polarity in *Bacillus subtilis:* effect of growth conditions on spore positions in sister cells. *J. Gen Microbiol.* **103:**201–205.
24. **Dunn, G., D. M. Torgersen, and J. Mandelstam.** 1976. Order of expression of genes affecting septum location during sporulation of *Bacillus subtilis. J. Bacteriol.* **125:**776–779.
25. **Errington, J.** 1991. A model for asymmetric septum formation during sporulation in *Bacillus subtilis. Mol. Microbiol.* **6:**785–789.
26. **Errington, J.** 1993. Sporulation in *Bacillus subtilis:* regulation of gene expression and control of morphogenesis. *Microbiol. Rev.* **57:**1–33.
27. **Errington, J., and N. Illing.** 1992. Establishment of cell-specific transcription during sporulation in *Bacillus subtilis. Mol. Microbiol.* **6:**689–695.
28. **Gholamhoseinian, A., and P. Piggot.** 1989. Timing of *spoII* gene expression to septum formation during sporulation of *Bacillus subtilis. J. Bacteriol.* **171:**5747–5749.
29. **Gholamhoseinian, A., Z. Shen, J.-J. Wu, and P. Piggot.** 1992. Regulation of transcription of the cell division gene *ftsA* during sporulation of *Bacillus subtilis. J. Bacteriol.* **174:**4647–4656.
30. **Gonzy-Treboul, G., C. Karmazyn-Campelli, and P. Stragier.** 1992. Developmental regulation of transcription of the *Bacillus subtilis ftsAZ* operon. *J. Mol. Biol.* **224:**967–979.
31. **Harry, E. J., and R. G. Wake.** 1989. Cloning and expression of a *Bacillus subtilis* division initiation gene for which a homolog has not been identified in another organism. *J. Bacteriol.* **171:**6835–6839.
32. **Healy, J., J. Weir, I. Smith, and R. Losick.** 1991. Post-transcriptional control of a sporulation regulatory gene encoding transcription factor σ^H in *Bacillus subtilis. Mol. Microbiol.* **5:**477–487.
33. **Higgins, M. L., and P. J. Piggot.** 1992. Septal membrane fusion—a pivotal event in bacterial spore formation. *Mol. Microbiol.* **6:**2565–2571.
34. **Hitchins, A. D., and R. A. Slepecky.** 1969. Bacterial spore formation as a modified prokaryotic cell division. *Nature* (London) **223:**804–807.

35. **Illing, N., and J. Errington.** 1991. Genetic regulation of morphogenesis in *Bacillus subtilis:* roles of σ^E and σ^F in prespore engulfment. *J. Bacteriol.* **173:**3159–3169.
36. **Ireton, K., and A. D. Grossman.** 1992. Coupling between gene expression and DNA synthesis early during development in *Bacillus subtilis. Proc. Natl. Acad. Sci. USA* **89:**8808–8812.
37. **Jonas, R. M., and W. G. Haldenwang.** 1989. Influence of *spo* mutations on σ^E synthesis in *Bacillus subtilis. J. Bacteriol.* **171:**5226–5228.
38. **Jonas, R. M., S. C. Holt, and W. G. Haldenwang.** 1990. Effects of antibiotics on synthesis and persistence of σ^E in sporulating *Bacillus subtilis. J. Bacteriol.* **172:**4616–4623.
39. **Karmazyn-Campelli, C., L. Fluss, T. Leighton, and P. Stragier.** 1992. The *spoIIN279* (ts) mutation affects the FtsA protein of *Bacillus subtilis. Biochimie* **74:**689–694.
40. **LaBell, T. L., J. E. Trempy, and W. J. Haldenwang.** 1987. Sporulation-specific sigma factor sigma 29 is synthesized for a precursor protein, P31. *Proc. Natl. Acad. Sci. USA* **84:**1784–1788.
41. **Levin, P. A., P. S. Margolis, P. Setlow, R. Losick, and D. Sun.** 1992. Identification of *Bacillus subtilis* genes for septum placement and shape determination. *J. Bacteriol.* **174:**7717–7728.
41a. **Losick, R.** Personal communication.
42. **Losick, R., and P. Stragier.** 1992. Crisscross regulation of cell-type-specific gene expression during development in *B. subtilis. Nature* (London) **355:**601–604.
43. **Losick, R., P. Youngman, and P. J. Piggot.** 1986. Genetics of endospore formation in *Bacillus subtilis. Annu. Rev. Genet.* **20:**625–669.
44. **Louie, P., A. Lee, K. Stansmore, R. Grant, C. Ginther, and T. Leighton.** 1992. Roles of *rpoD, spoIIF, spoIIJ, spoIIN* and *sin* in regulation of *Bacillus subtilis* stage II sporulation-specific transcription. *J. Bacteriol.* **174:**3570–3576.
45. **Lutkenhaus, J.** 1990. Regulation of cell division in *E. coli. Trends Genet.* **6:**22–25.
45a. **Lutkenhaus, J.** 1993. FtsZ ring in bacterial cytokinesis. *Mol. Microbiol.* **9:**403–409.
45b. **Lutkenhaus, J.** Unpublished data.
46. **Mandelstam, J. and S. A. Higgs.** 1974. Induction of sporulation during synchronized chromosome replication in *Bacillus subtilis. J. Bacteriol.* **120:**34–42.
47. **Margolis, P., A. Driks, and R. Losick.** 1991. Establishment of cell type by compartmentalized activation of a transcription factor. *Science* **254:**562–565.
48. **Margolis, P., A. Driks, and R. Losick.** 1993. Sporulation gene *spoIIB* from *Bacillus subtilis. J. Bacteriol.* **175:**528–540.
49. **Miyakawa, Y., and T. Komano.** 1981. Study on the cell cycle of *Bacillus subtilis* using temperature-sensitive mutants. 1. Isolation and genetic analysis of the mutants defective in septum formation. *Mol. Gen. Genet.* **181:**207–214.
50. **Mukherjee, A., K. Dai, and J. Lutkenhaus.** 1993. *E. coli* cell division protein FtsZ is a guanine nucleotide binding protein. *Proc. Natl. Acad. Sci. USA* **90:**1053–1057.
51. **Nanninga, N.** 1991. Cell division and peptidoglycan assembly in *Escherichia coli. Mol. Microbiol.* **5:**791–795.
52. **Nanninga, N., L. J. H. Koppes, and F. D. de Vries-Tijssen.** 1979. The cell cycle of *Bacillus subtilis* as studied by electron microscopy. *Arch. Microbiol.* **123:**173–181.

53. **Nukushina, J.-I., and Y. Ikeda.** 1968. Genetic analysis of the developmental processes during germination and outgrowth of *Bacillus subtilis* spores with temperature-sensitive mutants. *Genetics* **63:**63–74.
54. **Piggot, P. J., and J. G. Coote.** 1976. Genetic aspects of bacterial endospore formation. *Bacteriol. Rev.* **40:**908–962.
55. **RayChaudhuri, D., and J. T. Park.** 1992. *Escherichia coli* cell division gene *ftsZ* encodes a novel GTP-binding protein. *Nature* (London) **359:**251–254.
56. **Reeve, J. N., N. H. Mendelson, S. I. Coyne, L. L. Hallock, and R. M. Cole.** 1973. Minicells of *Bacillus subtilis. J. Bacteriol.* **114:**860–873.
57. **Ryter, A.** 1965. Etude morphologique de la sporulation de *Bacillus subtilis. Ann. Inst. Pasteur* (Paris) **108:**40–60.
58. **Sadaie, Y., and T. Kada.** 1983. Effect of septum-initiation mutations on sporulation and competent cell formation in *Bacillus subtilis. Mol. Gen. Genet.* **190:** 176–178.
59. **Sadaie, Y., J. Takamatsu, K. Nakamura, and K. Yamane.** 1991. Sequencing reveals similarity of the wild-type div^+ gene of *Bacillus subtilis* to the *Escherichia coli secA* gene. *Gene* **98:**101–105.
60. **Schmidt, R., P. Margolis, L. Duncan, R. Coppolecchia, C. P. Moran, Jr., and R. Losick.** 1990. Control of developmental transcription factor sF by sporulation regulatory proteins SpoIIA and SpoIIAB in *Bacillus subtilis. Proc. Natl. Acad. Sci. USA* **87:**9221–9225.
61. **Setlow, B., N. Magill, P. Febbroriello, L. Nakhimovsky, D. E. Koppel, and P. Setlow.** 1991. Condensation of the prespore nucleoid early in sporulation of *Bacillus* species. *J. Bacteriol.* **173:**6270–6278.
62. **Sowell, M. O., and C. E. Buchanan.** 1983. Changes in penicillin-binding proteins during sporulation of *Bacillus subtilis. J. Bacteriol.* **153:**1331–1337.
63. **Spratt, B. G.** 1975. Distinct penicillin binding proteins involved in the division, shape and elongation of *Escherichia coli* K12. *Proc. Natl. Acad. Sci. USA* **72:**2999–3003.
64. **Stragier, P., C. Bonamy, and C. Karmazyn-Campelli.** 1988. Processing of a sporulation sigma factor in *Bacillus subtilis:* how morphological structure could control gene expression. *Cell* **52:**697–704.
65. **Teather, R. M., J. F. Collins, and W. D. Donachie.** 1974. Quantal behavior of a diffusible factor which initiates septum formation at potential division sites in *Escherichia coli. J. Bacteriol.* **118:**407–413.
66. **Van Alstyne, D., and M. I. Simon.** 1971. Division mutants of *Bacillus subtilis:* isolation and PBS1 transduction of division-specific markers. *J. Bacteriol.* **108:**1366–1379.
67. **Varley, A., and Stewart, G.** 1992. The *divIVB* region of the *Bacillus subtilis* chromosome encodes homologs of *Escherichia coli* septum placement (MinCD) and cell shape (MreBCD) determinants. *J. Bacteriol.* **174:**6729–6742.
68. **Wang, X., and J. Lutkenhaus.** 1993. The FtsZ protein of *Bacillus subtilis* is localized to the division site and has GTPase activity that is dependent upon the FtsZ concentration. *Mol. Microbiol.* **9:**435–442.
69. **Ward, J. E., Jr., and J. Lutkenhaus.** 1984. Overproduction of FtsZ induces minicell formation in *E. coli. J. Bacteriol.* **157:**815–820.
70. **Young, M.** 1976. Use of temperature-sensitive mutants to study gene expression during sporulation in *Bacillus subtilis. J. Bacteriol.* **126:**928–936.

Regulation of Bacterial Differentiation
Edited by P. Piggot et al.

Chapter 6

Morphogenesis and Gene Expression during Sporulation

Patrick J. Piggot, James E. Bylund, and Michael L. Higgins

Seminal work some thirty years ago led to the definition of the stages of sporulation as we now recognize them (26, 68, 70, 86). At that time the genetic analysis of sporulation was in its infancy. Since then genetics has received a great deal of attention and there have been great strides in our understanding of gene regulation. In contrast, morphology has received very little attention. Nearly all the genetic analysis performed has been of *Bacillus subtilis,* whereas most of the morphological studies of endospore formation have been carried out in other species. The purpose of this chapter is to reanalyze aspects of the morphological process and to relate them to our knowledge of gene regulation during spore formation. We concentrate on the morphological changes leading to septation and to engulfment. (The process of spore septum formation is reviewed by Lutkenhaus [Chapter 5, this volume].) The process of endospore formation is essentially the same in all species that have been studied (26), and we have chosen our illustrations of particular structural features from micrographs of a range of species. Our discussions of particular genes are confined to *B. subtilis.*

INITIATION OF SPORULATION AND EVENTS LEADING TO AN ASYMMETRIC DIVISION (STAGE 0 TO STAGE II)

In response to starvation conditions, signal kinases (e.g., KinA, KinB) initiate the flow of phosphate down the phosphorelay, leading to the phosphorylation of the Spo0A protein. Activation of Spo0A by phos-

Patrick J. Piggot, James E. Bylund, and Michael L. Higgins, Department of Microbiology and Immunology, Temple University School of Medicine, Philadelphia, Pennsylvania 19140.

phorylation is the key signal that sets in motion the program of gene expression leading to spore formation (10; Hoch, Chapter 3, this volume). The phosphorelay also appears to be the target of cell cycle signals which presumably ensure that sporulation follows smoothly from the vegetative cell cycle (10, 47). Activation of Spo0A is, in turn, required for the asymmetric nucleoid condensation (72) and the asymmetric division (42, 70; Hoch, Chapter 3, this volume) that mark the early stages of sporulation as a modified cell division (40).

Changes in Nucleoid Morphology

Shortly after the onset of stationary conditions, the nucleoids of the vegetative cells (Fig. 1a) have rearranged to form axial filaments of chromatin (Fig. 1b and 2a). This has been defined as stage I of sporulation (70). Measurements of nucleoids in cells of *B. subtilis* stained with 4′,6-diaminidino-2-phenylindole, a fluorescent probe with a high affinity for DNA, support a model in which axial filaments result from the merger and elongation of adjacent pairs of nucleoids (35). The ability of nucleoids to elongate in a population experiencing step-down growth is growth-stage-dependent. For example, nucleoids form axial filaments in chloramphenicol-treated cells from late exponential cultures, but form spheres in chloramphenicol-treated cells from early exponential cultures (12). The reason for this difference in behavior is unknown.

The growth stage dependence of chloramphenicol-induced axial filament formation is reminiscent of the culture density dependence of sporulation efficiency characterized by Grossman and Losick (31). The latter behavior has been attributed to the accumulation of an extracellular differentiation factor, EDF-A. It has yet to be determined if the accumulation of EDF-A, or some related factor(s), is required for axial filament formation.

To our knowledge, axial filament formation during step-down growth conditions is unique to endospore-forming organisms and is observed in all systems of endospore formation that have been studied. In itself, this situation suggests that axial filaments might have a role in sporulation. Yet stage I is largely ignored, in part, because no asporogenous mutants have been described that are blocked in the transition from stage 0 to stage I. Despite their name, all *spo0* mutants that have been studied are blocked in the stage I to stage II transition (3, 42, 57, 64). (Either stage I or *spo0* should be renamed to be consistent; yet even in 1975 both names already seemed too ingrained for such a switch to be attempted.)

We have recently conducted an extensive analysis of a range of mutants, and the only ones that did not form axial filaments were *spo0A abrB* and *spo0B abrB* double mutants (13). We confirmed earlier observations (57) that *spo0A* and *spo0B* single mutants formed axial filaments; likewise *abrB* single mutants also formed axial filaments. The pleiotropic nature of *spo0* mutations and of *abrB* mutations makes interpretation of the observations difficult and the significance unclear; it may be relevant that *abrB* mutants were originally isolated because the mutations caused alterations in the membrane properties of *spo0* mutants (32, 33, 48, 80). Such alterations could affect nucleoid structure, since the nucleoid is thought to be associated with the membrane (7, 62).

The observation that mutations can prevent axial filament formation argues that the role of these structures should not be dismissed as unimportant, even though it continues to be obscure. Consider for the moment that axial filaments might be relevant to sporulation—then what purpose could such structures serve? We suggest that by transversing the length of the cell axial filaments could act to block further symmetric divisions. Woldringh and coworkers (59, 60, 85), in an impressive series of studies with *Escherichia coli*, have offered convincing evidence that the presence of a nucleoid at a given location in the cytoplasm can inhibit septum formation in that part of the cell. Thus, the axial filament may be a "veto" signal (34) that permanently blocks further symmetric division during sporulation and temporarily blocks asymmetric division until the asymmetric condensation (see below) of one nucleoid occurs, leaving a space for the sporulation septum to form.

Formation of axial filaments is the first of a series of changes in nucleoid structure that are probably crucial for spore formation. The next is an asymmetric polar condensation of one copy of the chromosome at one cell pole (Fig. 1c and 2b). The mechanism of condensation is unknown. We use the term "polar condensation" to refer to the fact that one nucleoid is drawn to one of the cell poles (Fig. 2b), and that on completion of this process, its volume will have been reduced to about 10 to 15% of that observed for vegetative nucleoids (26, 68, 70, 72). We should stress that the extent of nucleoid condensation during sporulation is much less than that observed in phage heads, for which the term "condensation" is used to describe the extraordinary concentrations that occur during phage morphogenesis.

Curiously, electron micrographs of prespore nucleoids at early stage II show little indication of the presence of nuclear material (Fig. 1c). It should be remembered that in electron micrographs of thin sections of exponential-phase bacteria one does not observe the entire chromosome (6, 18, 21, 51, 82). The centralized pools of widely spaced fibrils that are classically referred to in textbooks as "the nucleoid" (n in Fig. 1) represent only a portion of the genome. It is the portion that is not actively engaged in

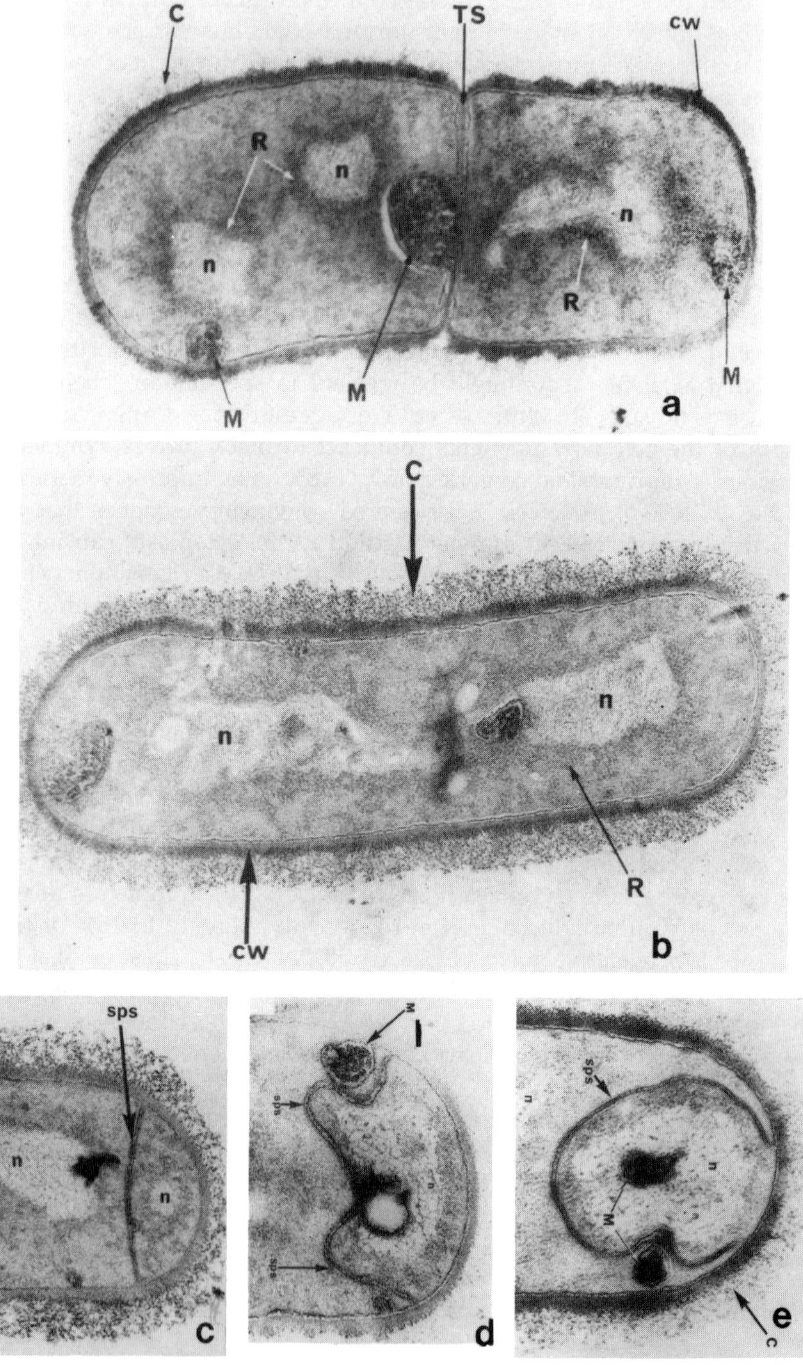
C
TS
cw
R
n
n
n
R
R
M
M
M
a
C
n
n
R
cw
b
sps
n
n
c
d
e

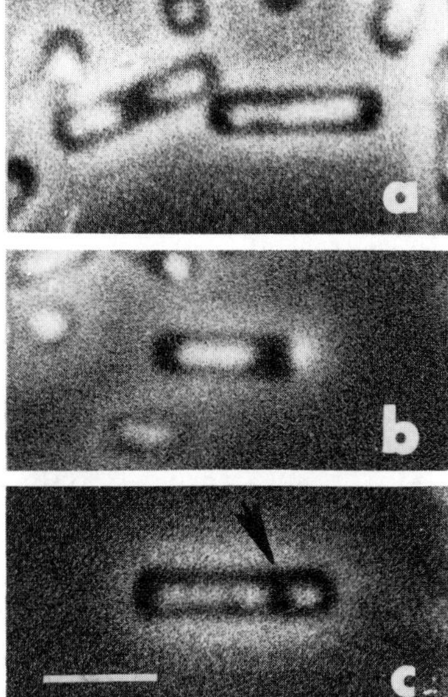

FIGURE 2. Light micrographs of sporulating cells of *B. subtilis* stained with 4′,6-diaminidino-2-phenylindole. The cells in a, b, and c are at stages I, IIi, and IIiii to III, respectively. The arrow denotes the nucleoid-free space discussed in the text. Bar = 2 μm.

transcription and replication (17, 41, 69). This portion of the genome forms lakes of fibers that bind water and form what is essentially a biogel. The binding of water by this portion of the resting nucleoplasm leads to a significant decrease in the density of the central portion of the cytoplasm of the bacterial cell (8, 81). The density difference is what enables the

FIGURE 1. Thin sections of cells showing the transition from stage 0 to stage IIiii of sporulation. (a) During vegetative growth (stage 0), only a portion of the nucleoid is visible. It can be seen as areas of coarse fibers, each fiber being surrounded by an area of low electron density (labeled n). These visible regions are thought to be made up of "resting DNA" which accumulates in the living cell in hydrated pools. In contrast, the invisible portion of the nucleoid, involved in replication and transcription-translation, is located in the ribosome-rich portions of the cytoplasm (R). (b) Axial filament formation (stage I). (c) Stage IIi, which is characterized by the formation of an asymmetrically located septum (sps). At this point, relatively little of the prespore nucleoid can be seen in individual sections. (d) The removal of all, or most of, the septal wall apparently renders the septum flexible and allows it to extend into the mother cell (stage IIiii). Note that as the prespore septum extends into the cell, the pool of hydrated nucleoid fibers grows in area (compare the region marked n in c with that in d and e). At stage IIiii the breaking of the connection between the septum and the cylindrical wall occurs. This allows the leading edge of septal annulus to surround the nucleoid progressively as it moves toward the apex of the pole (e). Other abbreviatons: C, capsule; cw, cell wall; M, mesosome; TS, transverse septum. All of the micrographs are of *Bacillus megaterium,* and are reprinted from Ellar et al. (22) with permission.

nucleoid to be distinguished from the (ribosome-rich) cytoplasm. The simplest interpretation of the relatively invisible nature of much of the prespore nucleoid in electron micrographs at the beginning of stage II (Fig. 1c) is that most of the nucleoid has been polarly concentrated until it has reached the packing density of the ribosome-rich cytosol (see area R in Fig. 1a and b). This state would render it most difficult to differentiate visually from the surrounding cytoplasm elements.

The mechanism for the polar condensation of the genome can only be speculated upon at this point, but it may, in part, require specific mechanicoproteins, a change in the number or type of histone-like proteins, and/or a change in the distribution or number of membrane-DNA attachment points. A change in linkage number is unlikely to be the cause as Nicholson and Setlow (61) have shown that such a change does not occur until after the chromosome condensation.

The polar condensation of the prespore chromosome occurs either before or concomitant with formation of the asymmetrically located sporulation septum. The condensation results in the creation of an asymmetrically located nucleoid-free space. From the finding of Woldringh and coworkers (59, 60, 85) that the interposition of a nucleoid inhibits septation in *E. coli*, it may be postulated that it is the position of this newly made nucleoid-free space (see arrow in Fig. 2c) that determines the location of the asymmetric septum. Consistent with this interpretation (and also others), the polar condensation and the asymmetric division are prevented by *spo0* mutations, but not by *spoII* mutations (13, 72).

Membrane Changes

Membrane changes early in sporulation have been detected by biochemical analysis: for example, there are changes in a membrane-associated transport system, glucose-phosphoenolpyruvate transferase (29), and there are changes in phospholipid composition which are grossly affected by *spo0* mutations (65, 66). It is intriguing that unsaturated fatty acids are the only organic molecules known to affect the activity of KinA, the key activator of the phosphorelay system (77). We do not attempt to incorporate these observations into our description of the morphological process, but it is important to emphasize at the outset that such changes have been observed.

The major morphological change in the membrane is in the mesosome. Mesosome is the name given to convoluted membrane structures seen in many micrographs of fixed bacteria. Fitz-James noted that a mesosome could be observed in a subpolar location in sporulating cells (25), possibly anticipating the formation of the sporulation division septum (Fig. 3a).

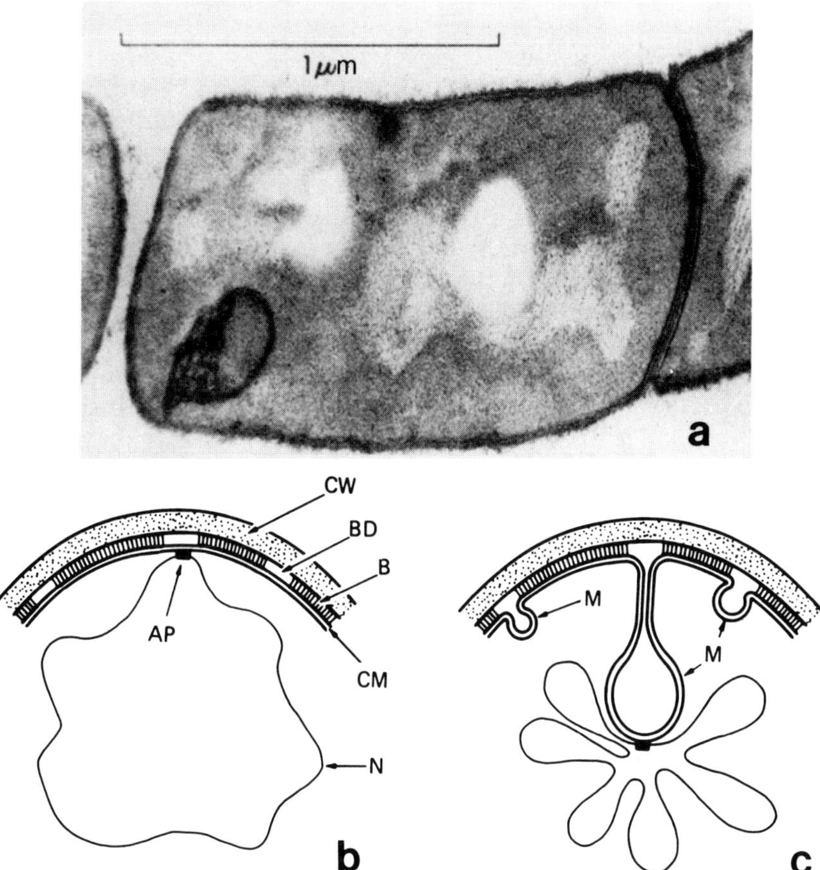

FIGURE 3. (a) Asymmetric mesosome formation preceding asymmetric division. (b, c) Diagrammatic representations of a model for mesosome formation which holds that mesosomes form in perturbed cells. The areas of the envelope which are destined to form mesosomes show a deficiency in hypothetical wall-membrane bridges. The bridge-deficient regions are pulled into the cytoplasm because of the shrinkage of the nucleoid and/or the contraction of cytoplasmic macromolecules which may have specific or nonspecific attachments to these portions of the membrane. The largest mesosomes are formed by those bridge-deficient portions of the membrane that are attached to the nucleoid. Abbreviations: AP, attachment point; B, bridge; BD, bridge-deficient regions; CM, cell membrane; CW, cell wall; M, mesosome; N, nucleoid. Reprinted from references 26 (a) and 36 (b, c) with permission. Panels b and c copyright © CRC Press, Boca Raton, Fla.

The mesosome is the first morphological marker to show gross asymmetry during sporulation. Its appearance in a subpolar location occurred within 20 min of the start of sporulation (57). In vegetative bacteria mesosomes are often associated with division sites (36). It has been proposed that large mesosomes result from a localized weakening between membrane-DNA attachment points and the cell wall (Fig. 3b and 3c) (36, 39). When cells are disturbed by events like a block in protein synthesis, centrifugation, or chemical fixation, the nucleoid often becomes more concentrated in the center of the cell. This concentration process appears to "pull" membrane-DNA attachment sites into the cytoplasm to form the membranous mesosomes (36). Consistent with this idea, it has been shown that the number of large mesosomes observed in fixed cells could be reduced in proportion to the number of double-strand breaks introduced into the chromosome before fixation (36, 62).

That nucleoid condensation might be the motor impelling DNA-membrane attachments into the cell seems reasonable; but what drives this condensation? It might be a purely physical process resulting from macromolecules repartitioning during periods when the cell cannot maintain the normal gradients of molecules across the cell membrane. If this theory were correct one could ask what maintains the distribution of macromolecules in energized cells. For example, it is often thought that the structure of the nucleoid is determined by having the right number of supercoils and histone-like proteins associated with it at the right place and time in relation to membrane attachment points. The suggestion that bacteria may have mechanicoskeletal proteins that could manage a cytoskeleton (44) prompts a reevaluation of this view.

What might be some of the implications of having a cytoskeleton?

One might be that deenergizing the system would cause a relaxation of the skeletal elements that help maintain nucleoid structure. Cytoskeletal changes would also be an attractive explanation for the contraction and occasional merger of nucleoids seen in disturbed cells (12, 71). In this view, mesosomes would be formed as a result of the collapse of cytoskeletal forces at key membrane-DNA attachment sites. Thus, the study of mesosome formation might be one means of studying the normal activity of proteins thought to have mechanical properties.

It is clear that the convoluted vesicular mesosome structure seen in many electron micrographs is an artifact of fixation (36). Nevertheless the frequent association of these membrane-DNA attachments with division, during both growth and sporulation, seems highly significant. Presumably the attachments are strong, as they survive the rigors of fixation. A further hint as to their function comes from biochemical studies of preparations of membrane fragments attached to DNA. These are enriched for penicillin binding proteins (7). Although it is not clear if these membrane fragments correspond to mesosomes, we can speculate that they do; this situation would be consistent with the septal biosynthetic machinery's being associated with mesosomes.

Spo0 mutants are reported to form asymmetrically located mesosomes (57) even though they do not form the sporulation septum (42, 57, 70) and do not show polar nucleoid condensation (72). This finding would suggest that the phosphorelay is required neither for the generation of the initial structural changes that produce axial filaments nor for the generation of asymmetry as indicated by the appearance of the asymmetrically located mesosomes.

STAGE II TO STAGE III

In the literature some authors use stage definitions to identify relatively precise intermediates in sporulation, whereas others use the stage definitions to describe relatively broad morphological transitions. We favor the more precise usage. The nomenclature introduced by Illing and Errington (46) provides a convenient base for naming intermediates that have been identified in the transition from stage II to stage III (28, 37, 45, 46, 86), and it is used here. An advantage of their system is that it names intermediates that are observed in *spoII* mutants in a way that does not cause confusion with the names of particular *spoII* loci. Expanding on their system, we suggest that at stage IIi the sporulation septum has been formed and autolysis of the septal wall has not started. At stage IIii wall material has been removed from the central part of the septum but not from its periphery. At stage IIiii wall material has largely disappeared from the entire septum. The definition of stage IIiii is loose regarding the status of the point of attachment of the septum to the peripheral membrane, which begins to move toward the cell pole when wall has disappeared from the septum; it may be that further intermediates will be identified in the transition to complete engulfment, which is defined as stage III.

Changes in Nucleoid Morphology

The condensed polar nucleoid of the prespore at stage IIi subsequently becomes less condensed as sporulation progresses (72). This decondensation is also seen in thin sections by electron microscopy as the growth in size of a central pool of nuclear fibrils (note the progression in size of the nuclear regions in Fig. 1c to 1e). The equivalent process can be seen in cells stained with 4′,6-diaminidino-2-phenylindole (contrast the size of the asymmetric nucleoid in Fig. 2b with that of the nucleoid in Fig. 2c). The decondensing nucleoid binds more water and thus becomes visible in thin sections as ribosome-free areas of the cytoplasm containing widely spaced fibrils. The differences in chromosome condensation between mother cell and prespore may be important for the establishment of different patterns of gene expression in the two cell compartments (63, 72).

A difficulty with the latter conclusion is that *spoIIE* mutants display asymmetric chromosome condensation (72) but do not display compartmentalized gene expression (56). However, the degree of condensation has not been quantitated in these mutants in relation to wild-type cells, and small differences (which might easily escape detection) could well explain the seeming unwillingness of the *spoIIE* mutants to support the hypothesis. Alternatively, it is possible that the initial condensation of the prespore genome inactivates transcription of it, and that it is the subsequent decondensation (which we would speculate does not occur to the needed extent in a *spoIIE* mutant) that allows selective activation of transcription of appropriate regions of the prespore chromosome (72). Selective activation of transcription in the prespore could then activate a cascade of compartmentalized gene expression (56). It is also, of course, possible that the condensation states of prespore and mother cell chromosomes are not the determining factors of compartmentalized gene expression.

Initial Changes in the Septum

In electron micrographs the wall of the spore septum is thinner and more electron-dense than the wall of the vegetative septum and the surrounding cylindrical wall (Fig. 1c). Electron density reflects the ability of a structure to deviate the path of electrons directed at it by a coherent electron-source. The greater the atomic mass of the structure, the more electrons will be "subtracted" from the image, and the darker (or more electron-dense) will be its image. The atomic masses of the constituents of biological materials are generally too low to deviate electrons significantly, so that it is the ability of these substances to attract heavy metal stains (usually used for examination of thin sections) that determines their electron density. Thus the greater the concentration of metal-attracting groups of a particular material, the darker it will appear in electron micrographs. In the gram-positive wall, metal-attracting groups are in the peptidoglycan, in accessory polymers, and in proteins (5). Since the spore septal wall may lack teichoic acid (spores lack wall teichoic acid [14, 49], but its absence in the sporulation septum is conjectured), its greater electron density may result from an increase in carboxyl groups in the peptidoglycan and/or from a change in protein composition relative to the vegetative wall.

Sporulation continues with the removal of wall from the center of the septum (45, 67). This mode of wall autolysis is highly unusual in the prokaryotic world. Usually it is the outer perimeter of the septal wall that is lytically attacked first, so that the septum can be bilaterally split to produce two new poles and allow the separation of daughter cells (11, 38). The autolysis of the sporulation septum wall is also highly unusual, in that ultimately much of the wall is removed. In contrast, the end walls of separating daughter cells during vegetative division are intact and indeed turn over more slowly than the cylindrical wall of the bacillus (52, 75).

Gated or ungated membrane pores (1, 74, 78) could provide access for lytic enzymes to specific portions of the wall of the sporulation septum. The mechanism could be akin to lytic removal of wall by certain phage autolysins, in which phage-specific membrane pores are opened at given times to allow the autolysins to bind to their substrate (87). Formation of these postulated pores in the septum could provide an exquisitely sensitive temporal regulation. The pores could be opened through the binding of a σ^F regulon product(s) (a possible mode of action of the "x" molecule postulated by Losick and Stragier [56] to mediate the activation of mother cell transcription by σ^E). Alternatively, the burst of lytic activity needed to remove the septal wall could result from some other type of change in the microenvironment of the septum (e.g., it is held that the activity of certain autolysins is modulated by the concentration of protons, lipids, and lipoteichoic acids [19, 73]).

Prespore wall autolysis appears to take place in two stages. *spoIID*, *spoIIM*, and *spoIIP* mutants display autolysis and membrane reorganization in the center but not the periphery of the septum (15, 46, 58, 64; Stragier, Chapter 11, this volume). This intermediate stage has been designated IIii (46). It is not clear why any of the mutations cause a block at stage IIii, although the sequence similarity between the SpoIID protein and a modifier of wall autolytic activity (54, 55) suggests that this protein may be required for subsequent wall autolysis.

The lytic removal of wall from the septum usually accompanies a change in the heavy metal staining pattern (electron density) seen in electron micrographs of the prespore septum (e.g., Fig. 1d and 1e). After wall has largely been removed, the observed structure of the septum is variable. Three examples are illustrated in Fig. 4e: (e1) four layers showing relatively equal but high amounts of electron density (Fig. 13a of ref. 22), (e2) two central electron-dense layers flanked by two outer layers showing much less electron density (Fig. 22 of ref. 22), or (e3) two layers of approx-

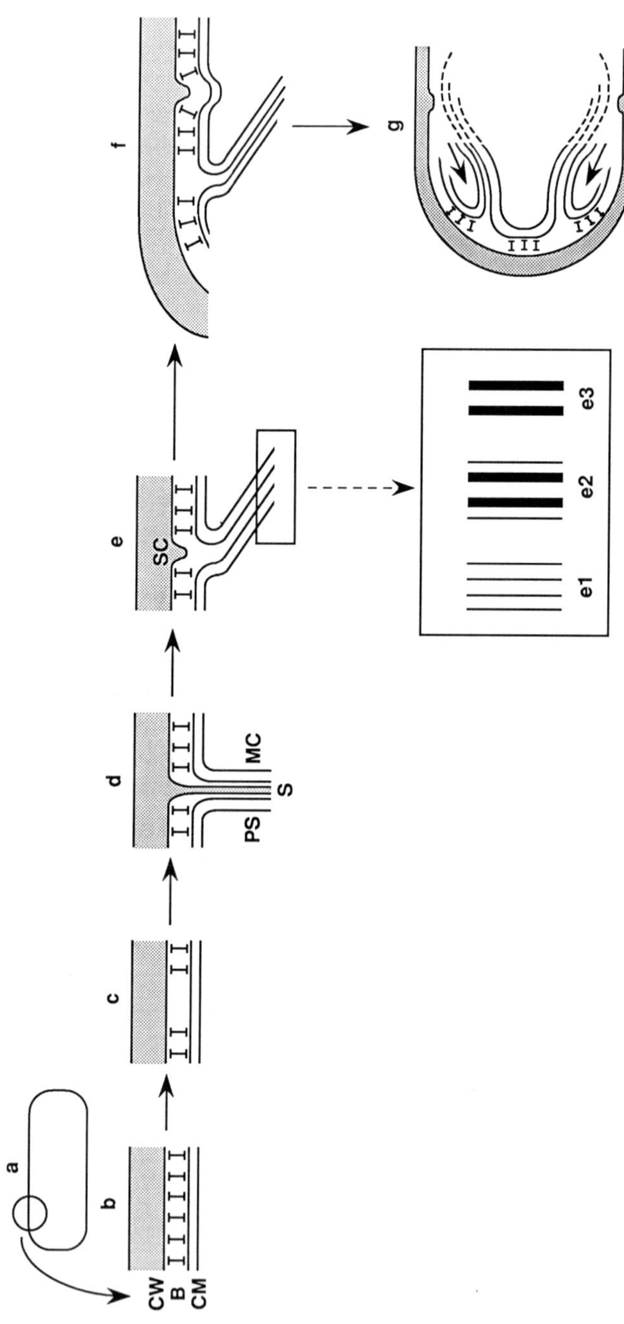
a
b
CW
B
CM
c
d
PS
S
MC
e
SC
f
g
e1
e2
e3

imately the same density (Fig. 3a of ref. 46). Each of these structures may contain remnants of intermediate wall material. Where more than one of this type of structure is apparent in a micrograph of a septum, the regions between the different structures often appear disorganized.

What do these changes in the heavy-metal-staining pattern of the septal membrane mean? It is possible that the variations result from differences in fixation and staining techniques, in growth or sporulation conditions, or in the bacterial species or strains used. However, it is more likely that they result from differences in membrane structure. Most of the heavy-metal-binding sites in membranes are contributed by various functional groups of membrane proteins, and by the head groups and the unsaturated groups of phospholipids. It may be that membrane components change or repartition in such a way that the inner two layers become more electron dense and can obscure the much less dense outer layers, i.e., e3 is an extreme form of e2. Or it may be that upon wall removal the membranes

FIGURE 4. Diagrammatic representation of a model for the proposed structural changes that occur in the envelope of sporulating cells during the transition from stage 0 to engulfment. (a) Outline of an endospore-forming cell. The circle indicates the area of the envelope whose morphogenesis is illustrated in b to f. (b) At stage 0, the cell wall (CW) is linked to the cell membrane by lysozyme-sensitive bridges (B). (c) The first event in septum formation is the lytic removal of a few of these bridges by the wall-membrane machinery that will assemble the septum; perturbation at this stage would result in mesosome formation (Fig. 3). (d) Junction with the newly formed septum (S). This septum separates the cell into the prespore (PS) and mother cell (MC) compartments. (e) The autolytic removal of the septal wall is usually manifested by a bowing of the septal membrane into the mother cell and a reorganization of the septal membranes. Frequently not all of the wall is removed, and a small annulus of wall extends into the cell to form a spore scar (SC). During stages IIii to IIiii, the septal membrane remains anchored here to the cylindrical wall. The septal reorganization takes in many guises, possibly dependent on the organism and/or the method of specimen preparation. The most frequently observed structures are (e1) four electron-dense layers of similar intensity, (e2) four electron-dense layers of which the inner two are denser than the outer two, and (e3) two layers of high electron density. (f) At stage IIiii the wall-membrane bridges surrounding the septal scar break. The removal of these bridges reduces the affinity of a ring of membrane for the wall. This portion of the membrane may then be drawn into the cytoplasm by a prespore which is growing in volume as its nucleoid decondenses. (g) The flow of the freed membrane into the cytoplasm relieves the stress placed on the trailing edge of the membrane, allowing new bridges to be formed between it and the wall (i.e., a repair process), while at the leading edge of the membrane, new rings of bridges are broken, allowing the neck of the engulfment membrane to decrease in diameter as it follows the contour of the polar cap.

fuse (37). It seems safe to conclude that a major structural change in the membrane occurs upon the loss of wall.

The autolysis of the septal wall is likely to be a pivotal point in the developmental sequence. It opens up communication between the compartments, so that development of the prespore is linked to mother-cell-specific gene expression. Further, it may provide directionality to that communication (37). Polarity of communication between mother cell and prespore may result in differences in the ion concentrations in the two compartments; this could have a variety of consequences, including the subsequent changes in prespore nucleoid structure. The initial restructuring of the septum upon removal of septal wall may, for example, be the event that confines σ^F activity to the prespore, and/or triggers conversion of pro-σ^E to σ^E in the mother cell (37).

Compartmentalization of Gene Expression

The earliest stage at which compartmentalized gene expression has been detected is stage IIii (20), and compartmentalization of σ^F and σ^E activity requires septum formation (4; Chapter 7, this volume). The dramatic asymmetry of the organism has already been established at this stage, as indicated by the asymmetry in mesosome partitioning, in nucleoid condensation, and in positioning of the septum. Thus, it seems likely that the organism is already primed for compartmentalized expression before the septum has been completed. The trigger may be nucleoid decondensation, or septal membrane reorganization, or the difference between mother cell and prespore in the ratio of DNA to some cytoplasmic or cell surface component. Mutations in *spoIIAA* and *spoIIE* prevent compartmentalization of gene expression but do not prevent spore septum formation; they may identify key components that somehow convert asymmetry into compartmentalized gene expression. Compartmentalization is discussed in detail by Stragier et al. (Chapter 7, this volume).

Commencement of Engulfment: Septal Enlargement

Removal of wall material from the septum often coincides with the bowing of the septum into the mother cell (Fig. 1d and 1e). The bowing appears to be correlated with an increase in the water binding capacity of the spore nucleoid (i.e., with decondensation of the nucleoid). As the nucleoid binds more water, the central pool of nuclear fibers increases in volume and the prespore septum extends further into the mother cell. It is possible that increases in nucleoid volume resulting from increasing hydration could, in part, drive the septal bowing and the consequent enlargement of the spore septum. At this period the septum increases greatly in surface area. Certainly, this could be accommodated to some extent by the stretching of the membrane(s) (16), but it also probably requires intercalation of considerable new material into the enlarging septal disc. The addition of new membrane material could allow for extensive changes in membrane composition beyond changes resulting from turnover and diffusion. Considering how much the septum must increase in area in order to surround the forespore, the material in the original septum (if conserved) would be greatly diluted by stage III. At stage III, and even at stage IIiii, much of the modified septum must be made up of material that was not present in the original IIi septum.

Further Changes in the Nucleoid

The contour of the enlarged septal membrane indicative of stage IIiii is frequently irregular (Fig. 1e and 5a). This irregularity may well be an artifact of fixation. In live organisms (i.e., before fixation) the membrane may assume some regular spheroid shape determined by the need to minimize free energy, rather than the prune-shaped structure frequently seen in electron micrographs. A possible explanation is that the irregular shape results from the highly hydrated state of the prespore nucleoid (but not of the mother cell nucleoid). At this stage dehydration of a sample during preparation for electron microscopy would cause water to flow out of the prespore, leading to a partial collapse of the membrane around the nucleoid. That the membrane does not have the exact contour of the nucleoid may indicate that the membrane is less flexible (i.e., has greater tensile strength) than is generally thought.

This situation has changed by the time stage III is reached. The membrane surrounding the forespore is ovoid rather than prune-shaped in electron micrographs (Fig. 5b). A major factor in this change is likely to be the reduced hydration of the forespore nuclear material compared to the hydration at stage IIiii (compare Fig. 5b and 5a); the change could also be assisted by an increase in strength of the forespore integument. The change in nucleoid hydration could well be the beginning of the process that eventually leads to the nucleoid's becoming refractile. It is intriguing to think of the effects that these various nucleoid changes might have on the expression of prespore/forespore genes.

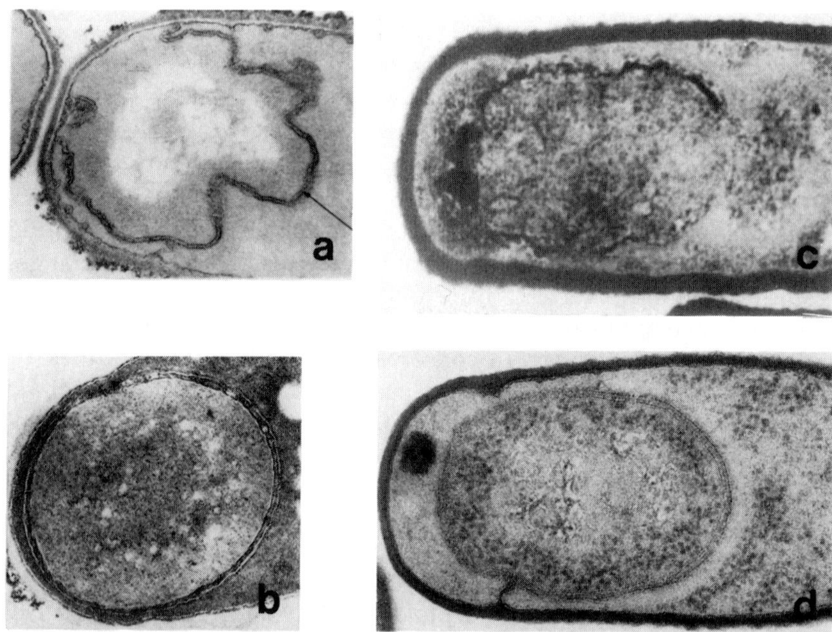

FIGURE 5. Thin sections of sporulating cells illustrating aspects of the conversion of cells from stage IIiii to stage III. (a) Often the engulfment membrane of stage IIiii cells appears irregular in outline. (b) During the cell's transition to stage III, the outline of the forespore becomes regular. It is proposed that the successful formation of a detached forespore requires that the tensile strength of the engulfment membrane be increased. If this does not happen, the forespore membranes will lyse, as observed in the case of some *spoIII* mutants (*spoIIIE36*) (c), but not others (*spoIIIG1*) (d). Micrographs a to d reprinted from references 84, 27, 76, and 50, respectively, with permission; panel d copyright © 1989 Cold Spring Harbor Laboratory Press.

Movement of the Septal-Cylindrical Wall Junction

The final part of the engulfment process involves the breakage of the connection of the surviving outer annulus of spore septal wall to the cylindrical wall (Fig. 4e to 4f). It also involves changes in the septal membrane. By stage III much of the prespore membrane appears to be bilayered, i.e., to have four electron-dense layers (Fig. 5b). The inner two are usually more electron-dense than the outer two. In addition to the increase in membrane electron density that occurs in the IIiii-to-III transition, there appears to be an increase in membrane tensile strength. It is as if an increase in membrane strength is required to break the attachment with the cylindrical wall and proceed to the apex of the cell pole. SpoIIA(P) mutants are blocked at stage IIiii, and it seems plausible that genes required for the completion of engulfment may be transcribed by E-σ^F (46). Below, we consider in detail the transition from stage IIiii to stage III.

The septal wall junction with the cylindrical wall must be lytically broken without a perforation of the cylindrical wall (Fig. 4d to 4f). This selective hydrolysis may require expression of a regulator of autolytic activity, or an autolysin, such that only bonds on the inner surface of the wall are attacked. The specificity could result from the bonds on the inner surface being under less stress (53), or from a difference in accessory polymer content in the inner wall surface. (The outside of the wall usually has much higher heavy metal binding capacity than does the inner surface of the wall, and this characteristic may in part be due to a difference in secondary polymer content [5].)

The membrane is thought to be bound to the cylindrical wall by lysozyme-sensitive linkers (30), except at the point at which the septum joins the cylindrical membrane (Fig. 4c). Engulfment proceeds by a constriction of the outer annulus of the septal membrane around the hydrated nucleoid. This in turn calls for the progressive breaking of the wall-membrane bonds in the leading edge of the annulus membrane as it approaches the apex of the polar cap (Fig. 4f to 4g). After a wall-membrane link is broken, an annular segment of membrane is pulled into the cytoplasm. It initially appears quite flexible but with time takes on the shape of the leading edge of a spheroid, which is the shape of the developing forespore (Fig. 1e and 5a to 5b). Through membrane synthesis, the trailing edge of membrane must be reattached to the cylindrical wall. By the progressive constrictive breakage and remaking of the wall-membrane along the contours of the cell pole, the old pole, in part, determines the shape of the prespore. As the annulus of membrane is freed from the inner surface of the pole, the released membrane moves around the hydrated nucleoid (i.e., Woldringh's model, in which a septum cannot go through a nucleoid [59, 60, 85]).

What could drive the constriction of the annulus? The process requires the septal annulus to break and remake wall-membrane junctions of decreasing circumference as the annulus of attachment moves to the apex of the cell pole. This might be accomplished by enzymes that only break bonds within the inner layer of the surface wall (as was discussed in relation to the enzymatic activity needed to break the wall-wall junction between the spore septum and the cylindrical wall). The progressive removal of this unstressed inner layer of the polar wall might serve as a trolley track to guide the engulfment process to the apex of the pole. The question remains as to what drives the constriction of the annulus after the wall-membrane junction has been broken. Two general models, which are not mutually exclusive, are suggested.

(i) Reduced surface tension model: Once a wall-membrane junction has been broken, the tensile strength of the double membrane would need to be low enough to form the shape of the leading edge of a spheroid. This would be the shape of lowest free energy state. The process would be like reducing the surface tension of a length of glass tubing by heating it in a local zone; the closing of the glass tube would be equivalent to the engulfment process during the transition from stage IIiii to stage III. Such a model has been suggested by Koch (52) to explain the constrictive division of some rod-shaped bacteria. After a period of time, as the detached membrane has assumed the shape of a portion of the spheroid, the tensile strength of the membrane layers could be gradually increased by the addition of structural materials or stress-bearing bonds to the engulfing membranes to lock in the shape of the prespore.

(ii) Physical-mechanical model: The transition from stage IIiii to stage III is a process akin to cell division. The annulus is closed by a contractile apparatus of mechanicoproteins similar to those that are thought to be needed to effect vegetative septal closure. In this view these proteins would direct the detachment of the septal membrane from the polar wall surface while shape is determined by the annulus moving through the region between the polar wall and the hydrated nucleoid.

ENGULFMENT OF THE PRESPORE BY THE MOTHER CELL

Engulfment occurs when the constrictive spore annulus has fused to complete what could be thought of as a second asymmetric division (Fig. 1e, 4g, and 5a). In order for development to continue, the tensile strength of the engulfing membrane must be increased. During the transition from stage IIiii to stage III, the increase in tensile strength is manifested by the engulfment membrane's appearing as a turgid spheroid (losing its earlier prune shape [Fig. 5b]). This strengthening may be effected by an intermediate structural layer between the engulfment membranes that appears at about this stage of sporulation (Fig. 35N in ref. 45). Unless the tensile strength of the engulfment membrane is raised, the forespore will rupture when packing density and/or osmotic pressure within the forespore increases. It is noteworthy that in several types of mutants blocked at this stage, with lesions in the *spoIIIA*, *spoIIIE*, or *spoIIIJ* loci, the forespore tends to lyse (references 83, 76, and 24, respectively) (Fig. 5c). The final closing of the noose requires either mechanicoproteins

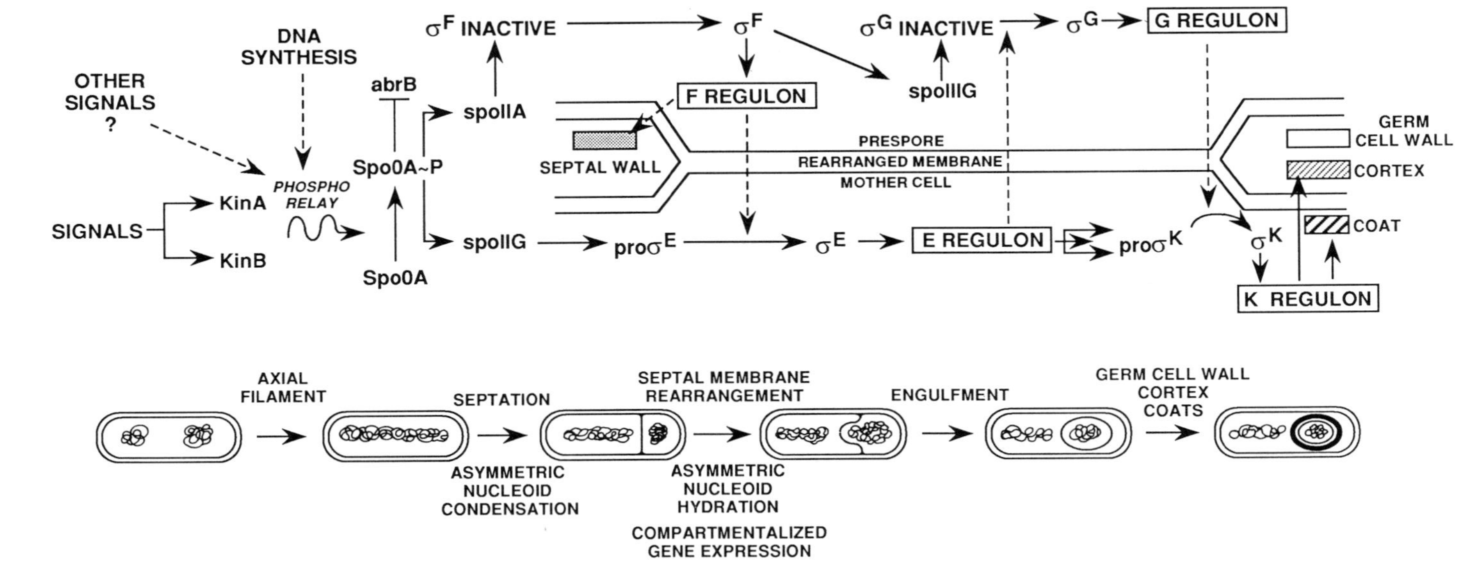

FIGURE 6. Diagrammatic representation of sequential genetic events in relation to key morphological changes that lead to spore formation. The temporal progression is from left to right. It is speculated that the rearranged septal membrane is crucial for establishing compartmentalized gene expression and for facilitating intercompartmental communication. It is thought that σ^F activity is required for the removal of septal wall and hence for the membrane rearrangement.

or some significant change in the rigidity of the engulfment membrane already formed. It may involve, or be regulated by, one or more of the *spoIII* gene products. Without question the rigidity and increased strength associated with the engulfed forespore involve synthesis of new envelope.

POSTENGULFMENT DEVELOPMENT

Two different types of wall are laid down around the engulfed forespore, the primordial germ cell wall (PGCW) and the cortex. Synthesis of these peptidoglycan layers might be expected to impair communication between the mother cell and the forespore. However, such communication is not blocked completely, as Ca^{2+} is transported to the forespore from the external medium after stage III (43), and dipicolinic acid is synthesized in the mother cell but accumulated in the forespore (2).

Synthesis of PGCW precedes that of the cortex. The available evidence indicates that cortex synthesis is directed from the mother cell whereas PGCW synthesis appears to be directed from the forespore (9, 79). The phenotype of *sigK* mutants suggests that cortex biosynthesis is under the control of σ^K, and this observation is entirely consistent with mother cell control (Chapter 8, this volume). The controls of PGCW are less clear, as strains mutated in *spoIIIG*, the structural gene for the forespore-specific σ^G, appear to have some wall-like material (Fig. 5d). Completion of engulfment is thought to activate σ^G, although the activation mechanism is unknown (56). Thus, it may be that PGCW begins to be synthesized before engulfment is completed and that PGCW synthesis is later directed from the forespore by σ^G after engulfment is complete. Synthesis of the spore coat is confined to the mother cell.

In Fig. 6 we have tried to summarize the links between morphogenesis and gene expression during spore formation. It will be appreciated that this scheme has benefited from the writings of others, summarized in several recent reviews (23, 37; Chapters 3, 7, 8, and 11, this volume). In this review we have tried to emphasize the importance to sporulation of changes in the nucleoid and in the spore septum. In the figure we attempt to emphasize the links between these events and changes in the regulation of gene expression.

We thank Michael Haines for help in preparation of the figures, Margaret Karow for helpful discussions about the manuscript, and Greg Harvey for editorial assistance. This work was supported in part by Public Health Service grants AI10971 (M.L.H.) and GM43577 (P.J.P.).

REFERENCES

1. **Alcayaga, C., R. Venegas, A. Carrasco, and D. Wolff.** 1992. Ion channels from the *Bacillus subtilis* plasma membrane incorporated into planar lipid bilayers. *FEBS Lett.* **311:**246–250.
2. **Andreoli, A. J., J. Saranto, P. A. Baecker, S. Suehiro, E. Escamilla, and A. Steiner.** 1975. Biochemical properties of forespores isolated from *Bacillus cereus*, p. 418–424. *In* P. Gerhardt, R. N. Costilow, and H. L. Sadoff (ed.), *Spores VI.* American Society for Microbiology, Washington, D.C.
3. **Balassa, G.** 1971. The genetic control of spore formation in *Bacilli. Curr. Top. Microbiol. Immunol.* **56:**101–192.
4. **Beall, B., and J. Lutkenhaus.** 1991. FtsZ in *Bacillus subtilis* is required for vegetative septation and for asymmetric septation during sporulation. *Genes Dev.* **5:**447–455.
5. **Beveridge, T. J.** 1988. Wall ultrastructure: how little we know, p. 3–20. *In* P. Actor, L. Daneo-Moore, M. L. Higgins, M. R. J. Salton, and G. D. Shockman (ed.), *Antibiotic Inhibition of Bacterial Cell Surface Assembly and Function.* American Society for Microbiology, Washington, D.C.
6. **Bohrmann, B., W. Villiger, R. Johansen, and E. Kellenberger.** 1991. Coralline shape of the bacterial nucleoid after cryofixation. *J. Bacteriol.* **173:**3149–3158.
7. **Bone, E. J., J. A. Todd, D. J. Ellar, M. G. Sargent, and A. W. Wyke.** 1985. Membrane particles from *Escherichia coli* and *Bacillus subtilis*, containing penicillin-binding proteins and enriched for chromosomal-origin DNA. *J. Bacteriol.* **164:**192–200.
8. **Bourbeau, P., D. Dicker, M. L. Higgins, and L. Daneo-Moore.** 1989. Effect of cell cycle stages on the central density of *Enterococcus faecium* ATCC 9790. *J. Bacteriol.* **171:**1982–1986.
9. **Buchanan, C. E., A. O. Henriques, and P. J. Piggot.** Cell wall changes during bacterial endospore formation. *In* J.-M. Ghuysen and H. R. Hakenbeck (ed.), *Bacterial Cell Walls.* Elsevier, Amsterdam, in press.
10. **Burbulys, D., K. A. Trach, and J. A. Hoch.** 1991. The initiation of sporulation in *Bacillus subtilis* is controlled by a multicomponent phosphorelay. *Cell* **64:**545–552.
11. **Burdett, I. D. J., and M. L. Higgins.** 1978. Study of pole assembly in *Bacillus subtilis* by computer reconstruction of septal growth zones seen in central, longitudinal thin sections of cells. *J. Bacteriol.* **133:**959–971.
12. **Bylund, J. E., M. A. Haines, P. J. Piggot, and M. L. Higgins.** 1993. Axial filament formation in *Bacillus subtilis:* induction of nucleoids of increasing length after addition of chloramphenicol to exponential-phase cultures approaching stationary phase. *J. Bacteriol.* **175:**1886–1890.
13. **Bylund, J. E., M. A. Haines, P. J. Piggot, and M. L. Higgins.** Unpublished data.
14. **Chin, T., J. Younger, and L. Glaser.** 1968. Synthesis of teichoic acids. VII. Synthesis of teichoic acids during spore germination. *J. Bacteriol.* **95:**2044–2050.
15. **Coote, J. G.** 1972. Sporulation in *Bacillus subtilis* characterization of oligosporogenous mutants and comparison of their phenotypes with those of asporogenous mutants. *J. Gen. Microbiol.* **71:**1–15.
16. **Corner, T. R., and R. E. Marquis.** 1969. Why do bacterial protoplasts burst in hypotonic solutions? *Biochim. Biophys. Acta* **183:**544–558.
17. **Daneo-Moore, L., D. Dicker, and M. L. Higgins.** 1980. Structure of the nucleoid in cells of *Streptococcus faecalis*. *J. Bacteriol.* **141:**928–937.

18. **Daneo-Moore, L., and M. L. Higgins.** 1972. Morphokinetic reaction of *Streptococcus faecalis* (ATCC 9790) cells to the specific inhibition of macromolecular synthesis: nucleoid condensation on the inhibition of protein synthesis. *J. Bacteriol.* **109:**1210–1220.
19. **Doyle, R. J., and A. L. Koch.** 1987. The functions of autolysins in the growth and division of *Bacillus subtilis*. *Crit. Rev. Microbiol.* **15:**169–222.
20. **Driks, A., and R. Losick.** 1991. Compartmentalized expression of a gene under the control of sporulation transcription factor σ^E in *Bacillus subtilis*. *Proc. Natl. Acad. Sci. USA* **88:**9934–9938.
21. **Edelstein, E., L. W. Parks, H.-C. Tsien, L. Daneo-Moore, and M. L. Higgins.** 1981. Nucleoid structure in freeze fractures of *Streptococcus faecalis:* effects of filtration and chilling. *J. Bacteriol.* **146:**798–803.
22. **Ellar, D. J., D. G. Lundgren, and R. A. Slepecky.** 1967. Fine structure of *Bacillus megaterium* during synchronous growth. *J. Bacteriol.* **94:**1189–1205.
23. **Errington, J.** 1993. *Bacillus subtilis* sporulation: regulation of gene expression and control of morphogenesis. *Microbiol. Rev.* **57:**1–33.
24. **Errington, J., L. Appleby, R. A. Daniel, H. Goodfellow, S. R. Partridge, and M. D. Yudkin.** 1992. Structure and function of the *spoIIIJ* gene of *Bacillus subtilis:* a vegetatively expressed gene that is essential for sigma G activity at an intermediate stage of sporulation. *J. Gen. Microbiol.* **138:**2609–2618.
25. **Fitz-James, P. C.** 1960. Participation of the cytoplasmic membrane in the growth and spore formation of bacilli. *J. Biophys. Biochem. Cytol.* **8:**507–528.
26. **Fitz-James, P., and E. Young.** 1969. Morphology of sporulation, p. 39–123. *In* G. W. Gould and A. Hurst (ed.), *The Bacterial Spore.* Academic Press, Inc., New York.
27. **Freese, E. B., P. Cooney, and E. Freese.** 1975. Conditions controlling commitment of differentiation in *Bacillus megaterium. Proc. Natl. Acad. Sci. USA* **72:** 4037–4041.
28. **Freese, E. B., and E. Freese.** 1977. The influence of the developing bacterial spore on the mother cell. *Dev. Biol.* **60:**453–462.
29. **Freese, E., W. Klofat, and E. Galliers.** 1970. Commitment to sporulation and induction of glucose-phosphoenolpyruvate-transferase. *Biochim. Biophys. Acta* **222:**265–289.
30. **Ghosh, B. K.** 1974. The mesosome—a clue to the evolution of the plasma membrane. *Subcell. Biochem.* **3:**311–369.
31. **Grossman, A. D., and R. Losick.** 1988. Extracellular control of spore formation in *Bacillus subtilis. J. Bacteriol.* **85:**4369–4373.
32. **Guespin-Michel, J. F.** 1971. Phenotypic reversion in some early blocked sporulation mutants of *Bacillus subtilis:* isolation and phenotypic identification of partial revertants. *J. Bacteriol.* **180:**241–247.
33. **Guespin-Michel, J. F.** 1971. Phenotypic reversion in some early blocked sporulation mutants of *Bacillus subtilis.* Genetic study of polymyxin resistant partial revertants. *Mol. Gen. Genet.* **112:**243–254.
34. **Helmstetter, C. E., O. Pierucci, M. Weinberger, M. Holmes, and M. S. Tang.** 1979. Control of cell division in *Escherichia coli,* p. 517–579. *In* J. R. Sokatch and L. N. Ornston (ed.), *The Bacteria,* vol. VII. Academic Press, Inc., New York.
35. **Higgins, M. L.** Unpublished data.
36. **Higgins, M. L., L. C. Parks, and L. Daneo-Moore.** 1981.The mesosome, p. 75–94. *In* B. K. Ghosh (ed.), *Organization of Prokaryotic Cell Membranes,* vol. II. CRC Press, Inc., Boca Raton, Fla.

37. **Higgins, M. L., and P. J. Piggot.** 1992. Septal membrane fusion—a pivotal event in bacterial spore formation? *Mol. Microbiol.* **6:**2565–2571.
38. **Higgins, M. L., and G. D. Shockman.** 1976. Study of cell wall assembly in *Streptococcus faecalis* by three-dimensional reconstructions of thin sections of cells. *J. Bacteriol.* **127:**1346–1358.
39. **Higgins, M. L., H.-C. Tsien, and L. Daneo-Moore.** 1976. Organization of mesosomes in fixed and unfixed cells. *J. Bacteriol.* **127:**1519–1528.
40. **Hitchins, A. D., and R. A. Slepecky.** 1969. Bacterial sporulation as a modified procaryotic cell division. *Nature* (London) **223:**804–807.
41. **Hobot, J. A., M. A. Bjornsti, and E. Kellenberger.** 1987. Use of on-section immunolabeling and cryosubstitution for studies of bacterial DNA distribution. *J. Bacteriol.* **169:**2055–2062.
42. **Hoch, J. A.** 1976. Genetics of bacterial sporulation. *Adv. Genet.* **18:**69–99.
43. **Hogarth, C., and D. J. Ellar.** 1979. Energy-dependence of calcium accumulation during sporulation of *Bacillus megaterium* KM. *Biochem. J.* **178:**627–632.
44. **Holland, I. B., S. Casaregola, and V. Norris.** 1990. Cytoskeletal elements and calcium: do they play a role in the *Escherichia coli* cell cycle? *Res. Microbiol.* **141:**131–136.
45. **Holt, S. C., J. J. Gauthier, and D. J. Tipper.** 1975. Ultrastructural studies of sporulation in *Bacillus sphaericus*. *J. Bacteriol.* **122:**1322–1338.
46. **Illing, N., and J. Errington.** 1991. Genetic regulation of morphogenesis in *Bacillus subtilis:* roles of sigma E and sigma F in prespore engulfment. *J. Bacteriol.* **173:**3159–3169.
47. **Ireton, K., and A. D. Grossman.** 1992. Coupling between gene expression and DNA synthesis early during development in *Bacillus subtilis*. *Proc. Natl. Acad. Sci. USA* **89:**8808–8812.
48. **Ito, J., G. Mildner, and J. Spizizen.** 1971. Early blocked asporogenous mutants of *Bacillus subtilis* 168. I. Isolation and characterization of mutants resistant to antibiotic(s) produced by sporulating *Bacillus subtilis* 168. *Mol. Gen. Genet.* **112:**104–109.
49. **Johnstone, K., F. A. Simion, and D. J. Ellar.** 1982. Teichoic acid and lipid metabolism during sporulation of *Bacillus megaterium* KM. *Biochem. J.* **202:**459–467.
50. **Karmazyn-Campelli, C., C. Bonamy, B. Savelli, and P. Stragier.** 1989. Tandem genes encoding σ-factors for consecutive steps of development in *Bacillus subtilis*. *Genes Dev.* **3:**150–157.
51. **Kellenberger, E.** 1991. Functional consequences of improved structural information on bacterial nucleoids. *Res. Microbiol.* **142:**229–238.
52. **Koch, A. L.** 1985. How bacteria grow and divide in spite of hydrostatic pressure. *Can. J. Microbiol.* **31:**1071–1084.
53. **Koch, A. L., M. L. Higgins, and R. J. Doyle.** 1981. Surface tension-like forces determine bacterial shapes: *Streptococcus faecium*. *J. Gen. Microbiol.* **123:**151–161.
54. **Kuroda, A., M. H. Rashid, and J. Sekiguchi.** 1992. Molecular cloning and sequencing of the upstream region of the major *Bacillus subtilis* autolysin gene: a modifier protein exhibiting sequence homology to the major autolysin and the *spoIID* product. *J. Gen. Microbiol.* **138:**1067–1076.
55. **Lazarevic, V., P. Margot, B. Doldo, and D. Karamata.** 1992. Sequencing and analysis of the *Bacillus subtilis lytRABC* divergon: a regulatory unit encompassing the structural genes of the *N*-acetylmuramoyl-L-alanine amidase and its modifier. *J. Gen. Microbiol.* **138:**1949–1961.

56. **Losick, R., and P. Stragier.** 1992. Crisscross regulation of cell-type-specific gene expression during development in *B. subtilis. Nature* (London) **355:**601–604.
57. **Mandelstam, J., D. Kay, and D. Hranueli.** 1975. Biochemistry and morphology of stage I in sporulation of *Bacillus subtilis* cells, p. 181–186. *In* P. Gerhardt, R. N. Costilow, and H. L. Sadoff (ed.), *Spores VI.* American Society for Microbiology, Washington, D.C.
58. **Margolis, P. S., A. Driks, and R. Losick.** 1993. Sporulation gene *spoIIB* from *Bacillus subtilis. J. Bacteriol.* **175:**528–540.
59. **Mulder, E., and C. L. Woldringh.** 1989. Actively replicating nucleoids influence positioning of division sites in *Escherichia coli* filaments forming cells lacking DNA. *J. Bacteriol.* **171:**4303–4314.
60. **Mulder, E., and C. L. Woldringh.** 1991. Autoradiographic analysis of diaminopimelic acid incorporation in filamentous cells of *Escherichia coli:* repression of peptidoglycan synthesis around the nucleoid. *J. Bacteriol.* **173:**4751–4756.
61. **Nicholson, W. L., and P. Setlow.** 1990. Dramatic increase in negative superhelicity of plasmid DNA in the forespore compartment of sporulating cells of *Bacillus subtilis. J. Bacteriol.* **172:**7–14.
62. **Parks, L. C., D. T. Dicker, A. D. Conger, L. Daneo-Moore, and M. L. Higgins.** 1981. Effect of chromosomal breaks induced by X-irradiation on the number of mesosomes and cytoplasmic organization of *Streptococcus faecalis. J. Mol. Biol.* **146:**413–431.
63. **Piggot, P. J.** 1991. Morphometric events leading to the asymmetric division during sporulation of *Bacillus subtilis. Semin. Dev. Biol.* **2:**47–53.
64. **Piggot, P. J., and J. G. Coote.** 1976. Genetic aspects of bacterial endospore formation. *Bacteriol. Rev.* **40:**908–962.
65. **Rigomier, D., C. Lacombe, and B. Lubochinsky.** 1978. Cardiolipin metabolism in growing and sporulating *Bacillus subtilis. FEBS. Lett.* **89:**131–135.
66. **Rigomier, D., B. Lubochinsky, and P. Schaeffer.** 1974. Composition en phospholipides de mutants asporogènes de *Bacillus subtilis. C. R. Acad. Sci. Ser. D* **278:**2059–2061.
67. **Rousseau, M., and J. Hermier.** 1975. Localisation en microscopie électronique des polysaccharides de la paroi chez les bactéries en sporulation. *J. Microsc. Biol. Cell.* **23:**237–248.
68. **Ryter, A.** 1964. Etude morphologique de la sporulation de *Bacillus subtilis. Ann. Inst. Pasteur* (Paris) **108:**305–315.
69. **Ryter, A., and A. Chang.** 1975. Location of transcribing genes in the bacterial cell by means of high resolution autoradiography. *J. Mol. Biol.* **98:**797–810.
70. **Ryter, A., P. Schaeffer, and H. Ionesco.** 1966. Classification cytologique, par leur stade de blocage, des mutants de sporulation de *Bacillus subtilis* Marburg. *Ann. Inst. Pasteur* (Paris) **110:**305–315.
71. **Schaechter, M., and V. O. Laing.** 1961. Direct observation of fusion of bacterial nuclei. *J. Bacteriol.* **81:**667–668.
72. **Setlow, B., N. Magill, F. Febbroriello, D. E. Nakhimovsky, D. E. Koppel, and P. Setlow.** 1991. Condensation of the forespore nucleoid early in sporulation of *Bacillus* species. *J. Bacteriol.* **173:**6270–6278.
73. **Shockman, G. D., and J.-V. Holtje.** Peptidoglycan (murein) hydrolases. *In* J.-M. Ghuysen and H. R. Hakenbeck (ed.), *Bacterial Cell Walls.* Elsevier, Amsterdam, in press.

74. **Simmon, S. M., and G. Blobel.** 1992. Signal peptides open protein-conducting channels in *E. coli. Cell* **65:**677–684.
75. **Sonnenfeld, E. M., T. J. Beveridge, and R. J. Doyle.** 1980. Discontinuity of charge on cell wall poles of *Bacillus subtilis. Appl. Microbiol.* **20:**409–415.
76. **Stragier, P.** 1989. Temporal and spatial control of gene expression during sporulation: from facts to speculation, p. 243–254. *In* I. Smith, R. A. Slepecky, and P. Setlow (ed.), *Regulation of Procaryotic Development.* American Society for Microbiology, Washington, D.C.
77. **Strauch, M. A., D. de Mendoza, and J. A. Hoch.** 1992. *cis*-Unsaturated fatty acids specifically inhibit a signal-transducing protein kinase required for initiation of sporulation in *Bacillus subtilis. Mol. Microbiol.* **6:**2909–2917.
78. **Szabo, I., V. Petronilli, and M. Zoratti.** 1992. A patch clamp study of *Bacillus subtilis. Biochim. Biophys. Acta* **1112:**29–38.
79. **Tipper, D. J., and P. E. Linnett.** 1976. Distribution of peptidoglycan synthetase activities between sporangia and forespores in sporulating cells of *Bacillus sphaericus. J. Bacteriol.* **126:**213–221.
80. **Trowsdale, J., S. M. H. Chen, and J. A. Hoch.** 1979. Genetic analysis of a class of polymyxin partial revertants of stage 0 sporulation mutants of *Bacillus subtilis:* a map of the chromosome region near the origin of replication. *Mol. Gen. Genet.* **173:**61–70.
81. **Valkenburg, J. A. C., and C. L. Woldringh.** 1984. Phase separation between nucleoid and cytoplasm in *Escherichia coli* as defined by immersive refractometery. *J. Bacteriol.* **160:**1151–1157.
82. **van Iterson, W.** 1966. The fine structure of the ribonucleoplasm in bacterial cytoplasm. *J. Cell. Biol.* **28:**563–570.
83. **Waites, W. M., D. Kay, I. W. Dawes, D. A. Wood, S. C. Warren, and J. Mandelstam.** 1970. Sporulation in *Bacillus subtilis.* Correlation of biochemical events with morphological changes in asporogenous mutants. *Biochem. J.* **118:**667–676.
84. **Walker, P. D.** 1970. Cytology of spore formation and germination. *J. Appl. Bacteriol.* **33:**1–12.
85. **Woldringh, C. L., E. Mulder, P. G. Huls, and N. O. E. Vischer.** 1991. Toporegulation of bacterial division according to the nucleoid occlusion model. *Res. Microbiol.* **142:**309–320.
86. **Young, I. E., and P. C. Fitz-James.** 1959. Chemical and morphological studies of bacterial spore formation. I. The formation of spores in *Bacillus cereus. J. Biophys. Biochem. Cytol.* **6:**467–482.
87. **Young, R.** 1992. Bacteriophage lysis: mechanism and regulation. *Microbiol. Rev.* **56:**430–481.

Regulation of Bacterial Differentiation
Edited by P. Piggot et al.

Chapter 7

Establishment of Compartment-Specific Gene Expression during Sporulation in *Bacillus subtilis*

Patrick Stragier, Peter Margolis, and Richard Losick

A general problem in developmental biology is the process by which cells of one type give rise to daughter cells, one or both of which differ in cell type from the progenitor cell. *Bacillus subtilis* is a favorable system in which to address this problem because of the unusually high accessibility of its developmental regimen for manipulation by the methods of molecular genetics (33, 40). During sporulation, a vegetative cell (the progenitor) gives rise to two specialized cells that differ in cell type both from each other and from the parent cell. The two cells are generated by the formation of an asymmetrically positioned septum that partitions the developing cell (the sporangium) into compartments of unequal size. The small compartment is known as the forespore whereas the large compartment is designated the mother cell. The compartments each capture a chromosome from the last round of vegetative DNA replication but follow dissimilar pathways of differentiation. The forespore is a germ line cell in the sense that it becomes the spore and gives rise to subsequent progeny. The mother cell, on the other hand, is a terminally differentiating cell type in that it nurtures the developing spore but is discarded by lysis when the developmental process is complete. In this chapter we summarize the current state of knowledge on the earliest events that give rise to differential gene expression after the formation of the sporulation septum. We begin, however, with a brief review of the basis for compartment-specific gene expression at later stages of development.

Patrick Stragier, Institut de Biologie Physico-Chimique, 13 rue Pierre et Marie Curie, 75005 Paris, France. ***Peter Margolis and Richard Losick,*** Department of Cellular and Developmental Biology, The Biological Laboratories, Harvard University, Cambridge, Massachusetts 02138.

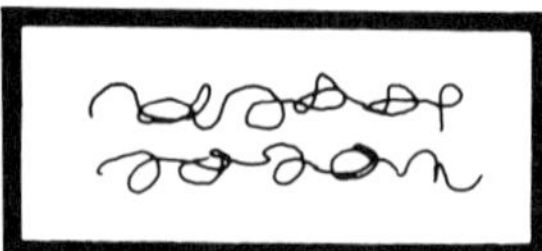

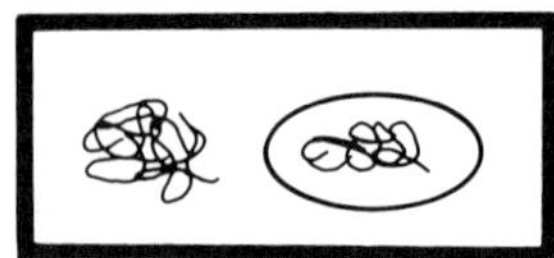

FIGURE 1. The early, middle, and late morphological stages of sporulation.

For the purposes of discussing the problem of compartment-specific gene expression it is convenient to group the morphological stages of sporulation into three principal categories (Fig. 1). These are the *early* stages (from the start of sporulation up to, but not including, septation), during which the developing cell consists of a single compartment; the *middle* stages (between septation and engulfment), during which the developing cell is partitioned into two compartments by the formation of the polar septum; and the *late* stages (after engulfment), during which the forespore is pinched off as a free protoplast within the mother cell and is about to, or has begun to, undergo subsequent morphogenesis (e.g., cortex and coat formation).

COMPARTMENT-SPECIFIC TRANSCRIPTION IN THE POSTENGULFMENT SPORANGIUM IS GOVERNED BY REGULATORY PROTEINS σ^G AND σ^K

Gene expression at late stages is principally governed by regulatory proteins σ^G and σ^K (see the reviews by Losick and Stragier [32] and Errington [14] and by Kroos and Cutting [Chapter 8, this volume] for detailed references). The σ^G factor, the product of sporulation gene *spoIIIG*, is produced selectively in the forespore and is responsible for the forespore-specific transcription of the *sspA-F* genes (which encode the small, acid-soluble proteins found in the core of the mature spore), the sporulation genes *spoIVB* and *spoVA,* and the germination operon *gerA.* According to current thinking, as discussed below, the coding gene for σ^G is itself selectively transcribed in the forespore; transcription of *spoIIIG* is induced in the forespore compartment of the middle-stage sporangium by the earlier-acting, forespore-specific transcription factor σ^F. Interestingly, however, σ^G is principally regulated at the level of its stability or activity. This posttranscriptional mode of regulation is correlated with, and is thought to depend upon, the pinching off of the forespore as a free protoplast within the mother cell as well as the action of *spoIIIA.* This unusually complex operon encodes eight polypeptides, all of which display features of integral membrane proteins (18). The pertinent point for our present discussion is that although *spoIIIG* is induced prior to engulfment, posttranscriptional mechanisms acting at the level of σ^G itself serve to restrict the action of the late-acting forespore transcription factor to the postengulfment stages of development.

The mother-cell counterpart to σ^G at late stages is transcription factor σ^K. The σ^K factor is responsible for the mother-cell-specific transcription of the *cotA-D* genes, which encode components of the outer shell of the mature spore, and the regulatory gene *gerE.* The gene for σ^K (*sigK*) is present as two partial coding elements in the chromosome of vegetative cells. These are *spoIVCB* and *spoIIIC,* which encode the NH_2- and COOH-terminal portions of σ^K, respectively. The *spoIVCB* and *spoIIIC* genes are separated by an intervening 42-kb DNA element known as *skin,* which is excised as a circle from the mother-cell chromosome by site-specific, reciprocal recombination during sporulation. Recombination depends on SpoIVCA, which is encoded within the *skin* element and is a member of the Gin Pin Hin TnpR family of recombinases, and on SpoIIID, a DNA-binding protein. The generation of the composite σ^K coding sequence uniquely in the mother-cell chromosome is accounted for by the fact that the synthesis of both SpoIVCA and SpoIIID is governed by σ^E, whose action, as discussed below, is believed to be confined to the mother cell. The σ^E factor and the DNA-binding protein SpoIIID also govern the compartment-specific transcription of *sigK,* acting from a promoter present at the 5′ end of the *spoIVCB* portion of the composite gene.

Interestingly, the product of the composite gene is not σ^K but rather an inactive proprotein, pro-σ^K. As reviewed in Chapter 8 in this volume, evidence indicates that pro-σ^K processing in the mother cell is controlled by an intercompartmental pathway under the control of σ^G in the forespore. The pathway consists of the products of at least four genes: *spoIVB,* which is transcribed in the forespore under the control of σ^G, and *bofA*, *spoIVFA*, and *spoIVFB*, which are transcribed in the mother cell under the control of σ^E. SpoIVFB acts positively in promoting pro-σ^K processing (and could be the protease), whereas BofA and SpoIVFA act negatively to inhibit processing. SpoIVB acts, directly or indirectly, across the membranes that separate the two compartments of the late-stage sporangium to overcome the inhibitory effect of BofA and SpoIVFA on SpoIVFB, thereby unleashing the conversion of pro-σ^K to its mature form. This complicated set of interactions is responsible for coordinating the timing of σ^K-directed gene expression in the mother cell with the onset of σ^G-directed gene expression in the forespore; mutants in which the appearance of mature σ^K is uncoupled from dependence on σ^G transcribe genes under the control of σ^K an hour prematurely and are somewhat defective in spore formation.

EVIDENCE FOR COMPARTMENTALIZATION OF THE ACTIVITIES OF EARLY-ACTING TRANSCRIPTION FACTORS σ^F AND σ^E

The σ^G and σ^K factors govern compartment-specific gene transcription at late stages of sporulation. A clue that σ^F and σ^E similarly govern compartment-specific gene expression at the middle stages emerges from the identification of genes under the control of these earlier-acting transcription factors. In the case of σ^F only two genes under its direct control have so far been identified. These are *gpr* (36, 53), which encodes a protease present in the forespore that is responsible for the degradation during germination of a family of small acid-soluble proteins called SASP (the products of the *sspA-F* genes), and *spoIIIG* (39, 43, 50, 52), which encodes the forespore transcription factor σ^G (see above). The expression of these two genes and the function of their products are associated with the forespore—observations compatible with the idea that the action of σ^F is limited to the forespore. However, both genes are additionally, and indeed principally (at least in the case of *gpr*), transcribed in a later phase of expression under the control of σ^G (26, 53). So it was uncertain whether the contribution of σ^F to the transcription of these genes was compartment-specific. Direct evidence that σ^F-directed gene expression is, in fact, limited to the forespore comes from immunoelectron microscopy experiments, which show that the β-galactosidase product of *lacZ* fused to a gene under σ^F control accumulates in the forespore compartment of mutant sporangia blocked in the production of σ^G (36, 51).

Similar considerations lead to the view that the action of σ^E is confined to the mother cell (15). Among the substantial collection of genes known to be under the direct control of σ^E (either σ^E alone or σ^E in conjunction with the SpoIIID DNA-binding protein) are at least six whose function is associated with events in the mother cell. These are the mother-cell-specific regulatory genes *spoIIID* and *sigK* (see above), *spoIVF* (7) (which governs pro-σ^K processing), the *cotE* gene (60, 61) (whose product is a component of the coat), and *spoIVA* (42, 48) and *spoVID* (1) (whose products are involved in coat morphogenesis). In addition, experiments involving the use of genetic mosaics show that the products of *spoIIID*, *sigK* (or more precisely, its *spoIVCB* coding portion), and the σ^E-transcribed *spoIIIA* operon (21) are required exclusively in the mother cell (9, 22, 28). In almost all of the cases cited, subcellular fractionation experiments and/or selective permeabilization experiments have been carried out to investigate the compartmentalization of β-galactosidase produced from fusions of *lacZ* to the σ^E-controlled genes (7, 28, 29). The results indicate a strong mother-cell bias in the localization of β-galactosidase produced under the control of σ^E. However, fractionation experiments of this kind can only be carried out with cells at late stages of sporulation when the forespore has acquired sufficient integrity to survive the fractionation procedure. Thus, the distribution of enzyme between the forespore and the mother cell in these experiments reflects the localization of residual β-galactosidase that has persisted after the period of σ^E-directed gene expression has ceased. The most direct evidence that σ^E-directed gene expression is confined to the mother cell comes from immunoelectron microscopy experiments using cells bearing *lacZ* fused to the σ^E-controlled *spoIID* gene (10). The results show a strong mother-cell bias in the accumulation of β-galactosidase at middle stages of sporulation (that is, at stages II to III) when σ^E is active.

One piece of evidence indicates, at least provisionally, that the expression of one σ^E-controlled gene may not be entirely confined to the mother cell. Sporulation gene *spoIIM* is under σ^E control, and subcellular fractionation experiments indicate a significant mother-cell bias in the compartmentalization of its expression (46, 47). However, the use of genetic mosaics indicates (in contrast to the case for all other σ^E-controlled genes so studied) that the *spoIIM* gene product is required in the forespore compartment of the sporangium. This result would appear to offer strong evidence that at least some σ^E-directed gene expression (and in the case of *spoIIM*, expression that is critical for sporulation) occurs in the forespore.

ACTIVITY OF σ^F IS GOVERNED BY A REGULATORY HIERARCHY INVOLVING AN ANTI-SIGMA FACTOR

The σ^F factor is encoded by the promoter-distal member of the three-cistron *spoIIA* operon, which consists of genes called *spoIIAA*, *spoIIAB*, and *spoIIAC* (16, 41, 59). Experiments based on the use of genetic mosaics and experiments in which the time of induction of the operon relative to the time of appearance of the sporulation septum was monitored indicate that σ^F is produced prior to septation (17, 38). If so, a mechanism must exist for restricting the activity of σ^F until after septation, when its action is confined to the forespore. This is most likely accomplished by a mechanism involving the products of the promoter-proximal cistrons *spoIIAA* and *spoIIAB*. Genetic and biochemical experiments indicate that SpoIIAB is an anti-sigma factor that binds to and blocks the activity of σ^F (11, 36, 37, 39, 43). Chemical cross-linking experiments suggest that the resulting complex has a stoichiometry of SpoIIAB$_2$-σ_2^F (11). The inhibition of σ^F by SpoIIAB is reversed by the action of SpoIIAA (36, 43), which can directly bind to SpoIIAB (37). Thus, SpoIIAA can be considered to be an anti-anti-sigma factor. Interestingly the nonsporulation (but related) sigma factor σ^B is similarly controlled by an anti-sigma factor called RsbW (a homolog of SpoIIAB) and an anti-anti-sigma factor called RsbV (a homolog of SpoIIAA) (3–5).

EVENTS INVOLVED IN THE RELEASE OF σ^F FROM INHIBITION BY SpoIIAB IN THE FORESPORE

If this regulatory hierarchy is involved in confining the activity of σ^F to the forespore, then how could this occur? A simple model holds that SpoIIAA exists in two states: an active state in which it is capable of binding to SpoIIAB and the default state, in which it is inactive (36). Alternatively, SpoIIAB could exist in two states: an active state in which it is susceptible to inhibition by SpoIIAA and a default state in which it is immune to the effect of SpoIIAA. If SpoIIAA or SpoIIAB is in the default state in the early-stage sporangium and in the mother-cell compartment of the middle-stage sporangium, then σ^F would be held in check in these cells by the action of SpoIIAB. This model, which is shown in Fig. 2, supposes that a special (as yet unidentified) feature of the forespore compartment drives SpoIIAA or SpoIIAB into an active state, thereby unleashing the action of σ^F. The discovery that a portion of SpoIIAB is similar in amino acid sequence to the histidine protein kinase SpoIIJ (but not in the region in which SpoIIJ undergoes autophosphorylation) raises the possibility that SpoIIAB could be driven between active and default states by interaction with a nucleotide (11).

In partial support of this model, the activation of σ^F has been shown to be strongly dependent on the formation of the sporulation septum, as

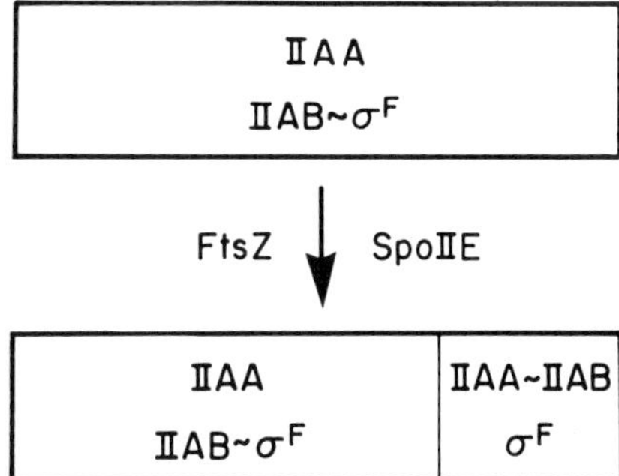

FIGURE 2. Interactions among SpoIIAA, SpoIIAB, and σ^F at the early and middle stages of sporulation. The wavy line indicates the existence of a complex between the indicated proteins.

judged by use of a fusion of the *ftsZ* septation gene to an inducible promoter (35). Also, immunoprecipitation experiments with antibodies to SpoIIAA and SpoIIAB demonstrate that SpoIIAA-SpoIIAB complexes are present at middle (presumably postseptation) but not early (predivisional) times during sporulation (37).

If the model for compartment-specific activation of σ^F is correct, then some aspect of septum formation must bring about a change in the state of SpoIIAA (or SpoIIAB) selectively in the forespore. How this occurs is a mystery at present and surely represents one of the major unsolved problems in the sporulation field. Nevertheless, a possible clue comes from studies on the stage II sporulation gene *spoIIE*. The *spoIIE* gene, which encodes a putative integral membrane protein (58), plays a unique role among sporulation genes in the activation of σ^F in that *spoIIE* mutations block σ^F-directed gene expression but not the transcription of the *spoIIA* operon (36). No other *spoII* mutations are known that have this effect other than mutations (e.g., *spoIIAA* and *spoIIAC* mutations) in the *spoIIA* operon itself. Transcription of *spoIIE* occurs in the predivisional cell (17, 57), but it remains to be investigated whether the SpoIIE protein must be present before septation, or if it is not needed until after septation, as in the case of σ^F. The latter result would suggest that SpoIIE acts as a sensor able to detect some specific feature of the forespore, whereas the former result would indicate that SpoIIE participates somehow in sporulation septum synthesis. *spoIIE* mutants are blocked at the septation stage of sporulation, producing sporulation septa with an aberrantly thick layer of cell wall material (20), a finding that reinforces the view that the sporulation septum plays a special role in the activation of σ^F. Conceivably, events occurring in the sporulation septum create a difference between the physiological states of the forespore and the mother cell to which the SpoIIAA protein is responsive.

IS PRO-σ^E PROCESSED SELECTIVELY IN THE MOTHER CELL?

Next, we turn to the question of how σ^E is activated selectively in the mother cell. The σ^E factor is encoded by the downstream member (*spoIIGB*) of the two-cistron *spoIIG* operon (25, 49, 54). Evidence indicates that *spoIIG* is induced prior to septation (17), but that σ^E is held in an inactive state early in development (30). The basis for inactivity is that the primary product of *spoIIGB* is an inactive proprotein bearing an NH_2-terminal extension of 27 amino acids (30, 37a, 54). The promoter-proximal member (*spoIIGA*) of the *spoIIG* operon is likely to be the structural gene for the processing enzyme that converts pro-σ^E to its active form (25, 49). Time course experiments and experiments based on the use of a fusion of the *ftsZ* septation gene to an inducible promoter have shown that processing of pro-σ^E does not commence until (and indeed, is dependent upon) completion of the sporulation septum (2, 10, 30, 49, 55). Therefore, some signal or auxiliary factor is required for SpoIIGA, a putative membrane-bound protein, to be able to process pro-σ^E.

In light of these considerations it has been attractive to suppose that the mother-cell bias in σ^E-directed gene expression is regulated at the level of compartment-specific processing of pro-σ^E. Unfortunately, subcellular fractionation experiments designed to investigate this hypothesis are technically difficult, and indeed initial efforts to compare the relative levels of pro-σ^E and mature σ^E in the mother cell versus the forespore seemed to indicate that the proprotein is processed with equal efficiency in both compartments (6). However, recent results of subcellular fractionation experiments indicate a substantial bias in the proportion of mature σ^E in the mother cell as compared to the forespore (27). It will be important to devise independent methods for assessing the contribution of compartment-specific processing to the selective action of σ^E in the mother cell. In the meantime, alternative models need to be considered, such as the propositions that processing occurs with equal efficiency in both compartments and that some unidentified antagonist of σ^E produced in the forespore (under the control of σ^F?) inhibits σ^E-directed gene expression in the forespore (Fig. 3) (see below).

EVIDENCE THAT PRO-σ^E PROCESSING DEPENDS ON THE PRODUCT OF A GENE UNDER σ^F CONTROL

A curious feature of pro-σ^E processing that may be relevant to models of selective processing in the mother cell is that the conversion of the proprotein to the active transcription factor σ^E depends on the forespore

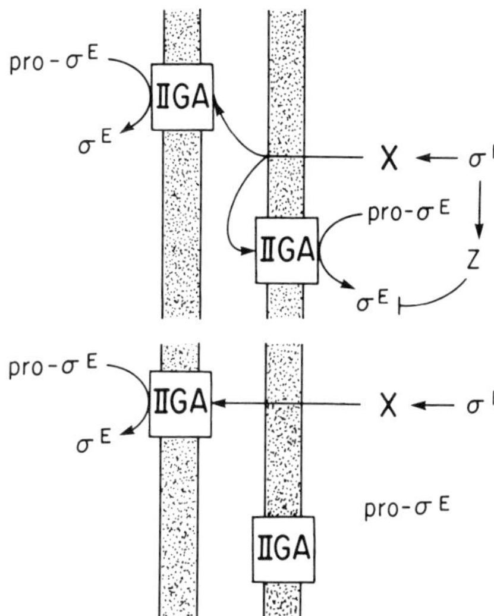

FIGURE 3. Alternative models for the dependence of pro-σ^E processing on the product (X) of a gene under the control of σ^F.

transcription factor σ^F (23, 49). Two models have been proposed to account for this dependence. In one, the σ^F protein (acting in a "structural" context, independent of its role as a transcription factor) forms a complex with and somehow activates the putative processing enzyme SpoIIGA (15). In the other model, σ^F turns on an unidentified gene called *X* whose product is responsible for stimulating the activity of SpoIIGA (10, 32, 36). Evidence in favor of the former model came from the observation that certain missense mutants of σ^F that were seemingly blocked in σ^F-directed gene expression (as measured from *spoIIIG* or *gpr* transcription) were still capable of allowing pro-σ^E processing (15, 20). Thus, if there is an *X* gene, then only a low level of σ^F-directed gene expression is needed to produce sufficient *X* gene product to support processing. To distinguish between these models, two mutant forms of σ^F were constructed whose putative –35 region recognition helices were partially converted (at residues believed to make amino acid-base pair contacts) to that of the primary sigma factor σ^A (45). These mutant forms of σ^F are expected to be structurally intact (and thus able to interact with SpoIIGA as proposed in the first model) but completely defective in directing transcription from σ^F-controlled promoters. Indeed, cells producing the mutant σ^F proteins are blocked not only in the expression of genes under σ^F control but also in the processing of pro-σ^E. This result is a strong indication that σ^F controls pro-σ^E processing through its transcriptional capacity. An important challenge, then, is to identify gene *X* and to determine the function of its product in pro-σ^E processing.

Despite our ignorance of the nature of gene *X* the discovery that pro-σ^E processing could depend on a gene under σ^F control suggests a model for how the processing of pro-σ^E could be limited to the mother cell (if, indeed, it is limited to the mother cell) (10, 32, 36). Since σ^F is active in the forespore, the *X* gene product is expected to be produced in the forespore compartment. If it acts in a directional fashion across the membranes that separate the two cells to stimulate SpoIIGA on the other side of the septum, then processing would only occur in the compartment opposite to the one in which σ^F is active (Fig. 3). This model is attractive because of its similarity to events controlling the processing of pro-σ^K (see above), in which the product of a gene (*spoIVB*) expressed in the forespore under the control of σ^G somehow acts across the membranes separating the two compartments to stimulate SpoIVFB-mediated processing of pro-σ^K in the mother cell.

In its simplest form, the model for compartmentalization of pro-σ^E processing suggests that the gene *X* product can only act vectorially, that is, across the septum. But some evidence indicates that processing can occur in the same cell in which gene *X* is expressed. For instance, processing is still efficient when septation is prevented by the addition of penicillin (24). Similarly, in some strains in which σ^F is excessively active (e.g., in cells bearing a *spoIIAB* mutation) septum formation is blocked but pro-σ^E is efficiently processed (45). Thus, at least under certain conditions the *X* gene product seems to be capable of working in a nondirectional fashion.

If the *X* gene product acts in a nondirectional fashion and if, therefore, processing occurs in both sporangial compartments, then how is the compartment-specific activity of σ^E achieved? In an alternative model, we imagine that in addition to inducing *X*, σ^F switches on the expression in the forespore of a gene that we call *Z* whose product is an antagonist of σ^E (Fig. 3). Thus, in this model the *X* gene product allows processing to occur in both cells, but the *Z* gene product blocks the action of σ^E specifically in the forespore.

Finally, we come to the issue of the dependence of pro-σ^E processing on septum formation. As indicated above, experiments involving the use of a fusion of the septation gene *ftsZ* to an inducible promoter indicated that pro-σ^E processing depends upon septum formation (2). However, the realization that processing depends on the product of a gene under σ^F control and that the activation of σ^F is itself septum-dependent indicates that the FtsZ-dependence of processing may be an indirect consequence of the dependence of σ^F-directed gene expression on septum formation. Alternatively, septum formation could be required both for activating σ^F (through the formation of a smaller cell compartment) and for activating σ^E (by allowing transduction of the signal generated by σ^F to the pro-σ^E processing machinery).

UNANSWERED QUESTIONS

Although differential gene expression is governed by several transcription factors, the primary event in compartment-specific gene expression seems to be the selective activation of σ^F in the forespore. This inference raises several unanswered questions. First, is the activation of σ^F, as we have suggested here, somehow a consequence of the polar placement of the sporulation septum? An answer to this question will require the isolation of mutants in which the sporulation septum is formed at a medial position. This will not be easy as not enough is known about the mechanism of septum placement to distinguish such mutants from known stage 0 mutants in which polar septation is prevented but which are unimpaired in normal binary fission.

Assuming that the asymmetric placement of the sporulation septum is the principal determinant of compartment-specific gene expression, a second unsolved issue is the nature of the difference between the compartments of unequal size that leads to the selective activation of σ^F in the forespore. One possibility rests on the fact that the forespore is much smaller than the mother cell. As a consequence, the concentration of DNA in the forespore is substantially higher than that in the mother cell. Also, the forespore nucleoid is more compact (as monitored by 4′,6-diamidino-2-phenylindole staining) than that of the mother cell (34, 44). Conceivably, a high threshold concentration or compactness of DNA somehow triggers the chain of events that leads to activation of σ^F. Another possibility is based on the difference in the ratio of surface area to volume between the two compartments (being higher in the forespore than in the mother cell). This difference could result in more rapid variations in the forespore in the concentration of some small molecule that is pumped into (or out of) the sporulating cell (36). Once again, a higher or lower concentration of this molecule in the forespore as compared to the mother cell could trigger events leading to activation of σ^F.

The final question is the basis for switching the site of septum formation from the medial position to the cell pole. Is this switch a reflection of an intrinsic asymmetry in the cell or the consequence of a stochastic event, and, in either event, by what mechanism is polar placement accomplished? Experiments with chains and pairs of sporulating cells show that in some species (e.g., *Bacillus megaterium*) the sporulation septum is preferentially formed near the "old" pole of the cell (that is, the pole generated two generations earlier) (19). But in *B. subtilis* the correlation with the old pole is weak and is seen in only certain media (12, 13). It appears therefore that the position of the sporulation septum is not rigidly determined by prior asymmetry of the cell.

Whatever the basis for generating asymmetry, we are still faced with the question of the nature of the machinery for bringing about a switch in the position of septum formation. A clue may come from the existence in *Escherichia coli* of mutations (in minicell or *min* genes) that cause the formation of asymmetrically positioned septa (8). Unlike sporulation septation, polar septation during minicell formation results in the release of free cells that are devoid of a nucleoid. Nevertheless, *B. subtilis* homologs to the *E. coli* minicell genes could play a role in placement of the sporulation septum. Three *min* genes are known in *E. coli* (8). These are called *minC, minD,* and *minE.* The *minC* and *minD* proteins are inhibitors of septation at both medial and polar sites, and homologs of these proteins are known in *B. subtilis* (31, 56). Topological specificity is believed to be determined by *minE,* whose product overcomes inhibition by MinC and MinD selectively at the medial position. Could a modification of a *B. subtilis* homolog to MinE or a sporulation-specific MinE have topological specificity for overcoming MinC and MinD inhibition selectively at a polar site? An answer to this question will have to await the identification of a gene equivalent to *minE* in *B. subtilis.*

This work was supported by a collaborative grant from the Human Frontier Science Program Organization.

REFERENCES

1. **Beall, B., A. Driks, R. Losick, and C. P. Moran, Jr.** 1993. Cloning and characterization of a gene required for assembly of the *Bacillus subtilis* spore coat. *J. Bacteriol.* **175:**1705–1716.
2. **Beall, B., and J. Lutkenhaus.** 1991. FtsZ in *Bacillus subtilis* is required for vegetative septation and for asymmetric septation during sporulation. *Genes Dev.* **5:**447–455.
3. **Benson, A. K., and W. G. Haldenwang.** 1992. Characterization of a regulatory network that controls σ^B expression in *Bacillus subtilis. J. Bacteriol.* **174:**749–757.
4. **Benson, A. K., and W. G. Haldenwang.** 1993. *Bacillus subtilis* σ^B is regulated by a binding protein (RsbW) that blocks its association with core RNA polymerase. *Proc. Natl. Acad. Sci. USA* **90:**2330–2334.
5. **Boylan, S., A. Rutherford, S. M. Thomas, and C. W. Price.** 1992. Activation of *Bacillus subtilis* transcription factor σ^B by a regulatory pathway responsive to stationary-phase signals. *J. Bacteriol.* **174:**3695–3706.
6. **Carlson, H. C., and W. G. Haldenwang.** 1989. The σ^E subunit of *Bacillus subtilis* RNA polymerase is present in both forespore and mother cell compartments. *J. Bacteriol.* **171:**2216–2218.

7. **Cutting, S., S. Roels, and R. Losick.** 1991. Sporulation operon *spoIVF* and the characterization of mutations that uncouple mother-cell from forespore gene expression in *Bacillus subtilis*. *J. Mol. Biol.* **221:**1237–1256.
8. **de Boer, P. A. J., R. E. Crossley, and L. I. Rothfield.** 1990. Bacterial cell division. *Annu. Rev. Genet.* **24:**249–274.
9. **De Lencastre, H., and P. Piggot.** 1979. Identification of different sites of expression for *spo* loci by transformation of *Bacillus subtilis*. *J. Gen. Microbiol.* **114:**377–389.
10. **Driks, A., and R. Losick.** 1991. Compartmentalized expression of a gene under the control of sporulation transcription factor σ^E in *Bacillus subtilis*. *Proc. Natl. Acad. Sci. USA* **88:**9934–9938.
11. **Duncan, L., and R. Losick.** 1993. SpoIIAB is an anti-sigma factor that binds to and inhibits transcription by regulatory protein σ^F from *Bacillus subtilis*. *Proc. Natl. Acad. Sci. USA* **90:**2325–2329.
12. **Dunn, G.** 1980. Cell polarity in *Bacillus subtilis:* statistical analysis of factors influencing the positions of spores in sister sporangia. *J. Gen. Microbiol.* **116:**33–40.
13. **Dunn, G., and J. Mandelstam.** 1977. Cell polarity in *Bacillus subtilis:* effect of growth conditions on spore positions in sister cells. *J. Gen. Microbiol.* **103:**201–205.
14. **Errington, J.** 1993. Sporulation in *Bacillus subtilis:* regulation of gene expression and control of morphogenesis. *Microbiol. Rev.* **57:**1–33.
15. **Errington, J., D. Foulger, N. Illing, S. R. Partridge, and C. M. Stevens.** 1990. Regulation of differential gene expression during sporulation in *Bacillus subtilis*, p. 257–267. *In* M. M. Zukowski, A. T. Ganesan, and J. A. Hoch (ed.), *Genetics and Biotechnology of Bacilli*, vol. 3. Academic Press, Inc., San Diego, Calif.
16. **Fort, P., and P. J. Piggot.** 1984. Nucleotide sequence of the sporulation locus *spoIIA* in *Bacillus subtilis*. *J. Gen. Microbiol.* **130:**2147–2153.
17. **Gholamhoseinian, A., and P. J. Piggot.** 1989. Timing of *spoII* gene expression relative to septum formation during sporulation of *Bacillus subtilis*. *J. Bacteriol.* **171:**5747–5749.
18. **Guerout-Fleury, A. M., G. Gonzy-Treboul, and P. Stragier.** Unpublished data.
19. **Hitchins, A. D.** 1975. Polarized relationship of bacterial spore loci to the "old" and "new" ends of sporangia. *J. Bacteriol.* **121:**518–523.
20. **Illing, N., and J. Errington.** 1991. Genetic regulation of morphogenesis in *Bacillus subtilis:* roles of σ^E and σ^F in prespore engulfment. *J. Bacteriol.* **173:**3159–3169.
21. **Illing, N., and J. Errington.** 1991. The *spoIIIA* operon of *Bacillus subtilis* defines a new temporal class of mother-cell-specific sporulation genes under the control of the σ^E form of RNA polymerase. *Mol. Microbiol.* **5:**1927–1940.
22. **Illing, N., M. Young, and J. Errington.** 1990. Use of integrational plasmid excision to identify cellular localization of gene expression during sporulation in *Bacillus subtilis*. *J. Bacteriol.* **172:**6937–6941.
23. **Jonas, R. M., and W. G. Haldenwang.** 1989. Influence of *spo* mutations on σ^E synthesis in *Bacillus subtilis*. *J. Bacteriol.* **171:**5226–5228.
24. **Jonas, R. M., S. C. Holt, and W. G. Haldenwang.** 1990. Effects of antibiotics on synthesis and persistence of σ^E in sporulating *Bacillus subtilis*. *J. Bacteriol.* **172:**4616–4623.
25. **Jonas, R. M., E. A. Weaver, T. J. Kenney, C. P. Moran, Jr., and W. G. Haldenwang.** 1988. The *Bacillus subtilis spoIIG* operon encodes both σ^E and a gene necessary for σ^E activation. *J. Bacteriol.* **170:**507–511.

26. **Karmazyn-Campelli, C., C. Bonamy, B. Savelli, and P. Stragier.** 1989. Tandem genes encoding σ-factors for consecutive steps of development in *Bacillus subtilis*. *Genes Dev.* **3:**150–157.
27. **Kirchman, P. A., H. DeGrazia, E. M. Kellner, and C. P. Moran, Jr.** 1993. Forespore-specific disappearance of the sigma factor antagonist SpoIIAB: implications for its role in determination of cell fate in *Bacillus subtilis*. *Mol. Microbiol.* **8:**663–671.
28. **Kunkel, B., L. Kroos, H. Poth, P. Youngman, and R. Losick.** 1989. Temporal and spatial control of the mother-cell regulatory gene *spoIIID* of *Bacillus subtilis*. *Genes Dev.* **3:**1735–1744.
29. **Kunkel, B., K. Sandman, S. Panzer, P. Youngman, and R. Losick.** 1988. The promoter for a sporulation gene in the *spoIVC* locus of *Bacillus subtilis* and its use in studies of temporal and spatial control of gene expression. *J. Bacteriol.* **170:**3513–3522.
30. **LaBell, T. L., J. E. Trempy, and W. G. Haldenwang.** 1987. Sporulation-specific σ factor σ^{29} of *Bacillus subtilis* is synthesized from a precursor protein, P^{31}. *Proc. Natl. Acad. Sci. USA* **84:**1784–1788.
31. **Levin, P. A., P. S. Margolis, P. Setlow, R. Losick, and D. Sun.** 1992. Identification of *Bacillus subtilis* genes for septum placement and shape determination. *J. Bacteriol.* **174:**6717–6728.
32. **Losick, R., and P. Stragier.** 1992. Crisscross regulation of cell-type-specific gene expression during development in *Bacillus subtilis*. *Nature* (London) **355:**601–604.
33. **Losick, R., P. Youngman, and P. J. Piggot.** 1986. Genetics of endospore formation in *Bacillus subtilis*. *Annu. Rev. Genet.* **20:**625–669.
34. **Magill, N., and P. Setlow.** 1992. Properties of purified sporelets produced by *spoII* mutants of *Bacillus subtilis*. *J. Bacteriol.* **174:**8148–8151.
35. **Margolis, P.** 1993. Establishment of cell type during sporulation in *Bacillus subtilis*. Ph.D. thesis. Harvard University, Cambridge, Mass.
36. **Margolis, P., A. Driks, and R. Losick.** 1991. Establishment of cell type by compartmentalized activation of a transcription factor. *Science* **254:**562–565.
37. **Min, K.-T., C. M. Hilditch, J. Errington, and M. D. Yudkin.** Transcription factor sigma-F of sporulating *Bacillus subtilis* is inhibited by a product of the sigma-F operon. Submitted for publication.
37a. **Moran, C. P., Jr.** Personal communication.
38. **Partridge, S. R., and J. Errington.** 1993. Importance of morphological events and intercellular interactions in the regulation of prespore-specific gene expression during sporulation in *Bacillus subtilis*. *Mol. Microbiol.* **8:**945–955.
39. **Partridge, S. R., D. Foulger, and J. Errington.** 1991. The role of σ^F in prespore-specific transcription in *Bacillus subtilis*. *Mol. Microbiol.* **5:**757–767.
40. **Piggot, P. J., and J. G. Coote.** 1976. Genetic aspects of bacterial endospore formation. *Bacteriol. Rev.* **40:**908–962.
41. **Piggot, P. J., C. A. Curtis, and H. DeLancastre.** 1984. Use of integrational plasmid vectors to demonstrate the polycistronic nature of a transcription unit (*spoIIA*) required for sporulation. *J. Gen. Microbiol.* **130:**2123–2126.
42. **Roels, S., A. Driks, and R. Losick.** 1992. Characterization of *spoIVA*, a sporulation gene involved in coat morphogenesis in *Bacillus subtilis*. *J. Bacteriol.* **174:**575–585.
43. **Schmidt, R., P. Margolis, L. Duncan, R. Coppolecchia, C.P. Moran, Jr., and R. Losick.** 1990. Control of developmental transcription factor σ^F by sporulation

regulatory proteins SpoIIAA and SpoIIAB in *Bacillus subtilis. Proc. Natl. Acad. Sci. USA* **87:**9221–9225.

44. **Setlow, B., N. Magill, P. Febbroriello, L. Nakhimousky, D. E. Koppel, and P. Setlow.** 1991. Condensation of the forespore nucleoid early in sporulation of *Bacillus* species. *J. Bacteriol.* **173:**6270–6278.
45. **Shazand, K., N. Frandsen, C. Karmazyn-Campelli, and P. Stragier.** Unpublished data.
46. **Smith, K., and P. Youngman.** 1993. Physical and functional characterization of the *Bacillus subtilis spoIIM* gene. *J. Bacteriol.* **175:**3607–3617.
47. **Smith, K., and P. Youngman.** 1993. Evidence that the *spoIIM* gene of *Bacillus subtilis* is transcribed by RNA polymerase associated with σ^E. *J. Bacteriol.* **175:**3618–3627.
48. **Stevens, C. M., R. Daniel, N. Illing, and J. Errington.** 1992. Characterization of a sporulation gene *spoIVA* involved in spore coat morphogenesis in *Bacillus subtilis. J. Bacteriol.* **174:**586–594.
49. **Stragier, P., C. Bonamy, and C. Karmazyn-Campelli.** 1988. Processing of a sporulation sigma factor in *Bacillus subtilis:* how morphological structure could control gene expression. *Cell* **52:**697–704.
50. **Sun, D., R. M. Cabrera-Martinez, and P. Setlow.** 1991. Control of transcription of the *Bacillus subtilis spoIIIG* gene, which codes for the forespore specific transcription factor σ^G. *J. Bacteriol.* **173:**2977–2984.
51. **Sun, D., P. Fajardo-Cavazos, M. D. Sussman, F. Tovar-Roja, R.-M. Cabrera-Martinez, and P. Setlow.** 1991. Effect of chromosome location of *Bacillus subtilis* forespore genes on their *spo* gene dependence and transcription by $E\sigma^F$: identification of features of good $E\sigma^F$-dependent promoters. *J. Bacteriol.* **173:**7867–7874.
52. **Sun, D., P. Stragier, and P. Setlow.** 1989. Identification of a new σ-factor involved in compartmentalized gene expression during sporulation of *Bacillus subtilis. Genes Dev.* **3:**141–149.
53. **Sussman, M. D., and P. Setlow.** 1991. Cloning, nucleotide sequence, and regulation of the *Bacillus subtilis gpr* gene which codes for the protease that initiates degradation of small, acid-soluble proteins during spore germination. *J. Bacteriol.* **173:**291–300.
54. **Trempy, J. E., C. Bonamy, J. Szulmajster, and W. G. Haldenwang.** 1985. *Bacillus subtilis* sigma factor, σ^{29}, is the product of the sporulation-essential gene *spoIIG. Proc. Natl. Acad. Sci. USA* **82:**4189–4192.
55. **Trempy, J. E., J. Morrison-Plummer, and W. G. Haldenwang.** 1985. Synthesis of σ^{29}, an RNA polymerase specificity determinant, is a developmentally regulated event in *Bacillus subtilis. J. Bacteriol.* **161:**340–346.
56. **Varley, A. W., and G. C. Stewart.** 1992. The *divIVB* region of the *Bacillus subtilis* chromosome encodes homologs of *Escherichia coli* septum placement (MinCD) and cell shape (MreBCD) determinants. *J. Bacteriol.* **174:**6729–6742.
57. **York, K., T. J. Kernney, S. Satola, C. P. Moran, Jr., H. Poth, and P. Youngman.** 1992. Spo0A controls the σ^A-dependent activation of *Bacillus subtilis* sporulation-specific transcription unit *spoIIE. J. Bacteriol.* **174:**2648–2658.
58. **Youngman, P.** Personal communication.
59. **Yudkin, M. D.** 1987. Structure and function in a *Bacillus subtilis* sporulation-specific sigma factor: molecular nature of mutations in *spoIIAC. J. Gen. Microbiol.* **133:**475–481.

60. **Zheng, L., W. P. Donovan, P. C. Fitz-James, and R. Losick.** 1988. Gene encoding a morphogenic protein required in the assembly of the outer coat of the *Bacillus subtilis* endospore. *Genes Dev.* **2:**1047–1054.

61. **Zheng, L., and R. Losick.** 1990. Cascade regulation of spore coat gene expression in *Bacillus subtilis. J. Mol. Biol.* **212:**645–660.

Regulation of Bacterial Differentiation
Edited by P. Piggot et al.

Chapter 8

Intercellular and Intercompartmental Communication during *Bacillus subtilis* Sporulation

Lee Kroos and Simon Cutting

Bacillus subtilis sporulation has emerged as an excellent model for the study of cell-cell communication. The process of endospore formation has long been appreciated as a paradigm for the investigation of both developmental gene regulation and cellular differentiation. In recent years these investigations have revealed several examples of cell-cell communication that are thought to coordinate the programs of gene expression and morphogenesis in the communicating cells. Here we review the current state of knowledge about these cell-cell communication events.

Figure 1 illustrates the difference between two types of cell-cell communication events that occur during *B. subtilis* sporulation. The first, which we will call "intercellular," refers to signaling between prokaryotic cells in the usual sense, in which both cells have their cell wall intact (Fig. 1A). The second, which we will call "intercompartmental," arises from the peculiar nature of the endosporulation process (Fig. 1B). Upon starvation the cell completes a round of DNA replication and partitions a genome to each of two compartments formed by septation. The sporulation septum is positioned asymmetrically, dividing the sporangium into a larger mother cell compartment and a smaller forespore compartment (stage II; note that the smaller compartment is sometimes called the prespore prior to the completion of engulfment, but we will use the term "forespore" here for simplicity). The two compartments are not distinct cells in the usual prokaryotic sense. The sporulation septum does not fill with a thick layer of

Lee Kroos, Departments of Biochemistry and Microbiology, Michigan State University, East Lansing, Michigan 48824. ***Simon Cutting,*** Department of Microbiology, University of Pennsylvania School of Medicine, 209 Johnson Pavilion, Philadelphia, Pennsylvania 19104.

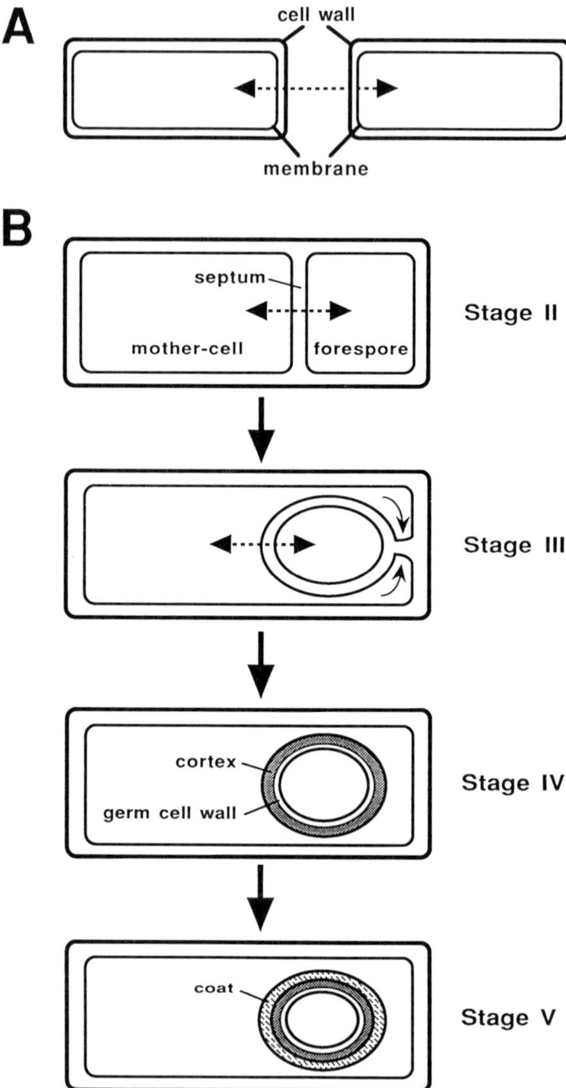

FIGURE 1. The difference between "intercellular" and "intercompartmental" communication. Dashed lines with arrows at each end symbolize communication events and highlight the barriers that signals must traverse. Intercellular communication (A) occurs very early during sporulation. Intercompartmental communication (B) occurs during morphological stages II and III of sporulation. Adapted from reference 40a with permission.

cell wall material as does the normal cell division septum. Rather, a thin layer of peptidoglycan appears to be present initially and is then removed (see reference 25 for a review). Also, the compartments remain in close proximity rather than dividing. In fact, during stage III the septum migrates, engulfing the forespore compartment in a double membrane and pinching it off as a protoplast within the mother cell compartment. The forespore can be thought of as a cell within the mother cell, but it is surrounded by two membranes, the inner one of normal polarity with respect to the forespore compartment and the outer one of opposite polarity since it was derived from the mother cell side of the septum. The two membranes may actually fuse into a single membrane, at least partially, during the process of engulfment (25) (this is not shown in Fig. 1B). After engulfment, peptidoglycan synthesis during stage IV produces the germ cell wall (proximal to the forespore) and the cortex between the two membranes surrounding the forespore. During stage V, proteins produced in the mother cell compartment assemble on the surface of the forespore, encasing it in a multilayered coat.

The lone example of *intercellular* communication occurs very early during the sporulation process, prior to asymmetric septum formation. Three apparent *intercompartmental* communication events occur between the time of septum formation and the time of cortex formation. During a portion of this period the usual cell wall barrier is absent and the two compartments begin to express different genetic programs. This makes the situation in the sporangium quite analogous to that found in the development of multicellular animals, in which daughter cells remain in proximity yet undergo different developmental fates. Thus, intercompartmental communication during *B. subtilis* sporulation may be a particularly good prokaryotic model for developmental cell-cell communication between eukaryotic cells. In this chapter we review the evidence for each of the four instances of cell-cell communication in their order of occurrence during sporulation, and we discuss models for possible mechanisms of signal transduction.

INTERCELLULAR COMMUNICATION

The observation that sporulation efficiency depends strongly on cell density stimulated Grossman and Losick (22) to search for an extracellular factor or factors that are required, in addition to starvation, for efficient sporulation. Cells induced to sporulate at a high cell density formed heat-resistant spores about 10^4-fold more efficiently than cells induced at a low cell density. The low-density cells appeared to be blocked at an early step in sporulation, prior to formation of the asymmetric septum, and exhibited reduced expression of *spoVG*, a gene whose expression depends on the earliest-acting sporulation-specific sigma factor, σ^H (108). The block to sporulation of low-density cells could be largely overcome by the addition of filter-sterilized culture supernatant from *B. subtilis* cells grown to a high density. The stimulatory factor(s) in the culture supernatant was called extracellular differentiation factor A (EDF-A). These results suggest that at low cell density EDF-A fails to accumulate sufficiently in the medium to support efficient sporulation.

EDF-A appears to be at least in part one or more oligopeptides (22). This conclusion is based on the findings that EDF-A is heat-stable (100°C for 15 min), protease-sensitive (pronase), and dialyzable (approximate molecular weight cutoff of 1,000 Da). However, attempts to purify EDF-A from culture supernatant have so far been unsuccessful (21a).

The requirements for production of EDF-A were examined by measuring the ability of sporulation mutants to stimulate sporulation of low-density wild-type cells (22). *spo0A* and *spo0B* mutants appeared to be completely defective in EDF-A production and *spo0E* and *spo0F* mutants appeared to be partially defective. Other stage 0 mutants, including *spo0H*, *spo0J*, and *spo0K*, appeared to produce EDF-A normally. Spo0B and Spo0F are components of a phosphorelay that phosphorylates Spo0A (4; Chapter 3, this volume). Spo0E negatively regulates this pathway in an unknown manner (63). Phosphorylated Spo0A is a transcriptional activator and repressor. It negatively regulates *abrB* (64, 92), which encodes a repressor of many operons that are expressed at the end of exponential growth (29, 63, 99, 100, 103, 109) and positively regulates several operons whose gene products are required early in sporulation (see below). Hence, production of phosphorylated Spo0A in response to starvation appears to be a key event in the initiation of sporulation. A *spo0A abrB* double mutant produced EDF-A, indicating that AbrB negatively regulates production of EDF-A, as it does the production of extracellular proteases and antibiotics and the acquisition of genetic competence (22). Figure 2 summarizes these regulatory interactions and additional information discussed below.

Once EDF-A is produced in response to formation of Spo0A phosphate and removal of AbrB repression, it may stimulate further synthesis of Spo0A phosphate, establishing an autoregulatory loop. Cells bearing a *spo0A* mutation that renders Spo0A constitutively active sporulate efficiently at low cell density (28). This observation suggests that the defect in low-density cells is the failure to accumulate adequate levels of Spo0A phosphate and that the role of EDF-A is to stimulate the phosphorelay that phosphorylates Spo0A. According to this model, EDF-A would be an intercellular signal that feeds into the phosphorelay and, like nutritional

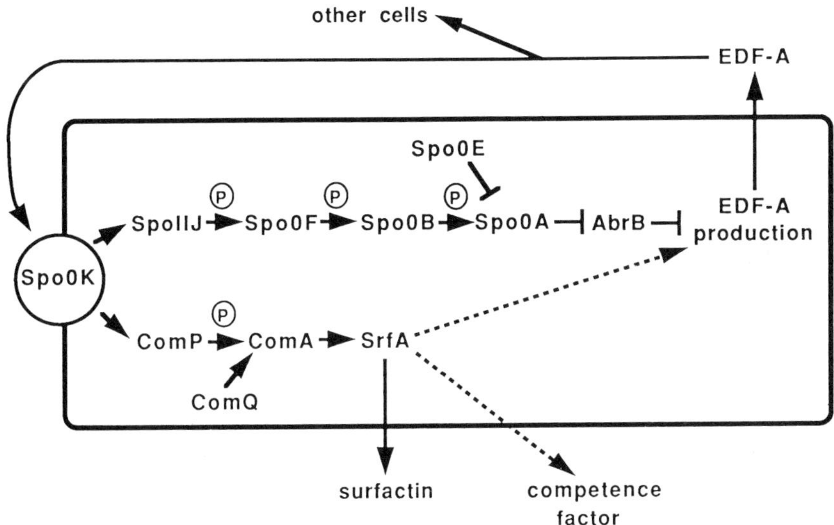

FIGURE 2. Model for regulatory interactions controlling the production of EDF-A, an intercellular signal. A circled P over an arrow indicates that regulation involves transfer of phosphate. The mechanisms by which Spo0E inhibits the accumulation of Spo0A phosphate and ComQ stimulates the accumulation of ComA phosphate are unknown. EDF-A may act as a cell density signal for sporulation by interacting with the Spo0K transport system and stimulating formation of Spo0A phospate (28, 76). The dashed lines illustrate the hypothesis that EDF-A and/or the extracellular competence factor may be peptide intermediates in the surfactin biosynthetic pathway (58, 102).

and cell cycle signals, would be integrated ultimately at the level of Spo0A phosphate production to determine whether sporulation is initiated (4, 21, 28).

How is the EDF-A signal perceived by recipient cells? One or more oligopeptides could interact with a receptor at the cell surface that mediates signal transduction across the membrane. Alternatively, it could be transported actively through the membrane and itself affect a component of the phosphorelay or affect a transport protein that in turn affects a component of the phosphorelay. *spo0K* encodes a transport system that may be involved in sensing EDF-A. The *spo0K* locus was shown to be an operon of five genes with sequence similarity to the genes of the oligopeptide permease operon of *Salmonella typhimurium* (62, 76). Two findings suggest that transport of EDF-A by the Spo0K system might activate SpoIIJ (also called KinA), a histidine kinase that initiates the phosphorelay leading to phosphorylation of Spo0A (1, 61). First, *spoIIJ spo0K* double mutants had a more severe sporulation defect than either single mutant (76). Second, overproduction of SpoIIJ partially suppressed the sporulation defect in *spo0K* mutants (76). An attractive feature of this model is that it readily explains how production of EDF-A could stimulate further synthesis of Spo0A phosphate. This is represented as a feedback loop in Fig. 2.

Transport of EDF-A or a similar factor by the Spo0K transport system may also play a role in the development of genetic competence. *B. subtilis* cells become competent for the uptake of exogenous DNA during the postexponential phase of growth (see reference 14 for a review). One or more extracellular factors appear to be one of the signals that trigger a regulatory cascade leading to the expression of genes whose products make the cell competent (30). It has been suggested that the products of *spo0K*, or at least the product of the fifth gene in the operon, Spo0KE, stimulates a histidine kinase, ComP, to phosphorylate ComA (14, 76). Overexpression of ComP partially suppressed the competence defect in *spo0KE* mutants (Y. Weinrauch and D. Dubnau, unpublished data cited in reference 14), a situation analogous to the suppression of the sporulation defect in *spo0K* mutants by overproduction of the SpoIIJ kinase (76). Accumulation of ComA phosphate stimulates transcription of *srfA* (59a), an operon whose products are involved in the nonribosomal synthesis of a cyclic lipopeptide antibiotic called surfactin (52a, 59, 102). This has led to the intriguing hypothesis that EDF-A and/or the extracellular competence factor may be peptide intermediates in the surfactin biosynthetic pathway (58, 102). The dashed lines in Fig. 2 illustrate this hypothesis. Recent progress toward the purification of the competence factor may clarify its relationship to EDF-A and surfactin (21a).

Extracellular peptide signals control the mating behavior of *Enterococcus faecalis* (6, 16) and *Saccharomyces cerevisiae* (24) and the multicellular development of *Myxococcus xanthus* (47). A particularly strong analogy can be made between the roles of EDF-A and A-factor in *B. subtilis* and *M. xanthus* development, respectively. A-factor is a mixture of peptides, amino acids, and proteases (47, 70). The protease component of A-factor is thought to release peptides and amino acids, which serve as intercellular signal molecules. As with *B. subtilis* cells, *M. xanthus* cells at low density fail to develop (104). Like EDF-A, A-factor stimulates the development of low-density cells (48). The analogy also extends to the proteins required for production and sensing of A-factor and EDF-A. Sequence analysis of *asgA*, a gene required for A-factor production (46), revealed domains with similarity to histidine kinases and response regulators (69a). In addition, sequence analysis of *sasA*, a locus that when mutated restores expression of some A-signal-dependent genes in *asg* mutants (36), showed similarity between two genes at the *sasA* locus and the family of transport proteins to which genes in the *spo0K* operon are similar (35a). It seems likely that *asgA* and *sasA* are components of a complex signal transduction network in *M. xanthus* that gathers and integrates nutritional, cell cycle, and intercellular signals to regulate properly the expression of a "postexponential super regulon," analogous to that proposed for *B. subtilis* (15).

Rescue of *M. xanthus* development by A-factor requires a threshold concentration of about 10 μM active amino acids, suggesting that A-signaling is a density-sensing device that specifies the minimum cell density required to initiate development (48). Intercellular communication employing EDF-A may play a similar role in controlling the initiation of *B. subtilis* sporulation. Why might development be coupled to cell density in these organisms? *M. xanthus* cells exhibit cooperative behaviors during growth as well as during development. These behaviors include cooperative feeding (75) and movement (35). Density-dependent developmental signaling may ensure that the *M. xanthus* fruiting body contains a sufficiently high density of spores for efficient cooperative behaviors upon germination. Obviously, *B. subtilis* cells do not form multicellular fruiting bodies. However, we might be mistaken if we assume that *B. subtilis* cells in nature do not exhibit cooperative behaviors during growth, especially in light of recent revelations about cell-cell interactions in colonies of *Escherichia coli* (3, 84). Survival of spores in a clump might also be enhanced relative to that of free spores. Density sensing may also alert cells to the rate of starvation and the likelihood of finding an adequate nutrient source. At high cell density starvation is rapid and the probability of finding nutrients is low, so the appropriate response is sporulation. Perhaps the decision to sporulate is deferred in low-density cells in hopes of finding an adequate nutrient source (suggested by A. Grossman [21a]). *B. subtilis* cells become motile upon starvation and are capable of chemotaxis toward nutrients. *M. xanthus* cells at low density may grow slowly under nutrient-poor conditions that would normally induce development of high-density cells, since this is the response of mutants defective in A-signaling (48). A portion of starved *E. coli* cells in a culture remain viable for months or years (see Chapter 2, this volume). Thus, a response that is intermediate between growth and sporulation may be most advantageous for survival of cells starved at low density.

INTERCOMPARTMENTAL COMMUNICATION

The morphological changes that result in the formation of a *B. subtilis* endospore are driven by a carefully regulated program of gene expression. Genes must be expressed at the proper time and level, and in the proper compartment (see Chapter 7, this volume). A cascade of five σ factors can

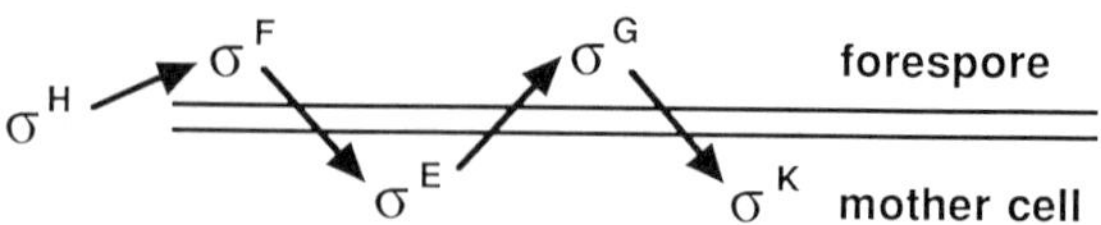

FIGURE 3. Order of action and location of activity of sporulation-specific σ factors. The double line represents the double membrane separating the forespore and mother cell compartments after formation of the sporulation septum.

account for much of the temporal and spatial regulation of gene expression during sporulation (51, 91). Figure 3 summarizes the order of action and the location of the five σ factors. Notice that three arrows cross the double line (representing the double membrane) separating the forespore and mother cell compartments. The three arrows represent three instances of intercompartmental communication. Each of these communication events is a signal transduction pathway that begins with an active σ factor in one compartment and leads to activation in the other compartment of the next σ factor in the cascade. Hence we will call the three pathways the σ^F to σ^E pathway, the σ^E to σ^G pathway, and the σ^G to σ^K pathway. Here we will focus on the evidence for the existence of each of these pathways and on the components of the signal transduction machinery. Each of the four compartment-specific σ factors (σ^F, σ^E, σ^G, and σ^K) appears to be inactive initially, so in each case the production of an active σ factor requires two steps, *synthesis* of the inactive form and subsequent *activation*. Table 1 summarizes the proteins that are thought to be most directly involved in the synthesis and activation of the compartment-specific σ factors. Each of the three instances of intercompartmental communication regulates the *activation* step, not the *synthesis* step, in the production of the next σ factor in the cascade. Thus, the last column of Table 1 identifies proteins that are

TABLE 1. Proteins involved in the synthesis and activation of compartment-specific σ factors

σ Factor (gene)	Synthesis	Activation
σ^F (*spoIIAC* or *sigF*)	σ^H, Spo0A	SpoIIAA, SpoIIAB, SpoIIE (3)[a]
σ^E (*spoIIGB* or *sigE*)	σ^A, Spo0A	σ^F, SpoIIGA
σ^G (*spoIIIG* or *sigG*)	σ^F, σ^G	σ^E, SpoIIAB, SpoIIB or SpoVG, SpoIID, SpoIIIA (7)
σ^K (*spoIVCB-spoIIIC* or *sigK*)	σ^E, SpoIIID, SpoIVCA, σ^K	σ^G, SpoIVB, SpoIVF (2), BofA

[a]The number of cistrons in the operon is given in parentheses.

likely to be components of the σ^F to σ^E, the σ^E to σ^G, and the σ^G to σ^K signal transduction pathways. These proteins serve to couple the programs of gene expression in the two compartments. They also operate in the context of a complex series of morphological changes. Presumably, activation of each σ factor in the cascade stimulates expression of a regulon whose products drive further morphogenesis. Whether intercompartmental communication serves to couple morphogenetic progress to the programs of gene expression in the two compartments has been the subject of much speculation. Resolution of this question will require elucidation of the temporal, spatial, and environmental requirements of the signal-transducing proteins.

THE σ^F TO σ^E PATHWAY

Synthesis of σ^F appears to be controlled by the earliest-acting sporulation-specific σ factor, σ^H (105). σ^F is encoded in the three-cistron *spoIIA* operon (17, 19, 69, 85, 94). Transcription of this operon begins about 1 h after the onset of sporulation (18, 68, 81), a point which is slightly later than that observed for other genes transcribed by σ^H RNA polymerase (95). The lag could reflect a lower affinity of the *spoIIA* promoter for σ^H RNA polymerase and/or the involvement of additional regulatory proteins. The cellular concentration of σ^H does increase at the onset of sporulation (23), and Spo0A phosphate has been reported to activate *spoIIA* transcription (4). The timing of *spoIIA* transcription suggests that σ^F is synthesized prior to septation, and the results of experiments with genetic mosaics support this idea (20).

Despite σ^F being synthesized before formation of the sporulation septum, its activity is confined to the forespore. This was shown using immunoelectron microscopy with antibodies against β-galactosidase to localize the site of expression of σ^F-dependent *lacZ* fusions (53). Activation of σ^F is controlled by the other two products of the *spoIIA* operon, SpoIIAA and SpoIIAB (53, 60, 82). Several observations support the idea that SpoIIAA is an antagonist of SpoIIAB, which is, in turn, an antagonist of σ^F (15a, 53, 82). Since SpoIIAA and SpoIIAB are also presumably synthesized prior to septation and are therefore expected to be present in both compartments after septation, this observation suggests that SpoIIAA is inactive prior to septation and becomes active only in the forespore after septation (53). If this model is correct, then understanding how SpoIIAA activity is regulated becomes the key issue in understanding how σ^F activity is compartmentalized. The products of the three-cistron *spoIIE* operon also play a role in σ^F activation, but it is unclear whether their primary effect is on SpoIIAA, SpoIIAB, or σ^F (53). *spoIIE* mutants appear to produce a thick layer of peptidoglycan in the sporulation septum (26), indicating the involvement of *spoIIE* products in the synthesis and/or regulation of the thin peptidoglycan layer that normally appears transiently in the sporulation septum. This finding has led to the suggestion that the SpoIIE proteins mediate or facilitate intercompartmental communication leading to σ^F activation (53).

σ^E is synthesized as an inactive precursor protein called pro-σ^E, which has an additional 27 to 29 amino acids at its amino terminus that are proteolytically removed in the activation step (49, 57a). Pro-σ^E is encoded in the two-cistron *spoIIG* operon (34, 88, 89, 97). This operon is transcribed with similar timing as the *spoIIA* operon (see above) during sporulation (39), but a different form of RNA polymerase is used. The *spoIIG* promoter is transcribed by σ^A RNA polymerase (38, 40), the major form of RNA polymerase in growing cells. However, transcription does not occur during growth, apparently due to the unusually great distance (22 bp) between the hexameric sequences recognized by σ^A in this promoter. In addition, binding of Spo0A to two sites in the *spoIIG* promoter region appears to activate transcription at the onset of sporulation (79, 80). As in the case of *spoIIA,* the timing of *spoIIG* transcription suggests that pro-σ^E is made prior to septation, so pro-σ^E is expected to be present in both compartments after septation.

Active σ^E RNA polymerase appears to be produced only in the mother cell. This conclusion is based on immunolocalization of β-galactosidase expressed from a σ^E-dependent *lacZ* fusion (13). It contradicts the result of an earlier study that had employed a similar approach (88). Also, physical separation of developing sporangia into forespore and mother cell fractions had suggested that σ^E is present in both compartments (5); however, the forespore fraction was contaminated with a considerable amount of mother-cell-specific alkaline phosphatase activity in this experiment. It now seems likely that active σ^E is produced only in the mother cell, but it remains possible that proteolytic processing of pro-σ^E to σ^E occurs in both compartments and that additional control mechanisms activate σ^E in the mother cell and/or inactivate it in the forespore. Since nothing is known about such control mechanisms and since it is clear that truncated forms of pro-σ^E missing part of the amino terminus possess σ^E activity in growing or sporulating *B. subtilis* (33, 65, 87a), we will focus our discussion of pro-σ^E activation on the proteolytic processing reaction.

SpoIIGA is encoded in the same operon as pro-σ^E and is required for the accumulation of σ^E (34, 88), which occurs shortly after formation of the sporulation septum between 1 and 2 h after the onset of sporulation. Furthermore, SpoIIGA appears to be sufficient to enhance accumulation of pro-σ^E in growing *B. subtilis* cells (88). This finding has led to the suggestion that SpoIIGA is the protease that processes pro-σ^E or that it enhances the susceptibility of pro-σ^E to one or more proteases present in growing and sporulating cells. The deduced amino acid sequence of SpoIIGA may bear some resemblance to aspartic or serine proteases in the C-terminal domain and is predicted to contain five membrane-spanning segments in the N-terminal domain (56, 88). Evidence that SpoIIGA is an integral membrane protein came from the fractionation properties of a *spoIIGA::lacZ* fusion protein (66). This study also suggested that SpoIIGA is synthesized much less efficiently than pro-σ^E. This difference could, at least in part, explain the observation that accumulation of σ^E lags about 1 h behind accumulation of its precursor during sporulation (98).

However, expression of the *spoIIG* operon (encoding both SpoIIGA and pro-σ^E) is not the only requirement for efficient processing during sporulation. Mutants that fail to make active σ^F fail to produce σ^E (31, 88), even though some of these mutants (e.g., *spoIIA* and *spoIIE* mutants) synthesize pro-σ^E (and presumably also synthesize SpoIIGA, although this hypothesis has not been tested directly). This dependence of the pro-σ^E processing reaction on σ^F, together with the findings that σ^F and σ^E activity are localized to the forespore and mother cell, respectively, constitutes the evidence for an intercompartmental communication event, which we call the σ^F to σ^E pathway (Fig. 4). This pathway begins with active σ^F in the forespore and results in the production of active σ^E in the mother cell. The membrane location of SpoIIGA and its critical role in σ^E accumulation make it a likely candidate for a protein involved in transducing a signal from the forespore to the mother cell (34, 66, 88). If SpoIIGA is initially inactive and it becomes active in response to a σ^F-dependent signal from the forespore, this situation could also explain the lag between the accumulation of pro-σ^E and the accumulation of σ^E (98).

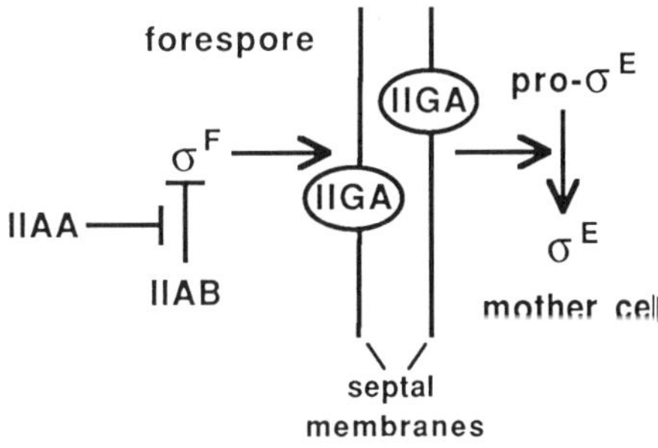

FIGURE 4. Model for the σ^F to σ^E signal transduction pathway. SpoIIAA removes SpoIIAB inhibition of σ^F activity in the forespore, generating a signal that may be transduced by SpoIIGA located in the septal membrane and resulting in accumulation of active σ^E in the mother cell.

What is the nature of the σ^F-dependent signal from the forespore? It is formally possible that σ^F itself or a byproduct of its activation (e.g., a SpoIIAA-SpoIIAB complex) is the signal. In this way, activation of σ^F in the forespore would be directly tied to activation of σ^E in the mother cell. Alternatively, σ^F RNA polymerase may direct the expression of one or more genes in the forespore whose product or products directly or indirectly act vectorially to permit σ^E activation in the mother cell (13, 51, 53). An attractive hypothesis is that σ^F-directed gene expression in the forespore leads to a modification of the sporulation septum that triggers pro-σ^E processing in the mother cell (25, 51). In this way, activation of σ^E in the mother cell would be tied not only to activation of σ^F, but to completion of a morphological step (49, 88). σ^F activity appears to be necessary for the removal of the thin layer of peptidoglycan that initially forms in the sporulation septum (25, 26). It has been suggested that removal of peptidoglycan from the sporulation septum and resulting fusion of the septal membranes triggers pro-σ^E processing (25). It is difficult to envision how such a mechanism could act vectorially and confine pro-σ^E processing to the mother cell. As noted above, it remains possible that processing occurs in both compartments and that σ^E is selectively activated in the mother cell and/or inactivated in the forespore as a result of σ^F activity.

Support for the idea that the sporulation septum plays a critical role in σ^E accumulation comes from a study in which cells depleted for FtsZ, a protein required to initiate septum formation, failed to make the sporulation septum and failed to accumulate σ^E (2). On the other hand, treatment of cells with penicillin at a particular time in development blocked septum formation, but not σ^E accumulation (32). These results, as well as the observation that SpoIIGA apparently enhances accumulation of σ^E in growing *B. subtilis* cells (88), can be reconciled by assuming that in growing or penicillin-treated cells a nascent septum can partially substitute for the sporulation septum in triggering σ^E accumulation.

Coupling the appearance of σ^E to some feature of the sporulation septum might ensure the completion of a critical morphological step prior to the period of σ^E activity in the mother cell. If so, earlier production of active σ^E should interfere with sporulation. Despite a systematic deletion analysis of the pro-region of the *sigE* gene (33, 65), no mutant has yet been generated that expresses σ^E-dependent genes earlier than normal. Coexpression of *spoIIGA* and *sigE* in growing *B. subtilis* resulted in a low level of σ^E-dependent gene expression, which had no adverse effect on subsequent sporulation (88). Thus, the biological significance of delaying the appearance of active σ^E remains uncertain.

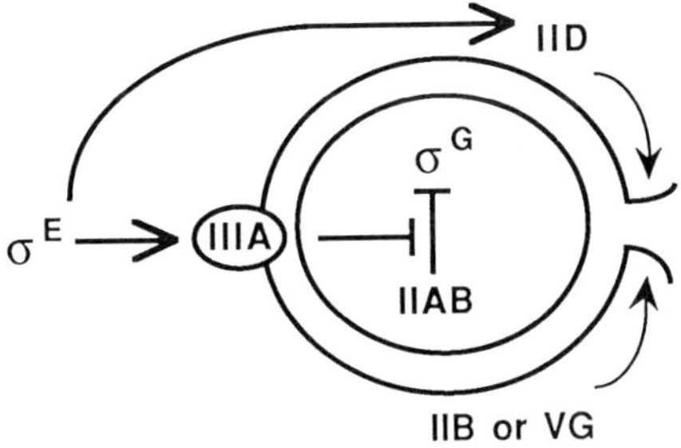

FIGURE 5. Model for the σ^E to σ^G signal transduction pathway. σ^E RNA polymerase transcribes the *spoIIIA* operon and the *spoIID* gene in the mother cell. SpoIID and proteins expressed earlier, like SpoIIB or SpoVG, drive the engulfment process. In the diagram, the outer forespore membrane is about to pinch off the forespore as a protoplast within the mother cell, completing engulfment. Some of the *spoIIIA* products may reside in the outer forespore membrane, where they sense completion of engulfment and generate a signal that results in the removal of SpoIIAB inhibition of σ^G activity in the forespore.

Whatever their precise roles, at least *spoIID* and *spoIIIA* are transcribed by σ^E in the mother cell, yet the products of these genes are involved in activating σ^G within the forespore compartment. This is the evidence for a signal transduction pathway leading from active σ^E in the mother cell to σ^G activation in the forespore (Fig. 5). Engulfment of the forespore then may serve as a "checkpoint" for delaying σ^G-directed gene expression until a critical time point in the developmental life cycle. The biological significance of fine-tuning the timing of σ^G-directed gene expression has not been elucidated in this pathway, but as in the example of the σ^K checkpoint discussed later, it may ensure the accurate synthesis and assembly of a complex morphological structure. The total number of genes involved in coupling σ^G-directed gene expression to engulfment is also unclear. *spoIIIA, spoIID, spoIIB,* and *spoVG* encode a total of 10 polypeptides. In addition to the SpoIIAB protein that may inhibit σ^G, it seems likely that other forespore-specific proteins, which have yet to be identified, are involved in the σ^E to σ^G pathway.

THE σ^G TO σ^K PATHWAY

One of the most completely studied σ factors is σ^K. This is the second and final σ factor known to be active in the mother cell compartment (13, 41). σ^K is responsible for transcribing a substantial number of genes that are involved in the synthesis and assembly of the spore coat. These genes include the *cot* genes (e.g., *cotA-D* and *cotF*), which encode spore coat proteins (11, 12, 77, 107), and also a DNA binding protein encoded by the *gerE* gene that regulates (negatively or positively) the transcription of some of the *cot* genes (9, 106). It seems likely that the σ^K regulon is comprised of many genes, of which only a handful have so far been discovered. Members of this regulon are transcribed exclusively in the mother cell compartment, as confirmed by both fractionation experiments (9, 44) and immunoelectron microscopy (13). Transcription by σ^K RNA polymerase commences at about the fourth hour of sporulation (9, 77) at a time when the germ cell wall has been deposited between the two layers of the forespore membrane but prior to synthesis of the cortex (σ^K-dependent genes may include those involved in not only spore coat synthesis but also cortex synthesis) (7).

One of the more interesting features of the regulation of σ^K synthesis is that its structural gene, *sigK*, is actually a composite gene made from two truncated genes called *spoIIIC* and *spoIVCB*. These two genes are joined by a chromosomal rearrangement at the third hour of sporulation exclusively in the mother cell compartment (43, 90). The rearrangement is confined to the mother cell because both the *spoIVCA* gene (encoding the recombinase [43, 78]) and the *spoIIID* gene (encoding a DNA binding protein required for the rearrangement [22a, 42, 90]) are transcribed by σ^E RNA polymerase (22a, 96). The role of SpoIIID in the rearrangement may be indirect, since SpoIIID stimulates *spoIVCA* transcription by σ^E RNA polymerase in vitro (22a), but SpoIIID may also participate directly by binding to DNA near the sites of recombination. Following rearrangement the *sigK* gene is subject to transcriptional control. The *sigK* gene is transcribed by σ^E RNA polymerase initially and by σ^K RNA polymerase later, in both cases with SpoIIID acting as a positive regulator (22a, 41, 44).

Activation of σ^K, like that of σ^E, involves proteolytic processing of an inactive precursor form. Comparison of the N-terminal amino acid sequence of purified σ^K with the nucleotide sequence of the *sigK* gene suggested that the primary translation product of *sigK* is a pro-protein (pro-σ^K) with a 20-amino-acid leader sequence (41, 90). Using an antibody to pro-σ^K, the existence of two forms of σ^K was demonstrated (51a). At the third hour of sporulation, immediately following the chromosomal rearrangement, the *sigK* gene is transcribed by σ^E RNA polymerase, and at this point pro-σ^K is detected using anti-pro-σ^K antibodies. However, σ^K is first detected at about the fourth hour of sporulation, almost 1 h after transcription of the *sigK* gene begins. Again, as in the case of the σ factors σ^F, σ^E, and σ^G, activation of σ^K appears to be delayed until a critical point in the developmental life cycle. In this example the signal for accumulation of σ^K emanates from within the forespore and is directly under the control of σ^G, since a null mutation in the *spoIIIG* gene abolishes σ^K accumulation (51a) yet does not interfere with either the chromosomal rearrangement (90) or the transcription of *sigK* (44). The precise nature of the signal that permits accumulation of σ^K is not yet understood. We do not know, for example, whether it represents a gross morphological change, although a suitable event occurring at this point in spore formation is the maturation of the germ cell wall between the two layers of forespore membrane. What is known, though, is that the signal for accumulation of σ^K is the end product of a signal transduction pathway that coordinates σ^K-directed gene expression in the mother cell with σ^G-directed gene expression in the forespore (7, 8, 10). A number of genes have now been identified that play a direct role in the σ^G to σ^K signal transduction pathway (Fig. 6), and each of these will be discussed below. It is likely, though, that some of the genes involved in this pathway have yet to be identified.

At the beginning of the σ^G to σ^K pathway is σ^G, which is activated upon completion of forespore engulfment, as discussed earlier. Once active, σ^G transcribes its target genes, at least one of which, *spoIVB*, encodes a 43-kDa protein that is involved in signaling the processing of pro-σ^K (7, 51a, 101). The *spoIVB* gene is transcribed only in the forespore, so presumably SpoIVB is confined to this chamber (7). SpoIVB may play a direct role in activating processing of pro-σ^K, possibly by interacting with the proteolytic enzyme. Alternatively, SpoIVB may have a structural or enzymatic role (in germ cell wall synthesis?), and its action may serve as part of a coordinated trigger that stimulates processing. If the requirement for processing pro-σ^K is relieved in *spoIVB* mutant cells, they are still unable to complete spore formation, suggesting that SpoIVB has another role in sporulation in addition to stimulating pro-σ^K processing (S. Cutting, unpublished data cited in reference 7). The requirement for *spoIVB* in processing pro-σ^K was not identified by a genetic screen, despite isolation of several alleles of two other genes (8), so it seems likely that *spoIVB*, and perhaps other forespore-specific genes, may be involved in generating a gross morphological change that is sensed by the proteolytic machinery.

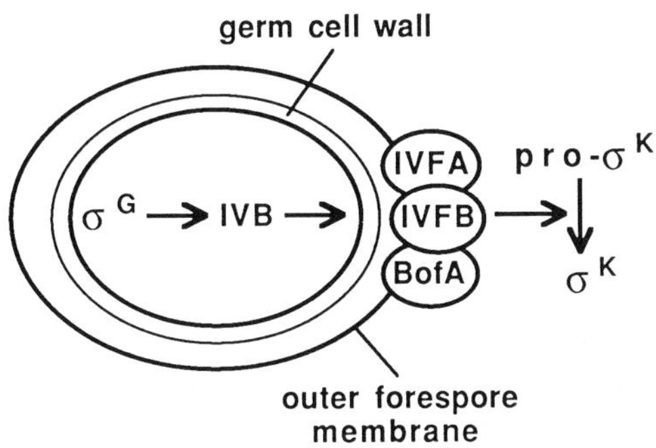

FIGURE 6. Model for the σ^G to σ^K signal transduction pathway. σ^G RNA polymerase transcribes the *spoIVB* gene in the forespore. SpoIVB directly or indirectly signals to SpoIVFB, which may reside in the outer forespore membrane as a heteromeric complex with SpoIVFA and BofA, resulting in proteolytic processing of pro-σ^K to produce active σ^K in the mother cell.

Acting after SpoIVB in the σ^G to σ^K signal transduction pathway are the *spoIVF* gene products. The *spoIVF* operon is transcribed by σ^E RNA polymerase in the mother cell compartment, and both its gene products, SpoIVFA (30 kDa) and SpoIVFB (33 kDa), are believed to be membrane-spanning proteins that can assemble into the outermost layers of the forespore membrane (10). Since the *spoIVF* operon is transcribed by σ^E RNA polymerase the SpoIVF proteins probably assemble directly into the asymmetric spore septum. Genetic evidence predicts that the SpoIVF proteins exist as an oligomeric protein complex containing more than one copy of SpoIVFA and SpoIVFB (10). Although neither protein appears to show similarity to known proteolytic enzymes, genetic evidence suggests that SpoIVFB is a strong candidate for the protease that cleaves pro-σ^K (10). Alternatively, the SpoIVF proteins could serve as a membrane-bound complex that transmits the forespore-derived signal to the proteolytic enzyme. Evidence that spoIVF might encode the pro-σ^K protease or its regulator comes from the identification of bypass mutations that relieve the requirement for σ^G or SpoIVB in processing of pro-σ^K (8). These suppressor mutations, termed *bofB* mutations (for bypass of forespore), lie in the *spoIVF* operon and appear to be change of function mutations that allow processing to occur in the absence of a forespore signal (8). A null mutation in the *spoIVF* operon abolishes pro-σ^K processing (52). Interestingly, the SpoIVFA protein appears to have two roles in regulating the activity of SpoIVFB (10). In its positive-acting role SpoIVFA is required to stabilize SpoIVFB and/or insert it into the membrane, since absence of the SpoIVFA protein renders SpoIVFB thermosensitive. In its negative-acting role SpoIVFA inhibits the activity of SpoIVFB until the appropriate signal is received. This signal may act directly on SpoIVFA or it may alter SpoIVFB such that inhibition is removed. The *bofB* mutations lie in the extreme carboxy terminus of *spoIVFA,* and presumably remove the inhibitory action of SpoIVFA on SpoIVFB even in the absence of the forespore signal, thus allowing constitutive activity of SpoIVFB.

The last gene known to be involved in processing pro-σ^K is the σ^E-dependent *bofA* gene, which encodes a small, 87-residue protein (8, 73). Isolated in the same genetic screen as the *bofB* mutations mentioned above, the *bofA* mutations relieve the requirement of the σ^G-directed forespore signal for processing of pro-σ^K. However, unlike the *spoIVF* operon, which is the site of the *bofB* alleles, a null mutation in the bofA gene does not seriously impair spore formation or pro-σ^K processing. BofA may form a heteromeric complex with the SpoIVFA/B proteins in the outer forespore membrane and inhibit the activity of SpoIVFB either directly or through SpoIVFA (73).

The precise nature of the signal emanating from within the forespore is unclear. It may be composed of several independent inputs that, together, comprise a unified signal that the forespore is ready to allow processing of pro-σ^K in the mother cell. Such a morphological signal might be completion of germ cell wall synthesis, and the SpoIVB protein may play a part in this process.

The signal transduction pathway that coordinates processing of pro-σ^K with forespore gene expression represents a developmental checkpoint that regulates the timing of gene expression in the mother cell compartment (8). In cells in which the requirement for pro-σ^K processing has been removed, transcription of σ^K-dependent genes is premature by about 1 h. When sporulation was monitored in these cells it was found that the frequency of sporulation was reduced almost tenfold, and those spores that were produced were defective in their ability to respond to germinants (8). Defective germination is presumably due to the premature synthesis and assembly of the spore coats, which, in turn, are due to the premature transcription of the σ^K regulon. These results then emphasize the biological importance of using intercompartmental communication to regulate σ^K activation.

SUMMARY

Efficient sporulation of *B. subtilis* requires that four cell-cell communication events occur. The first appears to involve one or more oligopeptides acting as an intercellular signal of cell density. If this signal, together with nutritional and cell cycle signals, drives the level of Spo0A phosphate high enough, sporulation is initiated. The other three cell-cell communication events occur between the forespore and mother cell compartments of the developing sporangium. Each of these intercompartmental signal transduction pathways begins with an active σ factor in one compartment and leads to activation in the other compartment of the next σ factor in a cascade that controls gene expression temporally and spatially. Proteins that participate in these signal-transduction pathways have been identified, but the signals and the mechanisms of signal transduction remain to be elucidated. A fascinating idea is that the signals are generated by completion of particular morphological structures, thus coupling the programs of gene expression and morphogenesis. Identifying the key signal-transducing proteins and determining how they function promises to be a challenging and fruitful endeavor.

We thank A. Grossman, L. Plamann, H. Kaplan, C. P. Moran, Jr., P. Stragier, R. Halberg, and S. Lu for communicating their results prior to publication. Unpublished work performed in L.K.'s laboratory was supported by the Michigan Agricultural Experiment Station and by grant GM43585 from the National Institutes of Health.

REFERENCES

1. **Antoniewski, C., B. Savelli, and P. Stragier.** 1990. The *spoIIJ* gene, which regulates early developmental steps in *Bacillus subtilis,* belongs to a class of environmentally responsive genes. *J. Bacteriol.* **172:**86–93.
2. **Beall, B., and J. Lutkenhaus.** 1991. FtsZ in *Bacillus subtilis* is required for vegetative and for asymmetric septation during sporulation. *Genes Dev.* **5:**447–455.
3. **Budrene, E. O., and H. C. Berg.** 1991. Complex patterns formed by motile cells of *Escherichia coli. Nature* (London) **349:**630–633.
4. **Burbulys, D., K. A. Trach, and J. A. Hoch.** 1991. Initiation of sporulation in *B. subtilis* is controlled by a multicomponent phosphorelay. *Cell* **64:**545–552.
5. **Carlson, H. C., and W. G. Haldenwang.** 1989. The σ^E subunit of *Bacillus subtilis* RNA polymerase is present in both forespore and mother cell compartments. *J. Bacteriol.* **171:**2216–2218.
6. **Clewell, D. B., and K. E. Weaver.** 1989. Sex pheromones and plasmid transfer in *Enterococcus faecalis. Plasmid* **21:**175–184.
7. **Cutting, S., A. Driks, R. Schmidt, B. Kunkel, and R. Losick.** 1991. Forespore-specific transcription of a gene in the signal transduction pathway that governs pro-σ^K processing in *Bacillus subtilis. Genes Dev.* **5:**456–466.
8. **Cutting, S., V. Oke, A. Driks, R. Losick, S. Lu, and L. Kroos.** 1990. A forespore checkpoint for mother-cell gene expression during development in *Bacillus subtilis. Cell* **62:**239–250.
9. **Cutting, S., S. Panzer, and R. Losick.** 1989. Regulatory studies on the promoter for a gene governing synthesis and assembly of the spore coat in *Bacillus subtilis. J. Mol. Biol.* **207:**393–404.
10. **Cutting, S., S. Roels, and R. Losick.** 1991. Sporulation operon *spoIVF* and the characterization of mutations that uncouple mother-cell from forespore gene expression in *Bacillus subtilis. J. Mol. Biol.* **221:**1237–1256.
11. **Cutting, S., L. Zheng, and R. Losick.** 1991. Gene encoding two alkali-soluble components of the spore coat from *Bacillus subtilis. J. Bacteriol.* **173:**2915–2919.
12. **Donovan, W., L. Zheng, K. Sandman, and R. Losick.** 1987. Genes encoding spore coat polypeptides from *Bacillus subtilis. J. Mol. Biol.* **196:**1–10.
13. **Driks, A., and R. Losick.** 1991. Compartmentalized expression of a gene under the control of sporulation transcription factor σ^E in *Bacillus subtilis. Proc. Natl. Acad. Sci. USA* **88:**9934–9938.
14. **Dubnau, D.** 1991. Genetic competence in *Bacillus subtilis. Microbiol. Rev.* **55:**395–424.
15. **Dubnau, D.** 1991. The regulation of genetic competence in *Bacillus subtilis. Mol. Microbiol.* **5:**11–18.

15a. **Duncan, L., and R. Losick.** 1993. SpoIIAB is an anti-σ factor that binds to and inhibits transcription by regulatory protein σ^F from *Bacillus subtilis. Proc. Natl. Acad. Sci. USA* **90:**2325–2329.

16. **Dunny, G. M.** 1990. Genetic functions and cell-cell interactions in the pheromone-inducible plasmid transfer system of *Enterococcus faecalis. Mol. Microbiol.* **4:**689–696.
17. **Errington, J., P. Fort, and J. Mandelstam.** 1985. Duplicated sporulation genes in bacteria: implication for simple developmental systems. *FEBS Lett.* **188:**184–188.
18. **Errington, J., and J. Mandelstam.** 1986. Use of a *lacZ* gene fusion to determine the dependence pattern of sporulation operon *spoIIA* in *spo* mutants of *Bacillus subtilis. J. Gen. Microbiol.* **132:**2967–2976.
19. **Fort, P., and P. J. Piggot.** 1984. Nucleotide sequence of the sporulation locus *spoIIA* in *Bacillus subtilis. J. Gen. Microbiol.* **130:**2147–2153.
20. **Gholamhoseinian, A., and P. J. Piggot.** 1989. Timing of *spoII* gene expression relative to septum formation during sporulation of *Bacillus subtilis. J. Bacteriol.* **171:**5747–5749.
21. **Grossman, A. D.** 1991. Integration of developmental signals and the initiation of sporulation in *B. subtilis. Cell* **65:**5–8.
21a. **Grossman, A. D.** Personal communication.
22. **Grossman, A. D., and R. Losick.** 1988. Extracellular control of spore formation in *Bacillus subtilis. Proc. Natl. Acad. Sci. USA* **85:**4369–4373.
22a. **Halberg, R., and L. Kroos.** Unpublished data.
23. **Healy, J., J. Weir, I. Smith, and R. Losick.** 1991. Post-transcriptional control of a sporulation regulatory gene encoding transcription factor σ^H in *Bacillus subtilis. Mol. Microbiol.* **5:**477–487.
24. **Herskowitz, I.** 1989. A regulatory hierarchy for cell specialization in yeast. *Nature* (London) **342:**749–757.
25. **Higgins, M. L., and P. J. Piggot.** 1992. Septal membrane fusion—a pivotal event in bacterial spore formation? *Mol. Microbiol.* **6:**2565–2571.
26. **Illing, N., and J. Errington.** 1991. Genetic regulation of morphogenesis in *Bacillus subtilis:* roles of σ^E and σ^F in prespore engulfment. *J. Bacteriol.* **173:**3159–3169.
27. **Illing, N., and J. Errington.** 1991. The *spoIIIA* operon of *Bacillus subtilis* defines a new temporal class of mother-cell-specific sporulation genes under the control of the σ^E form of RNA polymerase. *Mol. Microbiol.* **5:**1927–1940.
28. **Ireton, K., D. Z. Rudner, K. J. Siranosian, and A. D. Grossman.** 1993. Integration of multiple developmental signals in *Bacillus subtilis* through the *spo0A* transcription factor. *Genes Dev.* **7:**283–294.
29. **Jaacks, K. J., J. Healy, R. Losick, and A. D. Grossman.** 1989. Identification and characterization of genes controlled by the sporulation regulatory gene *spo0H* in *Bacillus subtilis. J. Bacteriol.* **171:**4121–4129.
30. **Joenje, H., M. Gruber, and G. Venema.** 1972. Stimulation of the development of competence by culture fluids in *Bacillus subtilis* transformation. *Biochim. Biophys. Acta* **262:**189–199.
31. **Jonas, R. M., and W. G. Haldenwang.** 1989. Influence of *spo* mutations on σ^E synthesis in *Bacillus subtilis. J. Bacteriol.* **171:**5226–5228.
32. **Jonas, R. M., S. C. Holt, and W. G. Haldenwang.** 1990. Effects of antibiotics on synthesis and persistence of σ^E in sporulating *Bacillus subtilis. J. Bacteriol.* **172:**4616–4623.
33. **Jonas, R. M., H. K. Peters III, and W. G. Haldenwang.** 1990. Phenotypes of *Bacillus subtilis* mutants altered in the precursor-specific region of σ^E. *J. Bacteriol.* **172:**4178–4186.

34. **Jonas, R. M., E. A. Weaver, T. J. Kenney, C. P. Moran, Jr., and W. G. Haldenwang.** 1988. The *Bacillus subtilis spoIIG* operon encodes both σ^E and a gene necessary for σ^E activation. *J. Bacteriol.* **170:**507–511.
35. **Kaiser, D., and C. Crosby.** 1983. Cell movement and its coordination in swarms of *Myxococcus xanthus*. *Cell Motility* **3:**227–245.
35a. **Kaplan, H. B.** Personal communication.
36. **Kaplan, H. B., A. Kuspa, and D. Kaiser.** 1991. Suppressors that permit A-signal-independent developmental gene expression in *Myxococcus xanthus*. *J. Bacteriol.* **173:**1460–1470.
37. **Karmazyn-Campelli, C., C. Bonamy, B. Savelli, and P. Stragier.** 1989. Tandem genes encoding σ-factors for consecutive steps of development in *Bacillus subtilis*. *Genes Dev.* **3:**150–157.
38. **Kenney, T. J., P. A. Kirchman, and C. P. Moran, Jr.** 1988. Gene encoding σ^E is transcribed from a σ^A-like promoter in *Bacillus subtilis*. *J. Bacteriol.* **170:**3058–3064.
39. **Kenney, T. J., and C. P. Moran, Jr.** 1987. Organization and regulation of an operon that encodes a sporulation-essential sigma factor in *Bacillus subtilis*. *J. Bacteriol.* **169:**3329–3339.
40. **Kenney, T. J., K. York, P. Youngman, and C. P. Moran, Jr.** 1989. Genetic evidence that RNA polymerase associated with σ^A uses a sporulation-specific promoter in *Bacillus subtilis*. *Proc. Natl. Acad. Sci. USA* **86:**9109–9113.
40a. **Kroos, L.** 1991. Gene regulation in the mother-cell compartment of sporulating *Bacillus subtilis*. *Semin. Dev. Biol.* **2:**63–71.
41. **Kroos, L., B. Kunkel, and R. Losick.** 1989. Switch protein alters specificity of RNA polymerase containing a compartment-specific sigma factor. *Science* **243:**526–529.
42. **Kunkel, B., L. Kroos, H. Poth, P. Youngman, and R. Losick.** 1989. Temporal and spatial control of the mother-cell regulatory gene *spoIIID* of *Bacillus subtilis*. *Genes Dev.* **3:**1735–1744.
43. **Kunkel, B., R. Losick, and P. Stragier.** 1990. The *Bacillus subtilis* gene for the developmental transcription factor σ^K is generated by excision of a dispensable DNA element containing a sporulation recombinase gene. *Genes Dev.* **4:**525–535.
44. **Kunkel, B., K. Sandman, S. Panzer, P. Youngman, and R. Losick.** 1988. The promoter for a sporulation gene in the *spoIVC* locus of *Bacillus subtilis* and its use in studies of temporal and spatial control of gene expression. *J. Bacteriol.* **170:**3513–3522.
45. **Kuroda, A., M. H. Rashid, and J. Sekiguchi.** 1992. Molecular cloning and sequencing of the upstream region of the major *Bacillus subtilis* autolysin gene: a modifier protein exhibiting sequence homology to the major autolysin and the *spoIID* product. *J. Gen. Microbiol.* **138:**1067–1076.
46. **Kuspa, A., and D. Kaiser.** 1989. Genes required for developmental signalling in *Myxococcus xanthus:* three *asg* loci. *J. Bacteriol.* **171:**2762–2772.
47. **Kuspa, A., L. Plamann, and D. Kaiser.** 1992. Identification of heat-stable A-factor from *Myxococcus xanthus*. *J. Bacteriol.* **174:**3319–3326.
48. **Kuspa, A., L. Plamann, and D. Kaiser.** 1992. A-signalling and the cell density requirement for *Myxococcus xanthus* development. *J. Bacteriol.* **174:**7360–7369.
49. **LaBell, T. L., J. E. Trempy, and W. G. Haldenwang.** 1987. Sporulation-specific sigma factor, σ^{29}, of *Bacillus subtilis* is synthesized from a precursor protein, P^{31}. *Proc. Natl. Acad. Sci. USA* **84:**1784–1788.

50. **Lazarevic, V., P. Margot, B. Soldo, and D. Karamata.** 1992. Sequencing and analysis of the *B. subtilis lytRABC* divergon: a regulatory unit encompassing the structural genes of the *N*-acetylmuramoyl-L-alanine amidase and its modifier. *J. Gen. Microbiol.* **138:**1949–1961.
51. **Losick, R., and P. Stragier.** 1992. Crisscross regulation of cell-type-specific gene expression during development in *B. subtilis. Nature* (London) **355:**601–604.
51a. **Lu, S., R. Halberg, and L. Kroos.** 1990. Processing of the mother-cell σ factor, σ^K, may depend on events occurring in the forespore during *Bacillus subtilis* development. *Proc. Natl. Acad. Sci. USA* **87:**9722–9726.
52. **Lu, S., and L. Kroos.** Unpublished data.
52a. **Marahiel, M. A., M. M. Nakano, and P. Zuber.** 1993. Regulation of peptide antibiotic production in *Bacillus. Mol. Microbiol.* **7:**631–636.
53. **Margolis, P., A. Driks, and R. Losick.** 1991. Establishment of cell type by compartmentalized activation of a transcription factor. *Science* **254:**562–565.
54. **Margolis, P. S., A. Driks, and R. Losick.** 1993. Sporulation gene *spoIIB* from *Bacillus subtilis. J. Bacteriol.* **175:**528–540.
55. **Mason, J. M., R. H. Hackett, and P. Setlow.** 1988. Regulation of expression of genes coding for small, acid-soluble proteins of *Bacillus subtilis* spores: studies using *lacZ* gene fusions. *J. Bacteriol.* **170:**239–244.
56. **Masuda, E. S., H. Anaguchi, T. Sato, M. Takeuchi, and Y. Kobayashi.** 1990. Nucleotide sequence of the sporulation gene *spoIIGA* from *Bacillus subtilis. Nucleic Acids Res.* **18:**657.
57. **Masuda, E. S., H. Anaguchi, K. Yamada, and Y. Kobayashi.** 1988. Two developmental genes encoding sigma factor homologs are arranged in tandem in *Bacillus subtilis. Proc. Natl. Acad. Sci. USA* **85:**7637–7641.
57a. **Moran, C. P., Jr.** Personal communication.
58. **Nakano, M. M., R. Magnuson, A. Myers, J. Curry, A. D. Grossman, and P. Zuber.** 1991. *srfA* is an operon required for surfactin production, competence development, and efficient sporulation in *Bacillus subtilis. J. Bacteriol.* **173:** 1770–1778.
59. **Nakano, M. M., M. A. Marahiel, and P. Zuber.** 1988. Identification of a genetic locus required for biosynthesis of the lipopeptide antibiotic surfactin in *Bacillus subtilis. J. Bacteriol.* **170:**5662–5668.
59a. **Nakano, M. M., and P. Zuber.** 1989. Cloning and characterization of *srfB,* a regulatory gene involved in surfactin production and competence in *Bacillus subtilis. J. Bacteriol.* **171:**5347–5353.
60. **Partridge, S. R., D. Foulger, and J. Errington.** 1991. The role of σ^F in prespore-specific transcription in *Bacillus subtilis. Mol. Microbiol.* **5:**757–767.
61. **Perego, M., S. P. Cole, D. Burbulys, K. Trach, and J. A. Hoch.** 1989. Characterization of the gene for a protein kinase which phosphorylates the sporulation-regulatory proteins Spo0A and Spo0F of *Bacillus subtilis. J. Bacteriol.* **171:** 6187–6196.
62. **Perego, M., C. F. Higgins, S. R. Pearce, M. P. Gallagher, and J. A. Hoch.** 1991. The oligopeptide transport system of *Bacillus subtilis* plays a role in the initiation of sporulation. *Mol. Microbiol.* **5:**173–185.
63. **Perego, M., and J. A. Hoch.** 1991. Negative regulation of *Bacillus subtilis* sporulation by the *spo0E* gene product. *J. Bacteriol.* **173:**2514–2520.
64. **Perego, M, G. B. Spiegelman, and J. A. Hoch.** 1988. Structure of the gene for the transition state regulator *abrB:* regulator synthesis is controlled by the *spo0A* sporulation gene in *Bacillus subtilis. Mol. Microbiol.* **2:**689–699.

65. **Peters, H. K., III, H. C. Carlson, and W. G. Haldenwang.** 1992. Mutational analysis of the precursor-specific region of *Bacillus subtilis* σ^E. *J. Bacteriol.* **174:**4629–4637.
66. **Peters, H. K., III, and W. G. Haldenwang.** 1991. Synthesis and fractionation properties of SpoIIGA, a protein essential for pro-σ^E processing in *Bacillus subtilis*. *J. Bacteriol.* **173:**7821–7827.
67. **Piggot, P. J., and J. G. Coote.** 1976. Genetic aspects of bacterial endospore formation. *Bacteriol. Rev.* **40:**908–962.
68. **Piggot, P. J., and C. A. M. Curtis.** 1987. Analysis of the regulation of gene expression during *Bacillus subtilis* sporulation by manipulation of the copy number of *spo-lacZ* fusions. *J. Bacteriol.* **169:**1260–1266.
69. **Piggot, P. J., C. A. Curtis, and H. DeLancastre.** 1984. Use of integrational plasmid vectors to demonstrate the polycistronic nature of a transcription unit (*spoIIA*) required for sporulation. *J. Gen. Microbiol.* **130:**2123–2126.

69a. **Plamann, L.** Personal communication.

70. **Plamann, L., A. Kuspa, and D. Kaiser.** 1992. Proteins that rescue A-signal-defective mutants of *Myxococcus xanthus*. *J. Bacteriol.* **174:**3311–3318.
71. **Rather, P. N., R. Coppolecchia, H. DeGrazia, and C. P. Moran, Jr.** 1990. Negative regulator of σ^G-controlled gene expression in stationary-phase *Bacillus subtilis*. *J. Bacteriol.* **172:**709–715.
72. **Rather, P. N., and C. P. Moran, Jr.** 1988. Compartment-specific transcription in *Bacillus subtilis:* identification of the promoter for *gdh*. *J. Bacteriol.* **170:**5086–5092.
73. **Ricca, E., S. Cutting, and R. Losick.** 1992. Characterization of *bofA,* a gene involved in intercompartmental regulation of pro-σ^K processing during sporulation in *Bacillus subtilis*. *J. Bacteriol.* **174:**3177–3184.
74. **Rong, S., M. S. Rosenkrantz, and A. L. Sonenshein.** 1986. Transcriptional control of the *Bacillus subtilis spoIID* gene. *J. Bacteriol.* **165:**771–779.
75. **Rosenberg, E., K. Keller, and M. Dworkin.** 1977. Cell-density dependent growth of *Myxococcus xanthus* on casein. *J. Bacteriol.* **129:**770–777.
76. **Rudner, D. Z., J. R. LeDeaux, K. Ireton, and A. D. Grossman.** 1991. The *spo0K* locus of *Bacillus subtilis* is homologous to the oligopeptide permease locus and is required for sporulation and competence. *J. Bacteriol.* **173:**1388–1398.
77. **Sandman, K., L. Kroos, S. Cutting, P. Youngman, and R. Losick.** 1988. Identification of the promoter for a spore coat protein gene in *Bacillus subtilis* and studies on the regulation of its induction at a late stage of sporulation. *J. Mol. Biol.* **200:**461–473.
78. **Sato, T., Y. Samori, and Y. Kobayashi.** 1990. The *cisA* cistron of *Bacillus subtilis* sporulation gene *spoIVC* encodes a protein homologous to a site-specific recombinase. *J. Bacteriol.* **172:**1092–1098.
79. **Satola, S. W., J. M. Baldus, and C. P. Moran, Jr.** 1992. Binding of Spo0A stimulates *spoIIG* promoter activity in *Bacillus subtilis*. *J. Bacteriol.* **174:**1448–1453.
80. **Satola, S., P. A. Kirchman, and C. P. Moran, Jr.** 1991. Spo0A binds to a promoter used by σ^A RNA polymerase during sporulation in *Bacillus subtilis*. *Proc. Natl. Acad. Sci. USA* **88:**4533–4537.
81. **Savva, D., and J. Mandelstam.** 1986. Synthesis of *spoIIA* and *spoVA* mRNA in *Bacillus subtilis*. *J. Gen. Microbiol.* **132:**3005–3011.
82. **Schmidt, R., P. Margolis, L. Duncan, R. Coppolecchia, C. P. Moran, Jr., and R. Losick.** 1990. Control of developmental transcription factor σ^F by sporula-

tion regulatory proteins SpoIIAA and SpoIIAB in *Bacillus subtilis. Proc. Natl. Acad. Sci. USA* **87:**9221–9225.

83. **Setlow, P.** 1989. Forespore-specific genes of *Bacillus subtilis:* function and regulation of expression, p. 211–221. *In* I. Smith, R. A. Slepecky, and P. Setlow (ed.), *Regulation of Procaryotic Development.* American Society for Microbiology, Washington, D.C.
84. **Shapiro, J. A., and C. Hsu.** 1989. *Escherichia coli* K-12 cell-cell interactions seen by time-lapse video. *J. Bacteriol.* **171:**5963–5974.
85. **Stragier, P.** 1986. Comment on "Duplicated sporulation genes in bacteria." *FEBS Lett.* **195:**9–11.
86. **Stragier, P.** 1989. Temporal and spatial control of gene expression during sporulation: from facts to speculations, p. 243–254. *In* I. Smith, R. A. Slepecky, and P. Setlow (ed.), *Regulation of Procaryotic Development.* American Society for Microbiology, Washington, D.C.
87. **Stragier, P.** 1992. Establishment of forespore-specific gene expression during sporulation of *Bacillus subtilis,* p. 297–310. *In* S. Mohan, C. Dow, and J. A. Cole (ed.), *Prokaryotic Structure and Function: A New Perspective,* vol. 47. Society for General Microbiology/Cambridge University Press, Cambridge.

87a. **Stragier, P.** Personal communication.

88. **Stragier, P., C. Bonamy, and C. Karmazyn-Campelli.** 1988. Processing of a sporulation sigma factor in *Bacillus subtilis:* how morphological structure could control gene expression. *Cell* **52:**697–704.
89. **Stragier, P., J. Bouvier, C. Bonamy, and J. Szulmajster.** 1984. A developmental gene product of *Bacillus subtilis* homologous to the sigma factor of *Escherichia coli. Nature* (London) **312:**376–378.
90. **Stragier, P., B. Kunkel, L. Kroos, and R. Losick.** 1989. Chromosomal rearrangement generating a composite gene for a developmental transcription factor. *Science* **243:**507–512.
91. **Stragier, P., and R. Losick.** 1990. Cascades of sigma factors revisited. *Mol. Microbiol.* **4:**1801–1806.
92. **Strauch, M., V. Webb, G. Spiegelman, and J. A. Hoch.** 1990. The Spo0A protein of *Bacillus subtilis* is a repressor of the *abrB* gene. *Proc. Natl. Acad. Sci. USA* **87:**1801–1805.
93. **Sun, D., R. M. Cabrera-Martinez, and P. Setlow.** 1991. Control of transcription of the *Bacillus subtilis spoIIIG* gene, which codes for the forespore specific transcription factor σ^G. *J. Bacteriol.* **173:**2977–2984.
94. **Sun, D., P. Stragier, and P. Setlow.** 1989. Identification of a new σ-factor involved in compartmentalized gene expression during sporulation of *Bacillus subtilis. Genes Dev.* **3:**141–149.
95. **Tatti, K. M., H. L. Carter III, A. Moir, and C. P. Moran, Jr.** 1989. Sigma H-directed transcription of *citG* in *Bacillus subtilis. J. Bacteriol.* **171:**5928–5932.
96. **Tatti, K. M., C. H. Jones, and C. P. Moran, Jr.** 1991. Genetic evidence for interaction of σ^E with the *spoIIID* promoter in *Bacillus subtilis. J. Bacteriol.* **173:**7828–7833.
97. **Trempy, J. E., C. Bonamy, J. Szulmajster, and W. G. Haldenwang.** 1985. *Bacillus subtilis* sigma factor, σ^{29}, is the product of the sporulation-essential gene *spoIIG. Proc. Natl. Acad. Sci. USA* **82:**4189–4192.
98. **Trempy, J. E., J. Morrison-Plummer, and W. G. Haldenwang.** 1985. Synthesis of σ^{29}, an RNA polymerase specificity determinant, is a developmentally regulated event in *Bacillus subtilis. J. Bacteriol.* **161:**340–346.

99. **Trowsdale, J., S. M. Chen, and J. A. Hoch.** 1978. Genetic analysis of phenotypic revertants of *spo0A* mutants in *Bacillus subtilis:* a new cluster of ribosomal genes, p. 131–135. *In* G. Chambliss and J. C. Vary (ed.), *Spores VII.* American Society for Microbiology, Washington, D.C.
100. **Trowsdale, J., S. M. Chen, and J. A. Hoch.** 1979. Genetic analysis of a class of polymixin resistant partial revertants of stage 0 sporulation mutants of *Bacillus subtilis:* a map of the chromosomal region near the origin of replication. *Mol. Gen. Genet.* **173:**61–70.
101. **Van Hoy, B. E., and J. A. Hoch.** 1990. Characterization of the *spoIVB* and *recN* loci of *Bacillus subtilis. J. Bacteriol.* **172:**1306–1311.
102. **Van Sinderen, D., S. Withoff, H. Boels, and G. Venema.** 1990. Isolation and characterization of *comL,* a transcription unit involved in competence development in *Bacillus subtilis. Mol. Gen. Genet.* **224:**396–404.
103. **Weir, J., M. Predich, E. Dubnau, G. Nair, and I. Smith.** 1991. Regulation of *spo0H,* a gene coding for the *Bacillus subtilis* σ^H factor. *J. Bacteriol.* **173:**521–529.
104. **Wireman, J. W., and M. Dworkin.** 1975. Morphogenesis and developmental interactions in myxobacteria. *Science* **189:**516–523.
105. **Wu, J., M. G. Howard, and P. J. Piggot.** 1989. Regulation of transcription of the *Bacillus subtilis spoIIA* locus. *J. Bacteriol.* **171:**692–698.
106. **Zheng, L., R. Halberg, S. Roels, H. Ichikawa, L. Kroos, and R. Losick.** 1992. Sporulation regulatory protein GerE from *Bacillus subtilis* binds to and can activate or repress transcription from promoters for mother-cell-specific genes. *J. Mol. Biol.* **226:**1037–1050.
107. **Zheng, L., and R. Losick.** 1990. Cascade regulation of spore coat gene expression in *Bacillus subtilis. J. Mol. Biol.* **212:**645–660.
108. **Zuber, P., J. Healy, H. L. Carter III, S. Cutting, C. P. Moran, Jr., and R. Losick.** 1989. Mutation changing the specificity of an RNA polymerase sigma factor. *J. Mol. Biol.* **206:**605–614.
109. **Zuber, P., and R. Losick.** 1987. Role of AbrB in Spo0A- and Spo0B-dependent utilization of a sporulation promoter in *Bacillus subtilis. J. Bacteriol.* **169:**2223–2230.

Regulation of Bacterial Differentiation
Edited by P. Piggot et al.

Chapter 9

DNA Structure, Spore Formation, and Spore Properties

Peter Setlow

A major feature of the process of sporulation in *Bacillus* species is a difference in the properties of the DNA in the forespore and the mother cell. Although both mother cell and forespore have equal amounts of DNA (31), presumably completed chromosomes, the DNA in these two compartments differs in (i) recognition by RNA polymerase (14, 37), (ii) the degree of chromosome condensation (31), and (iii) UV photochemistry (36). Additionally, as sporulation proceeds and the forespore is converted into a dormant spore, the spore's DNA becomes extremely resistant to a variety of types of damage, including depurination and oxidative cleavage (6, 11). Presumably, these latter changes promote the long-term survival of the dormant spore. This review will concentrate on the properties of DNA in the forespore and dormant spore, in particular as these DNA properties are involved in spore function and spore properties.

RECOGNITION BY RNA POLYMERASE

Much work has established that there is differential gene expression in the mother cell and forespore compartments during sporulation, and that this is regulated primarily at the transcriptional level (14, 37). This finding indicates that the DNA in the two compartments of the sporulating cell is recognized differently by RNA polymerase. There is much evidence indicating that changes in the σ-factor complement of RNA polymerase are involved in the differential DNA recognition in mother cell and forespore, and both mother-cell- and forespore-specific σ-factors have been identified (14, 15, 22, 37). However, it is still not clear how the differential gene

Peter Setlow, Department of Biochemistry, University of Connecticut Health Center, Farmington, Connecticut 06030-3305.

expression in the two compartments is initially established, i.e., what triggers synthesis or activity of the first compartment-specific σ-factor. It is formally possible that changes in the DNA template itself might be involved in establishment of compartment-specific DNA recognition by RNA polymerase. The evidence for this suggestion is that the forespore chromosome undergoes a macroscopic change in its condensation state, amounting to a two- to fourfold increase in the DNA per unit volume, at about the time of establishment of compartment-specific gene expression (31, 38). Given the effect that chromosome condensation can have on gene expression in other systems (16), it is tempting to speculate that forespore chromosome condensation might drastically affect access of RNA polymerase to certain regions of the chromosome, and thus effect regulation of gene expression. Forespore chromosome condensation has been seen in both *Bacillus subtilis* and *Bacillus megaterium* using several different techniques (27, 31). In *B. subtilis* forespore chromosome condensation does not take place in *spo0* mutants, in which forespore septum formation is blocked, but is unaffected in *spo* mutants blocked after forespore septum formation (31). A key but as yet unanswered question is precisely when the chromosome condensation takes place, i.e., whether there is significant condensation before the forespore septum is complete. If the latter is the case, then chromosome condensation might play a key role in establishment of forespore-specific gene expression even prior to septum formation. Unfortunately, definitive data on the timing of forespore chromosome condensation relative to forespore septum formation are not available. Similarly, the forespore chromosome condensation mechanism is not understood, although changes in forespore DNA supercoiling and global DNA binding proteins appear not to be involved (18, 38). Possibly the signal to form the asymmetric forespore septum also results in an asymmetric distribution of DNA attachment sites on the membrane in the region to become the forespore compartment.

Although there is evidence from other systems that chromosome condensation can have drastic effects on gene expression (16), there is no direct evidence for this in the sporulating cell. However, there is one bit of indirect evidence, as the expression of a number of forespore-specific genes varies significantly depending on the position of these genes on the chromosome (43). There are a number of explanations for this phenomenon, none of which is completely convincing. One explanation is that there are differences in the access of RNA polymerase to different regions of the forespore chromosome, possibly due to its condensation state. The role of changes in the DNA template in modulating gene expression in the forespore seems a fruitful area for further study.

UV PHOTOCHEMISTRY

At about the third hour of sporulation (about 1 h after forespore chromosome condensation) the UV photochemistry of DNA in the forespore begins to undergo a dramatic change (3, 36). The major DNA photoproducts produced by UV irradiation of vegetative cells or mother cells are cyclobutane-type dimers between adjacent pyrimidines, predominantly between adjacent thymines (TT) (Fig. 1A, Table 1). However, at about T_3 of sporulation the yield of TT from forespores begins to decrease and a new photoproduct appears (3, 9, 32, 36). This new photoproduct, initially termed spore photoproduct (SP) (Fig. 1B), is a thyminyl-thymine adduct formed between adjacent thymines on the same DNA strand. UV irradiation of dormant spores yields no detectable cyclobutane-type pyrimidine dimers, but a high level of SP (Table 1).

The generation of SP instead of TT upon UV irradiation of spores appears to be the reason that spores are 10- to 50-fold more UV-resistant than growing cells (36) (Table 1). Whereas TT and SP are formed with approximately equal yields per incident dose in cells and spores, respectively (5, 32), SP is repaired during spore germination by a rather error-free system which monomerizes SP to two thymine residues (45). The change in forespore DNA UV photochemistry from TT to SP production takes place in parallel with both a physical change in forespore DNA to a more fibrillar appearance in the electron microscope and the acquisition of forespore UV resistance (42). Strikingly, when forespores first acquire UV resistance they

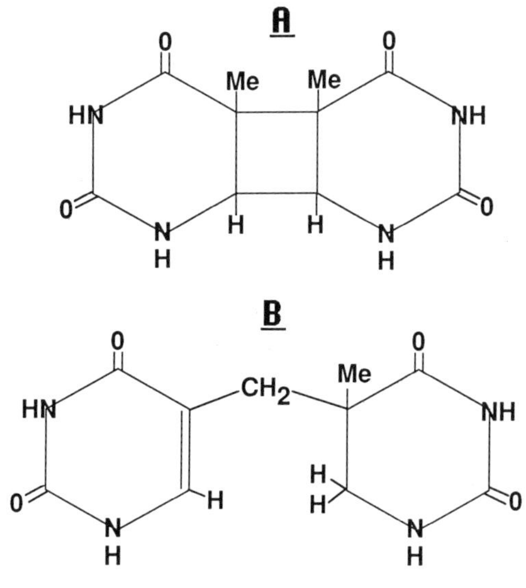

FIGURE 1. Structure of major UV photoproducts from DNA in (A) vegetative cells: a *cis, syn*-cyclobutane-type thymine-thymine dimer (TT); or (B) spores: a 5-thyminyl-5,6-dihydrothymine adduct (SP). Abbreviation: Me, methyl group.

TABLE 1. UV resistance and DNA photoproducts from *B. subtilis* cells and spores, and UV photoproducts from DNA and an α/β-type SASP-DNA complex in vitro [a]

Sample analyzed	Dose to give 90% killing (kJ/m²)	DNA photoproduct formation (% total thymine/kJ/m²)	
		TT	SP
Analyzed in vivo			
Wild-type or $\alpha^-\beta^-$ vegetative cells	40	5	< 0.1
Mother cells	40	5	< 0.1
Forespores with SASP but without dipicolinic acid	> 1,000	< 0.3	0.4
Dormant spores	315	< 0.2	7.5
$\alpha^-\beta^-$ Dormant spores	25	3.1	3.3
Wild-type spores germinated 5 min	> 1,000	< 0.2	0.5
Wild-type spores germinated 90 min	40	5.9	0.3
Analyzed in vitro			
DNA		> 4.1	0.3
α/β-type SASP/DNA complex		< 0.1	0.5
α/β-type SASP/DNA complex plus dipicolinic acid		< 0.1	3.0

[a]Data are taken from references 24, 29, 32, and 36.

are actually three to eight times *more* UV-resistant than are dormant spores (Table 1). The decrease in UV resistance of the dormant spore compared to the young forespore appears to be due to the high level of dipicolinic acid (~10% of dry weight) accumulated by the dormant spore, as dipicolinic acid (DPA) sensitizes spore DNA to UV (9, 10, 32). DPA is excreted in the first seconds of germination, and these DPA-free germinated spores transiently exhibit a very high UV resistance, associated with a very low production of both SP and TT as a function of incident dose (29, 32, 36). As germination proceeds the UV resistance of the spore eventually falls to that of growing cells, as TT production returns (Table 1).

As noted above, forespore DNA appears to undergo a structural change at the time of the change in its UV photochemistry. At this same time the forespore DNA becomes saturated with a group of small, acid-soluble spore proteins (SASPs) of the α/β type—so named for the two major proteins of this type in *B. subtilis*, SASP-α and -β (35). The α/β-type SASPs are coded for by a multigene family of at least seven monocistronic genes in *Bacillus* species, all of which are expressed in parallel only in the forespore beginning at about T_3 of sporulation. The primary sequences of these small proteins have been highly conserved, both within and across species. In the *Bacillus* line of spore-formers, α/β-type SASP sequences exhibit 26 absolutely conserved residues, with a number of other similar residues (Fig. 2). Most of the absolutely conserved residues are also conserved in α/β-type SASPs of *Clostridium* species (5). These proteins exhibit no significant sequence similarity to any other protein in available data bases. The α/β-type SASPs are degraded during spore germination well after DPA excretion; this degradation is initiated by a SASP-specific protease (35). This protease cleaves only once in α/β-type SASPs (arrow in Fig. 2), within a region whose sequence has been highly conserved. Further digestion of the resultant oligopeptides is carried out by various peptidases. The free amino acid end products support much of the protein synthesis early in spore germination.

Use of *B. subtilis* mutants lacking the genes coding for SASP-α and -β ($\alpha^-\beta^-$ strains) has shown that the presence of these proteins is the major reason for spore UV resistance and spore DNA's UV photochemistry, as $\alpha^-\beta^-$ spores are UV-sensitive and their UV irradiation generates reduced SP levels and significant levels of TT (Table 1). The UV resistance of $\alpha^-\beta^-$ spores can be restored to the wild-type level by synthesis of sufficient amounts of any wild-type α/β-type SASP—even if it is from another species (20, 44). However, α/β-type SASPs mutated in residues conserved throughout evolution are ineffective in this regard (44; see Fig. 2). The effects of α/β-type SASPs on the UV photochemistry of DNA have been duplicated both in *Escherichia coli* induced to synthesize an α/β-type SASP and in vitro (24, 30). The latter work has shown that binding of α/β-type SASPs to DNA in dilute buffer suppresses formation of 6/4 photoproducts and all cyclobutane-type dimers and promotes SP formation (7, 24) (Table 1). If DPA is included in an α/β-type SASP-DNA complex irradiated in vitro, then the yield of SP per incident fluence approaches that found in dormant spores (32) (Table 1).

As indicated above, α/β-type SASPs are DNA binding proteins which are specific for double-stranded DNA, with poly(dG)·poly(dC) bound most strongly (33). In addition, an oligo(dG)·oligo(dC) as small as 12 bp is bound. The only double-stranded DNA not bound by α/β-type SASPs is poly(dA)·poly(dT). However, in natural DNAs A-tracts of at least 12 residues are coated by these proteins. Studies with purified α/β-type SASPs from *Bacillus* as well as *Clostridium* species indicate that all these proteins exhibit almost identical DNA binding specificity. However, the mutant α/β-type SASPs noted above in which residues conserved throughout evolution are altered have lost their DNA binding capacity (44). A significant part of the DNA binding region of α/β-type SASPs appears to be in the highly conserved carboxy-terminal half of these proteins (Fig. 2), as a synthetic peptide modeled on this region binds DNA (28). In vitro the stoichiometry of α/β-type SASPs to

```
Bce1:     MGKNNSGSRNEVLVRGAEQALDQMKYEIAQEFGVQLGADTTARSNGSVGGEITKRLVAMAEQQLGGRANR
Bce2:         MSRST-KLAVPGAESALD-M-Y-I-Q----Q--ADATA-A-------I-----SL-EQQLG-YQK
BmeA:          MANT-KLVAPGSAAAID-M-Y-I-S----N--PEATA-A-------I-----QM-EQQLG-K
BmeC: MANYQNASNRNSS-KLVAPGAQAAID-M-F-I-S----N--PDATA-A-------I-----QL-EQNLG-KY
Bme3:     MANNNSSNN-ELLVYGAEQAID-M-Y-I-S----N--ADTTA-A-------I-----QL-EQQLG-GRF
Bme4:     MANNKSSNN-ELLVYGAEQAID-M-Y-I-S----N--ADTTA-A-------I-----QL-EQQLG-GRSKTTL
Bme5:          MART-KLLTPGVEQFLD-Y-Y-I-Q----T--SDTAA-S-------I-----QQ-QAHLS-STQK
Bme6:     MANNKSSNN-ELLVYGAEQAID-M-Y-I-S----N--ADTTA-A-------I-----QL-EQQLG-GRF
Bme7:     MANSRNKSS-ELAVHGAQQAID-M-Y-I-S----T--PDTTA-A-------I-----QM-EQQLG-GRSKSLS
Bst1:    MPNQSGSNSS-QLLVPGAAQVID-M-F-I-S----N--AETTS-A-------I-----SF-QQQMG-GVQ
BsuA:     MANNNSGNS-NLLVPGAAQAID-M-L-I-S----N--ADTTS-A-------I-----SF-QQNMG-GQF
BsuB:       MANQNSS-DLLVPGAAQAID-M-L-I-S----N--ADTTS-A-------I-----SF-QQQMG-RVQ
BsuC:  MAQQSRSRSNNN-DLLIPQAASAIE-M-L-I-A----Q--AETTS-A-------I-----RL-QQNMG-GQFH
BsuD:          MASR-KLVVPGVEQALD-F-L-V-Q----N--SDTVA-A-------M-----QQ-QSQLN-TTK
Sha1:       MANNNSS-ELVVPGVQQALD-M-Y-I-Q----Q--ADSTS-A-------I-----QM-EQQFG-QQYGQQQK
Sur1:     MTNNNNSNS-QLLVPGVQQAIN-M-E-I-N----N--PDSTS-A-------I-----RQ-QSQMN-YTK
Sur2:       MPNNNSS-QLLVPGVQQALN-M-E-I-S----Q--PDASS-A-------I-----RQ-QSQMN-YTK
Tth1:    MAQQGRNRSS-QLLVAGAAQAID-M-F-I-Q----T--ADTTS-A-------I-----SL-QQQLG-GTSF
```

FIGURE 2. Comparison of primary sequences of α/β-type SASPs from the "*Bacillus*" line of gram-positive spore-formers. Sequences are for proteins from *Bacillus cereus* (Bce), *Bacillus megaterium* (Bme), *Bacillus stearothermophilus* (Bst), *B. subtilis* (Bsu), *Sporosarcina halophala* (Sha), *Sporosarcina ureae* (Sur), and "*Thermoactinomyces thalpophila*" (Tth) and are given in the one-letter code. Residues which are identical to those in Bce1 are denoted by dashes; underlined residues are those in which mutation (G → A or K → Q in BsuC) destroys DNA binding in vivo and in vitro. The arrow shows the cleavage site of the SASP-specific protease. Data are taken from references 5, 17, 35, and 44.

DNA at saturation is ~1 SASP per 5 bp; this is approximately the ratio found in spores. Although the binding constant for α/β-type SASP-DNA interaction is not extremely strong ($K_a < 10^6$), the concentration of both protein and DNA components of this complex in vivo is >1 mM, a concentration which appears to drive complex formation to completion.

In addition to the effects on UV photochemistry, α/β-type SASP binding has a number of other effects on DNA properties (Table 2). These include provision of resistance to backbone cleavage by nucleases and hydroxyl radicals, as well as stiffening the DNA backbone, resulting in an increase in DNA persistence length of >20-fold (11a). The DNA also appears to be converted to an A-like conformation by α/β-type SASP binding, based on a variety of spectroscopic measurements (21). This change in DNA conformation from B to A on α/β-type SASP binding is consistent with the DNA binding specificity of these proteins, as poly(dG)·poly(dC) is in or close to being in an A-like conformation in solution (2, 26), whereas poly(dA)· poly(dT) has never been seen to adopt an A-like conformation (1). The change in DNA conformation on α/β-type SASP binding is also accompanied by a drastic change in the protein conformation, from the relative

TABLE 2. Effects of α/β-type SASP binding on DNA properties[a]

Property	DNA alone	α/β-Type SASP/DNA complex
1. Hydroxyl radical sensitivity	Backbone cleaved	Backbone resistant to cleavage
2. Restriction endonuclease or DNase I or II sensitivity	Backbone cleaved	Backbone resistant to cleavage
3. Dimethyl sulfate sensitivity	Purines methylated	Purines methylated
4. Conformation of helix	B-like	A-like
5. Rise per base pair	~3.3 A	~3.3 A
6. Predicted base pairs per helical turn	10.5	11
7. Persistence length	~150 bp	> 2.7 kb
8. Number of negative supertwists per kilobase in a relaxed circular DNA	0	6–8
9. Major UV photoproduct	TT	SP
10. Depurination rate (poly[dG]·poly[dC]; pH 5.0; 70°C)	3%/24 h	< 0.1%/24 h

[a]Data are for pUC18 or pUC19 and $SspC^{wt}$ unless otherwise noted, and are taken from references 6, 11a, 23, 24, 36, and 41.

absence of defined structure in the free protein to a compact, highly α-helical structure when the protein is bound to DNA (11c).

The precise parameters of the DNA's A-like structure induced by α/β-type SASP binding are not clear, but the DNA length is not altered significantly (Table 2). One would, however, predict that a covalently closed DNA going from B to A would undergo a significant topological change because of predicted differences in the number of base pairs per helical turn in the two conformations (Table 2). Indeed, α/β-type SASP binding does induce formation of six to eight negative supertwists per kilobase of relaxed, covalently closed DNA (23), a value higher than that predicted by changes in the number of base pairs per helical turn alone. However, recent work has suggested that α/β-type SASPs can also induce negative supertwists in DNA by bringing two DNA helices together in side-to-side association and wrapping them gently around each other (11b). Further work is needed to establish the relative contribution of these two mechanisms whereby α/β-type SASPs alter the DNA topology of covalently closed plasmids. In confirmation of the in vitro results, synthesis of saturating levels of α/β-type SASPs in vivo (either in spores or in *E. coli*) results in a large increase in the negative superhelical density of plasmid DNAs (25, 30). The absolute value for the supertwists per kilobase induced in vivo by α/β-type SASPs is ~60% of that seen in vitro.

Given the striking effects of α/β-type SASPs on protection of the DNA backbone from enzymatic or chemical attack, as well as the lack of sequence specificity in their binding, it seems likely that the proteins interact primarily with the DNA backbone. Indeed, purine methylation is not affected by α/β-type SASP binding (33) (Table 2). Since the DNA length is not appreciably altered by SASP binding, the DNA does not wrap around the protein. Rather, it appears likely that the protein may itself oligomerize on the DNA to form a protein helix around the DNA helix. Although the free protein itself does not oligomerize, it is clear that the protein does bind cooperatively to DNA (11b, 32). Since α/β-type SASPs can bind to small oligonucleotides, there is hope that the structure of an α/β-type SASP/DNA complex may eventually be determined with precision. The resultant data may then give us insight into the molecular mechanisms whereby α/β-type SASPs interact with DNA and alter DNA properties.

OTHER CHANGES IN SPORE DNA PROPERTIES

The concordance between the topological and UV photochemical properties of spore DNA, which is complexed with α/β-type SASPs in vivo, and those of an α/β-type SASP/DNA complex in which the DNA is in an A-like conformation in vitro, has led to the suggestion that the DNA in spores is also in an A-like conformation (40). If this is indeed the case, it would be the first clear role for A-like DNA in vivo. Although this DNA structure appears crucial to the spore DNA's UV photochemistry, and hence UV resistance, this DNA structure (plus the associated α/β-type SASPs) also appears involved in several other spore DNA properties.

It has been known for many years that spores are much more resistant than growing cells to chemical poisons, including agents such as hydrogen peroxide which can cause DNA damage by generation of hydroxyl radicals (11, 12) (Table 3). A significant portion of a spore's hydrogen peroxide resistance is probably due to the decreased permeability of spores to this agent compared to the permeability of a growing cell (11). However, $\alpha^-\beta^-$ spores exhibit a significant decrease in hydrogen peroxide resistance compared to wild-type spores (Table 3). Furthermore, many of the survivors of a hydrogen peroxide treatment of $\alpha^-\beta^-$ spores contain obvious mutations. This suggests that DNA is the target for at least some of the killing of $\alpha^-\beta^-$ spores by hydrogen peroxide, although the precise nature of the DNA damage has not been determined. In contrast, survivors of hydrogen peroxide treatment of wild-type spores are relatively mutation-free (Table 3), suggesting that their DNA is protected from hydrogen peroxide damage such that destruction of another target kills wild-type spores. The effects of α/β-type SASPs on spore resistance to hydrogen peroxide can be duplicated in vitro with an α/β-type SASP/DNA complex, which is much more resistant to cleavage by hydrogen peroxide or hydroxyl radicals than DNA by itself (32a, 37).

A second hallmark of bacterial spores is their increased resistance to heat compared to that of growing cells; spores of some species can survive many minutes at temperatures >90°C (8, 11). This resistance to killing at

TABLE 3. Survival and mutagenesis of *B. subtilis* cells and spores after hydrogen peroxide treatment or incubation at various temperatures[a]

Cells or spores	Time of H_2O_2 treatment[b]		Incubation conditions in water		
	10 min	30 min	93°, 30 min	85°, 30 min	22°, 6 mo
Wild-type vegetative cells	< 0.001				
Wild-type spores	30	4 (0.2)	1.3 (< 0.1)	67 (< 0.1)	53 (< 0.1)
$\alpha^-\beta^-$ spores	3 (12)	0.04 (14)	< 0.001	1.3 (14–21)	1.2 (17)

[a]Data are expressed as percent survival, with the percentage with mutations (both auxotrophic and asporogenous) in parentheses, and are taken from references 6 and 32.

[b]10% H_2O_2.

elevated temperatures is accompanied by even longer periods of survival at ambient temperatures. There are reports of survival of spores for over 500 years, and retention of much viability over periods of 6 months to 1 year in water at 10 to 25°C are not uncommon (6, 42). Obviously, during these extended periods of survival, DNA must be protected from damage, as there is no possibility of DNA repair because of the absence of nucleoside triphosphates (34, 39). One likely source of DNA damage which will accumulate over time, and at faster rates as the temperature is elevated, is DNA depurination. Even at 25°C DNA depurination in the dormant spore could result in loss of ~10 purines per spore genome per day (13). In growing cells, such damage would normally be rapidly repaired, but this repair cannot occur in dormant spores which lack nucleoside triphosphates (34). Thus DNA must be protected against this type of damage. One likely means of protecting DNA against reactions such as depurination is by decreasing the water content in the spore. Indeed, reduced spore core water is a major cause of spore heat resistance and presumably spore longevity (8). However, it appears likely that there are multiple factors involved in spore heat resistance (8), and a role for α/β-type SASPs is suggested by the decreased survival of $\alpha^-\beta^-$ spores compared to wild-type spores not only at high temperatures, but also at much lower temperatures (6, 19) (Table 3). In addition, as noted above for hydrogen peroxide treatment, the survivors of incubation of $\alpha^-\beta^-$ spores at either high or low temperatures exhibited a high frequency of mutations, in contrast to results with wild-type spores (6) (Table 3). This finding suggests that $\alpha^-\beta^-$ spores are dying upon incubation because of accumulation of DNA damage, damage which is prevented in wild-type spores such that they die from other causes. The precise nature of the DNA damage killing $\alpha^-\beta^-$ spores is not clear, but DNA from heat-killed (~99%) $\alpha^-\beta^-$ spores has ~1 single strand break per 2 kb (6). It has been suggested (but not yet proven) that the single-strand breaks in DNA are due to depurination events followed by backbone cleavage (6). Providentially, binding of α/β-type SASPs to DNA in vitro reduces the rate of depurination >20-fold (Table 2). The conclusion to be drawn from these data is that α/β-type SASP binding is a key component of spore heat resistance and extended survival. This binding greatly decreases DNA's reactivity, in particular its susceptibility to depurination. As a consequence, in wild-type spores it is usually not DNA damage that kills spores, but rather some other event such as breakdown of membrane permeability or destruction of a key protein (4). However, in $\alpha^-\beta^-$ spores DNA damage can now be faster than other killing mechanisms, resulting in decreased spore survival at all temperatures and an increase in mutations in the survivors.

CONCLUSIONS

The dramatic changes in DNA properties which accompany spore formation clearly have resulted in novel mechanisms to bring about these spore properties. The precise role of one such mechanism, forespore chromosome condensation, is unclear at present, but it may be an evolutionary forerunner of the chromosome condensation seen in many higher organisms. The second mechanism, the synthesis of a novel group of DNA binding proteins—α/β-type SASPs—which alter DNA properties to ensure survival during extended dormancy, is clearly a mechanism peculiar to spores. This is undoubtedly true because of spore dormancy, such that the entire genome can be maintained in an inactive state until the "return to life" accompanying spore germination, at which time the proteins are degraded. These novel proteins in essence provide a protected environment for spore DNA to ride out dormancy without accumulation of damage that could otherwise overwhelm damage repair systems, which can only begin to act early in spore germination. Even when spores germinate and α/β-type SASPs are no longer needed, these proteins continue to serve, as their degradation provides amino acids for much of the protein synthesis early in spore germination. It is also possible that α/β-type SASPs can play an additional role, as they could be involved in regulating gene expression during sporulation. Studies in vitro and in vivo have shown that α/β-type SASPs block transcription of many genes (20a, 29, 30, 33a)—certainly not a surprising property for a DNA binding protein which can completely cover DNA. However, α/β-type SASPs do show preferred sites of binding to DNA. Consequently it is possible that during the period in sporulation when α/β-type SASPs are synthesized, and while their level is subsaturating relative to DNA, these proteins might serve to modulate expression of many genes on the chromosome. The system of bacterial sporulation and its product, the dormant spore, continue to provide fascinating insights into the methods used to solve the problems facing biological systems.

Work in the author's laboratory has been supported by grants from the Army Research Office and the National Institutes of Health (GM19698).

REFERENCES

1. **Arnott, S., and E. Selsing.** 1974. Structures for the polynucleotide complexes poly(dA)·poly(dT) and poly(dT)·poly(dA)·poly(dT). *J. Mol. Biol.* **88:**509–521.
2. **Arnott, S., and E. Selsing.** 1974. The structure of polydeoxyguanylic acid·polydeoxycytidylic acid. *J. Mol. Biol.* **88:**551–552.

3. **Baillie, E., G. R. Germaine, W. G. Murrell, and D. F. Ohye.** 1974. Photoreactivation, photoproduct formation, and deoxyribonucleic acid state in ultraviolet-irradiated sporulating cultures of *Bacillus cereus*. *J. Bacteriol.* **120:**516–523.
4. **Belliveau, B. H., T. C. Beaman, H. S. Pankratz, and P. Gerhardt.** 1992. Heat killing of bacterial spores analyzed by differential scanning calorimetry. *J. Bacteriol.* **174:**4463–4474.
5. **Cabrera-Martinez, R. M., and P. Setlow.** 1991. Cloning and nucleotide sequence of three genes coding for small, acid-soluble proteins of *Clostridium pefringens* spores. *FEMS Microbiol. Lett.* **77:**127–132.
6. **Fairhead, H., B. Setlow, and P. Setlow.** 1993. Prevention of DNA damage in spores and in vitro by small, acid-soluble proteins from *Bacillus* species. *J. Bacteriol.* **175:**1367–1374.
7. **Fairhead, H., and P. Setlow.** 1992. Binding of DNA to α/β-type small, acid-soluble proteins from spores of *Bacillus* or *Clostridium* species prevents formation of cytosine dimers, cytosine-thymine dimers, and bipyrimidine photoadducts after UV irradiation. *J. Bacteriol.* **174:**2874–2880.
8. **Gerhardt, P., and R. E. Marquis.** 1989. Spore thermoresistance mechanisms, p. 43–63. *In* I. Smith, R. A. Slepecky, and P. Setlow (ed.), *Regulation of Procaryotic Development: Structural and Functional Analysis of Bacterial Sporulation and Germination*. American Society for Microbiology, Washington, D.C.
9. **Germaine, G. R., E. Coggiola, and W. G. Murrell.** 1973. Development of ultraviolet resistance in sporulating *Bacillus cereus* T. *J. Bacteriol.* **116:**823–831.
10. **Germaine, G. R., and W. G. Murrell.** 1973. Effect of dipicolinic acid on the ultraviolet radiation resistance of *Bacillus cereus* spores. *Photochem. Photobiol.* **17:**145–154.
11. **Gould, G. W.** 1983. Mechanisms of resistance and dormancy, p. 173–209. *In* A. Hurst and G. W. Gould (ed.), *The Bacterial Spore*, vol. 2. Academic Press, Inc., New York.
11a. **Griffith, J., L. Santiago-Lara, and P. Setlow.** Unpublished data.
11b. **Griffith, J., and P. Setlow.** Unpublished data.
11c. **He, C., B. Setlow, P. Setlow, and S. C. Mohr.** Unpublished data.
12. **Imlay, J. A., and S. Linn.** 1988. DNA damage and oxygen radical toxicity. *Science* **240:**1302–1309.
13. **Lindahl, T., and B. Nyberg.** 1972. Rate of depurination of native deoxyribonucleic acid. *Biochemistry* **11:**3610–3618.
14. **Losick, R., and L. Kroos.** 1989. Dependence pathways for expression of genes involved in endospore formation in *Bacillus subtilis*, p. 223–242. *In* I. Smith, R. A. Slepecky, and P. Setlow (ed.), *Regulation of Procaryotic Development: Structural and Functional Analysis of Bacterial Sporulation and Germination*. American Society for Microbiology, Washington, D.C.
15. **Losick, R., and P. Stragier.** 1992. Crisscross regulation of cell-type-specific gene expression during development in *B. subtilis*. *Nature* (London) **355:**601–604.
16. **Lyon, M.** 1988. X-chromosome inactivation and the location and expression of X-linked genes. The William Allan memorial address. *Am. J. Hum. Genet.* **42:**8–16.
17. **Magill, N. G., C. A. Loshon, and P. Setlow.** 1990. Small, acid-soluble, spore proteins and their genes from two species of *Sporosarcina*. *FEMS Microbiol. Lett.* **72:**293–298.
18. **Magill, N. G., and P. Setlow.** 1992. Properties of purified sporlets produced by *spoII* mutants of *Bacillus subtilis*. *J. Bacteriol.* **174:**8148–8151.

19. **Mason, J. M., and P. Setlow.** 1986. Evidence for an essential role for small, acid-soluble, spore proteins in the resistance of *Bacillus subtilis* spores to UV light. *J. Bacteriol.* **167:**174–178.
20. **Mason, J. M., and P. Setlow.** 1987. Different small, acid-soluble proteins of the α/β-type have interchangeable roles in the heat and UV radiation resistance of *Bacillus subtilis* spores. *J. Bacteriol.* **169:**3633–3637.
20a. **McGinnis, K., and P. Setlow.** Unpublished data.
21. **Mohr, S. C., N. V. H. A. Sokolov, C. He, and P. Setlow.** 1991. Binding of small acid-soluble spore proteins from *Bacillus subtilis* changes the conformation of DNA from B to A. *Proc. Natl. Acad. Sci. USA* **88:**77–81.
22. **Moran, C. P., Jr.** 1989. Sigma factors and the regulation of transcription, p. 167–184. *In* I. Smith, R. A. Slepecky, and P. Setlow (ed.), *Regulation of Procaryotic Development: Structural and Functional Analysis of Bacterial Sporulation and Germination.* American Society for Microbiology, Washington, D.C.
23. **Nicholson, W. L., B. Setlow, and P. Setlow.** 1990. Binding of DNA *in vitro* by a small, acid-soluble spore protein and its effect on DNA topology. *J. Bacteriol.* **172:**6900–6906.
24. **Nicholson, W. L., B. Setlow, and P. Setlow.** 1991. Ultraviolet irradiation of DNA complexed with α/β-type small, acid-soluble proteins from spores of *Bacillus* or *Clostridium* species makes spore photoproduct but not thymine dimers. *Proc. Natl. Acad. Sci. USA* **88:**8288–8292.
25. **Nicholson, W. L., and P. Setlow.** 1989. Dramatic increase in the negative superhelicity of plasmid DNA in the forespore compartment of sporulating cells of *Bacillus subtilis. J. Bacteriol.* **172:**7–14.
26. **Nishimura, Y., C. Torigoe, and M. Tsuboi.** 1985. An A-form poly(dG)·poly(dC) in H_2O solution. *Biopolymers* **24:**1841–1844.
27. **Piggot, P. J.** 1991. Morphometric events leading to the asymmetric division during sporulation of *Bacillus subtilis. Semin. Dev. Biol.* **2:**47–53.
28. **Rao, H., S. C. Mohr, H. Fairhead, and P. Setlow.** 1992. Synthesis and characterization of a 29-amino acid residue DNA-binding peptide derived from α/β-type small, acid-soluble spore proteins (SASP) of bacteria. *FEBS Lett.* **305:**115–120.
29. **Sanchez-Salas, J.-L., M. L. Santiago-Lara, B. Setlow, M. D. Sussman, and P. Setlow.** 1992. Properties of *Bacillus megaterium* and *Bacillus subtilis* mutants which lack the protease that degrades small, acid-soluble proteins during spore germination. *J. Bacteriol.* **174:**807–814.
30. **Setlow, B., A. R. Hand, and P. Setlow.** 1991. Synthesis of a *Bacillus subtilis* small, acid-soluble spore protein in *Escherichia coli* causes cell DNA to assume some characteristics of spore DNA. *J. Bacteriol.* **173:**1642–1653.
31. **Setlow, B., N. Magill, P. Febbroriello, L. Nakhimovsky, D. E. Koppel, and P. Setlow.** 1991. Condensation of the forespore nucleoid early in sporulation of *Bacillus* species. *J. Bacteriol.* **173:**6270–6278.
32. **Setlow, B., and P. Setlow.** 1993. Dipicolinic acid greatly enhances production of spore photoproduct in bacterial spores upon UV irradiation. *Appl. Environ. Microbiol.* **59:**640–643.
32a. **Setlow, B., and P. Setlow.** Unpublished data.
33. **Setlow, B., D. Sun, and P. Setlow.** 1992. Studies of the interaction between DNA and α/β-type small, acid-soluble spore proteins: a new class of DNA binding protein. *J. Bacteriol.* **174:**2312–2322.
33a. **Setlow, J. K., B. Setlow, and P. Setlow.** Unpublished data.

34. **Setlow, P.** 1981. Biochemistry of bacterial forespore development and spore germination, p. 13–18. *In* H. S. Levinson, D. J. Tipper, and A. L. Sonenshein (ed.), *Sporulation and Germination.* American Society for Microbiology, Washington, D.C.
35. **Setlow, P.** 1988. Small, acid-soluble spore proteins of *Bacillus* species: structure, synthesis, genetics, function, and degradation. *Annu. Rev. Microbiol.* **42:**319–338.
36. **Setlow, P.** 1988. Resistance of bacterial spores to ultraviolet light. *Comments Mol. Cell. Biophys.* **5:**253–264.
37. **Setlow, P.** 1989. Forespore-specific genes of *Bacillus subtilis:* function and regulation of expression, p. 211–222. *In* I. Smith, R. A. Slepecky, and P. Setlow (ed.), *Regulation of Procaryotic Development: Structural and Functional Analysis of Bacterial Sporulation and Germination.* American Society for Microbiology, Washington, D.C.
38. **Setlow, P.** 1991. Changes in forespore chromosome structure during sporulation in *Bacillus* species. *Semin. Dev. Biol.* **2:**55–62.
39. **Setlow, P.** 1992. I will survive: protecting and repairing spore DNA. *J. Bacteriol.* **174:**2737–2741.
40. **Setlow, P.** 1992. DNA in dormant spores of *Bacillus* species is in an A-like conformation. *Mol. Microbiol.* **6:**563–567.
41. **Shore, D., J. Langowski, and R. L. Baldwin.** 1981. DNA flexibility studied by covalent closure of short fragments into circles. *Proc. Natl. Acad. Sci. USA* **78:**4833–4837.
42. **Slepecky, R. A., and E. R. Leadbetter.** 1983. On the prevalence and roles of spore-forming bacteria and their spores in nature, p. 79–99. *In* A. Hurst and G. W. Gould (ed.), *The Bacterial Spore,* vol. 2. Academic Press, Inc., New York.
43. **Sun, D., P. Fajardo-Cavazos, M. D. Sussman, F. Tovar-Rojo, R.-M. Cabrera-Martinez, and P. Setlow.** 1991. Analysis of the effect of chromosome location of *Bacillus subtilis* forespore specific genes on their *spo* gene dependence and transcription by $E\sigma^F$: identification of features of good $E\sigma^F$ dependent promoters. *J. Bacteriol.* **173:**7867–7874.
44. **Tovar-Rojo, F., and P. Setlow.** 1991. Analysis of the effects of mutant small, acid-soluble spore proteins from *Bacillus subtilis* on DNA *in vivo* and *in vitro. J. Bacteriol.* **173:**4827–4835.
45. **Wang, T.-C. V., and C. S. Rupert.** 1977. Evidence for the monomerization of spore photoproduct to two thymines by the light-independent "spore repair" process in *Bacillus subtilis. Photochem. Photobiol.* **25:**123–127.

Regulation of Bacterial Differentiation
Edited by P. Piggot et al.

Chapter 10

Ecology and Relationships of Endospore-Forming Bacteria: Changing Perspectives

R. A. Slepecky and E. R. Leadbetter

Largely because of the practical ramifications of their formation and presence, bacterial endospores (and particularly the basis of their heat resistance and factors affecting their germination) and the organisms that form them were the focus of intense curiosity during the first half of this century. Only in the latter half of the century did the aerobic *Bacillus* spp. become the focus of attention in terms of their remarkable morphogenesis and the factors controlling it (10).

As a result of such attention we are by now well aware of many exciting details regarding the physiology, biochemistry, and, now, molecular biology of endospore formation and germination. However, we are far less cognizant of the roles that endospore-forming organisms play in natural habitats. There is obvious logic in focusing attention on only a few selected strains as one means of aiding advances in understanding. This outlook, however, creates imbalances and perhaps distortions when we fail to remember that there appear to be quite significant differences in some aspects of endospore formation and structure (19). For example, generalizations about the sequential events that result in the eventual formation of the mature endospore most often refer to those events as they have become understood in bacilli that form their spores near one pole of the cell. Although it seems likely that the principles describing sporulation events will prove applicable to organisms that form spores in a more lateral position (e.g., *Bacillus laterosporus*) or to cells that are more spherical in

R. A. Slepecky, Biological Research Laboratories, Syracuse University, Syracuse, New York 13244-1220. ***E. R. Leadbetter,*** Graduate Program in Microbiology, Department of Molecular and Cell Biology, The University of Connecticut, Storrs, Connecticut 06269-2131.

shape (e.g., *Sporosarcina* spp.), it is also possible that an understanding of the events in such bacteria will reveal significant deviations from the events characteristic of, for example, *Bacillus subtilis*.

The long-recognized diversity among the endospore-forming bacteria was at first focused on the differences between the rod-shaped *Bacillus* (mostly strictly aerobic and catalase-positive) and *Clostridium* (strictly anaerobic) spp. Now the assemblage includes other rods, such as *Sporolactobacillus* (microaerophilic, catalase-negative, homolactic fermentation) and *Thermoactinomyces* spp. (branching filaments), *Desulfotomaculum* spp. (anaerobic, sulfate respiration), and cocci (*Sporosarcina* spp.). Thus differences in cell morphology, sites of spore formation, and details of spore ultrastructure (19) have now also become important considerations.

In addition to these traits, we are now becoming increasingly aware of the nutritional diversity of spore-forming bacteria, a diversity that has significant implications for the habitats in which these bacteria are, and will be, found and the transformations they may be expected to undergo and the effects they may be expected to exert in such habitats. A very real set of differences in the relationships of spore-forming bacteria and in the possible origins of spore formation itself has long been perceived by those interested in the biology of these bacteria. Such suggestions and concerns have been strengthened enormously by recent molecular biological analyses of apparent phylogenetic relationships within this group of organisms (see below). The implications of such much-needed studies for other groups of endospore-formers are likely to be significant. In this chapter, we selectively focus our attention on these newer findings regarding the habitat diversity, nutritional diversity, and genetic diversity of the endospore-forming bacteria.

NEWLY RECOGNIZED ECOLOGICAL ROLES OF ANAEROBES

Evidence has been available for some time that different members of the genus *Clostridium* play significant roles in events that transpire early in anaerobic metabolic food chains. Solubilization of biopolymers such as cellulose and starch by hydrolyses, resulting in the release of their component monomers, has been recognized as an important event in the mineralization process in diverse anaerobic habits—both mesophilic and thermophilic. Recent developments have focused attention on an equally significant role that other, sometimes only recently characterized, anaerobic endospore-forming bacteria play in the terminal aspects of anaerobic metabolic food chains as well.

The adverse effect of the accumulation of even modest amounts of molecular hydrogen on the continued operation of such food chains makes clear the important role of organisms able to consume H_2 and thus maintain a low partial pressure of the gas in the many habitats where anaerobic metabolism is *the* way of life (15, 38). The evidence, nearly a decade ago, for the new genus *Sporomusa* (30) is a case in point; the physiological traits and natural distribution of its members are one example of the convincing evidence for unanticipated ecological roles of anaerobic endospore-forming bacteria. The members of this genus constitute an interesting group not only because their cells appear gram-negative as judged by staining procedures, but also because transmission electron microscopy of thin sections reveals a cell wall structure comparable to that of classic gram-negative cells—an outer, membrane-like bilayer is present. Lipopolysaccharide has been detected. These spore-formers (*Sporomusa acidovorans, Sporomusa malonica, Sporomusa ovata,* and *Sporomusa termitida;* only *Sporomusa paucivorans* fails to form endospores) differ from some (e.g., *Desulfotomaculum* spp.) whose cells are judged gram-negative by staining but appear gram-positive as judged by transmission electron microscopy of thin sections (2). *Sporohalobacter* spp. cells also appear to be truly gram-negative. Clearly, it will be intriguing to unravel the morphological and anatomical changes accompanying the morphogenesis of the gram-negative cell into an endospore with classical features, and to compare those sequential events to those already demonstrated for gram-positive spore-formers.

The metabolism of members of the genus *Sporomusa* is homoacetogenic. Consumption of H_2 and CO_2 is often the basis for synthesis of acetate, but in these organisms a variety of other substrates, such as carbon monoxide, formate, or methanol, as well as certain sugars, organic acids, and methoxylated aromatic compounds, can be metabolized (2, 3). *S. termitida* is abundant in the hindgut of certain "higher" termites that are widely distributed. Thus, considering the cellulose decomposition functions of these insects, the significance of these bacteria in the global carbon cycle—of which anaerobic cellulose degradation is an important component—is clearly enormous. The importance of the metabolism of this genus is further dramatized by recognition that *Sporomusa* spp. exist in other anaerobic habitats as free-living anaerobes, and by considering that some *Sporomusa* spp. are even able to obtain energy for growth by decarboxylation of organic acids, another important set of end products of many fermentative bacteria.

Yet another newly described group of gram-negative, anaerobic, endospore-forming bacteria is the genus *Acetonema; Acetonema longum,* a slender rod, is found in the hindgut of a wood-feeding "lower" termite

(*Pterotermes occidentis*) and has a physiology and metabolism akin to that of *Sporomusa* spp. (H_2 and CO_2 are also consumed during its homoacetogenesis). Again, other carbon compounds can serve as substrates for fermentation (23) as well.

Still other studies of different termites, like the soil-feeding *Cubitermes speciosus,* reveal that H_2/CO_2 acetogenesis is a significant property of a *Clostridium* sp. associated with the hindgut function of the termite (22). Since bacteria still presumed to be deserved members of the genus *Clostridium* are also able to carry out such H_2/CO_2 acetogenesis, the impact of such an array of acetogenic spore-forming bacteria on the function of anaerobic habitats is likely to emerge as a dominant consideration as new emphasis is focused on the in situ activites of this physiological type.

Another equally fascinating and exciting development that serves to alter and enlarge our perceptions of the significant roles that spore-forming bacteria play in anaerobic metabolic food chains is the discovery of endosporulation in phototrophic bacteria (26, 34). The heliobacters are unusual not only because they represent the first demonstrated instance of endospores in the physiological category, but also because of the novel bacteriochlorophyll ("*g*") present. Of the four members of the *Heliobacteriaceae* described, two—*Heliobacterium fasciculum* and *Heliobacterium gestii*—form endospores; another member of this genus, *Heliobacterium chlorum,* is not known to do so. As is the case for many other non-sulfur-producing phototrophs, members of this group are able to photometabolize organic acids for their growth; unlike many other phototrophs, however, the heliobacters appear to be more common residents of soils than of aqueous habitats. It will be of significant interest to determine whether the environmental factors affecting endospore formation during phototrophic growth are comparable to those believed to play dominant roles in heterotrophs. Although the walls of heliobacters appear gram-negative as judged by staining, chemical analyses suggest a gram-positive character (e.g., lipopolysaccharide is absent) but with perhaps either a low peptidoglycan content or an unusual chemical composition of the peptidoglycan that is present (26).

Recognition that still other anaerobic spore-forming bacteria play important roles in natural processes is indicated by the names of the genera *Syntrophospora* (53), *Thermoanaerobacter,* and *Thermoanaerobacterium* (25).

WHAT CONSTITUTES THE GENUS *BACILLUS?*

The long-standing discord between the "lumpers" and the "splitters" in taxonomic thinking has been apparent, even for a group of organisms that, at first glance, appeared to have a unique unifying anatomical characteristic in the endospore. It appears certain that the genus *Bacillus* will soon be divided and several new genera created to accommodate the members of the genus. For too long, any respiring isolate that survived a "pasteurization" regimen of exposure to a temperature of 80°C for 10 min and formed visible endospores was denoted a member of the genus *Bacillus.* The range of genomic guanine-plus-cytosine content (32 to 69 mol%), coupled with the wide array of physiological and biochemical phenotypes served to indicate the diversity within the genus (4, 42).

Substrates utilized for growth include cellulose, starch, chitin, agar, proteins, and hydrocarbons, as well as a variety of low-molecular-weight organic compounds. The ability to carry out dinitrogen fixation, nitrification, or denitrification, to oxidize manganese or selenium, and to reduce manganese and to precipitate iron reflects considerable physiological diversity as well. The life-styles of these bacteria include chemolithotrophy as well as chemoorganotrophy, and the range of environments in which they are found includes acidic as well as alkaline ones, and temperatures ranging from cold to hot. Relatively few members of the genus are known to cause disease. A recent compendium (43) of "validly published species" listed 56 members; the list enlarges regularly (35), as witness the recent descriptions of *Bacillus cycloheptanicus* (7) and *Bacillus acidoterris* (6), both of which also figure significantly in phylogenetic considerations (see below).

More recent indications of phylogenetic diversity in the genus are based on rRNA sequencing. A close relationship was indicated among the genera *Bacillus, Planococcus, Staphylococcus,* and *Thermoactinomyces* (46). In another study, *B. subtilis, Bacillus cereus,* and *Bacillus megaterium* of the elliposidal spore group were seen to form a coherent cluster, whereas members of the spherical spore group (*Bacillus sphaericus, Bacillus globisporus,* and "*Bacillus aminovorans*") did not appear to cluster (41). This latter group appeared to be phylogenetically closer to the non-spore-forming bacteria *Caryophanon latum, Filibacter limicola,* and *Planococcus citreus,* respectively. *Bacillus pasteurii* was judged to be closely related to the spore-forming coccus *Sporosarcina ureae;* both also happen to grow well in alkaline environments. The thermophile *Bacillus stearothermophilus* did not form a cluster with the main *Bacillus* group, but appeared to be related to *Thermoactinomyces vulgaris,* also noted for its thermophilic traits as well as endospore formation. Three major clusters were defined based on sequences of more than 1,100 nucleotides of the 16S rRNA of some 35 different reference strains of the genus—a *B. subtilis* cluster with 19 species, a *Bacillus alvei* cluster with 6, and one for *Bacillus brevis* which contained just 2 species. A fourth cluster, a "*Bacillus cycloheptanicus* branch," has also been suggested by these studies (37, 50).

Using a similar approach, but focusing on the small subunit rRNA sequences, Ash et al. (1) argue for five phylogenetically distinct clusters in the strains they studied. Taken together, the two sets of results, even though not in total agreement, make apparent the real need for serious consideration of taxonomic revision of the genus *Bacillus* with a view to establishing not merely determinative distinctions, but rather phylogenetic relationships. Consideration of the latter may provide insights into the evolutionary origin(s) of endospore formation. As suggested earlier in this chapter, the diversity seen in endspore structure and in the physiological activities and anatomical features of the organisms that form the spores may cause us to be concerned about the supposed unity of factors affecting or regulating endospore formation or germination. Concern with such possible relationships may also provide insights into the significance of such features as the presence of alicyclic fatty acids in some spore-formers, as represented by the proposed new genus *Alicyclobacillus* (51).

The interplay between phylogenetic implications derived from consideration of phenotypic traits and those derived from analyses of presumably ancient chronometers (rRNA) may be complicated, or constrained, by the prospects of genetic exchanges occurring at the present time. Plasmids and bacteriophages for *Bacillus* spp. abound (21, 43). These have been employed usefully in studies of the genetics of sporulation and as vectors in recombinant DNA technology for production of commerically useful products (29). However, whether either plasmids or phage are significant in effecting substantial genetic exchange in natural habitats is somewhat uncertain. Strong evidence exists for interaction between different *Bacillus* species and their viruses, and for the effects of environmental factors that may alter the sensitive relationships between viruses and host cells (36). Using genetically labeled strains of *B. subtilis* growing together in soils, Graham and Istock (16) have demonstrated the exchange of blocks of linked genes. Transfer of DNA, both between and within species, is known (5, 11, 12, 14, 28, 47–49). Taken together these prospective mechanisms for genetic exchange may have as yet unrecognized effects on identification of new isolates from various natural habitats. The loss of characteristics, reflecting plasmid loss for example, may also have unrecognized effects and taxonomic implications. Perhaps, then, it will not be surprising if we come to learn that apparently phylogenetically related organisms may have quite different key physiological traits and may fill quite diverse niches.

EVOLUTION OF ENDOSPORE FORMATION

As we have earlier argued (45), "conventional considerations of the evolution of spore-formers usually have revolved around the spore's resistance to stress, particularly the dramatic resistance to heat. In any evolutionary assessment there is difficulty in knowing whether natural selection has indeed operated on, or for, a given trait or whether the trait has been co-selected with an unperceived but evolutionarily significant one." It seems quite likely that if we understood the basis of spore heat resistance on the one hand, or resistance to lysis, desiccation, or radiation on the other, we could be in a better position to contemplate what selective factors might have been operating and might have led to the clearly complex set of events that transpire in the cell and culminate in the formation of a new potential or incipient cell-within-a-cell.

In a thoughtful consideration of the basis for and significance of spore heat resistance, Murrell (31) noted that

> an adequate explanation of the chemical and biophysical basis of heat resistance needs to explain (i) the increase in heat resistance of the vegetative cell-to-spore transition, and (ii) the large range in heat resistance of different species of spores. Most bacteria form spores roughly similar in cytological composition and in (dipicolinic acid) contents and yet the spores differ in their level of heat resistance by as much as 100,000 times. What is the basis for this difference? It is clear that there is no single chemical determinant that can explain both aspects of heat resistance. Rather, the spore is a complex cytological and chemical structure whose properties, and in particular heat resistance, depend on the integrity and necessary complementation of many structural components and chemical constituents. Most of these are known to be involved both in formation of a heat resistant spore and in inter-species differences in heat resistance.

The mechanisms of spore thermoresistance remain enigmatic despite extensive studies (13, 32), but they clearly involve such factors as dehydration (13), mineralization events (27), alteration of membrane structural and functional properties (24), and protective effects of certain proteins (39, 41). It would seem certain that, although other imposed insults or stresses have not been nearly so well studied, the basis for spore heat resistance to these will also be multifactorial.

The difficulty in understanding just which spore structural or chemical traits are involved in resistance to heat or other stresses is related to the manner in which the stress damage or response is necessarily assessed. The spore must be able to germinate and proceed through outgrowth to form a vegetative cell, and that cell must multiply scores of times before the appearance of a visible colony that can be scored, thus indicating the survivorship of the stressed spore. For example, the level of heat and UV resistance attained by spores and their vegetative cells has been partly affected by the efficiency or effectiveness of DNA repair (17); survivorship thus depends on both the degree of protection of essential structures and macromolecules and the ability to recover from and repair any induced injury (20). Setlow (39) has noted that protection and repair of spore DNA affects the ability of spores to survive long periods of time in a dormant state. Damage to DNA seems deterred by decreased spore water content, and this retards chemical reactions affecting DNA. Small, acid-soluble spore proteins bind to the DNA and serve to dampen DNA reactivity. Finally, DNA repair processes play a role. There is ample evidence that DNA damage occurs upon exposure of spores to heat (33); an example is the induction of mutations (52). It is not unreasonable to suppose that mechanisms proposed by Setlow and colleagues (40) will be shown to be involved in spore thermoresistance. Involvement of small, acid-soluble spore proteins in UV resistance in spores has been demonstrated (40). Perhaps, as we have previously speculated (44), "in evolutionary terms, might the goal of the sporulating cell not only be 'to parcel in an insulated chamber the functioning unit of chromatin' (9) but to partition sufficient DNA to increase its odds for survival?" Perhaps *this* is what dormancy is really all about (40)?

The "alternate means of packaging genetic information" view provides another way of thinking about the origins of endosporulation: rather than a nonsporulating cell evolving into one capable of endospore formation, might not a primitive replicating system have acquired protection against environmental stresses by acquisition of (i) a cortex (which does, after all, have some chemical similarity to the peptidoglycan of a cell wall) and (ii) biodegradation-resistant spore coats?

Since sporulation may be considered a modified form of cell division (18) (a view increasingly supported by molecular genetic evidence [8]), the "alternate packaging" notion becomes additionally attractive. As implied earlier in this chapter, continued assessment of phylogenetic relationships of the many bacteria that form endospores may give new insights into mono- versus polyphyletic origin(s) of spore formation or provide new outlooks on (i) a proposed evolutionary link between eukaryotes and prokaryotes or (ii) a view that the forespore was the evolutionary precursor of the gram-negative cell (summarized in reference 44).

The significance of the (putative) antiquity of bacterial endospores has long been the subject of speculation from many biological points of view, and interest in dormancy (and even a fear of it!) is far from dormant. Perhaps studies employing polymerase chain reaction and nucleic acid sequencing approaches will combine to shed light on the origins of the endospore.

REFERENCES

1. **Ash, C., J. A. E. Farrow, S. Wallbanks, and M. D. Collins.** 1991. Phylogenetic heterogeneity of the genus *Bacillus* revealed by comparative analysis of small subunit ribosomal RNA sequences. *Lett. Appl. Microbiol.* **13:**202–206.
2. **Breznak, J. A.** 1992. The genus *Sporomusa,* p. 2014–2021. *In* A. Balows, H. G. Trüper, M. Dworkin, W. Harder, and K. H. Schleifer (ed.), *The Prokaryotes,* 2nd ed. Springer-Verlag, New York.
3. **Breznak, J. A., and J. S. Blum.** 1991. Mixotrophy in the termite gut acetogen, *Sporomusa termitida. Arch. Microbiol.* **156:**105–110.
4. **Claus, D., and R. C. W. Berkeley.** 1986. The genus *Bacillus,* p. 1105–1139. *In* P. H. A. Sneath (ed.), *Bergey's Manual of Systematic Bacteriology,* vol. 2. The Williams & Wilkins Co., Baltimore.
5. **Cornelis, P., C. Digneffe, and K. Willemot.** 1982. Cloning and expression of a *Bacillus coagulans* amylase gene in *Escherichia coli. Mol. Gen. Genet.* **186:**507–511.
6. **Deinhard, G., P. Blanz, K. Poralla, and E. Altan.** 1987. *Bacillus acidoterrestris* sp. nov., a new thermotolerant acidophile isolated from different soils. *Syst. Appl. Microbiol.* **10:**47–53.
7. **Deinhard, G., J. Saar, W. Krischke, and K. Poralla.** 1987. *Bacillus cycloheptanicus* sp. nov., a new thermoacidophile containing w-cycloheptane fatty acids. *Syst. Appl. Microbiol.* **10:**68–73.
8. **Errington, J.** 1993. *Bacillus subtilis* sporulation: regulation of gene expression and control of morphogenesis. *Microbiol. Rev.* **57:**1–33.
9. **Fitz-James, P. C.** 1957. Discussion on cytological changes during germination, p. 85–92. *In* H. O. Halvorson (ed.), *Spores.* American Institute of Biological Sciences, Washington, D.C.
10. **Foster, J. W.** 1956. Morphogenesis in bacteria: some aspects of spore formation. *Q. Rev. Biol.* **31:**102–118.
11. **Fuji, M., T. Imanaka, and S. Aiba.** 1982. Molecular cloning and expression of penicillinase genes from *Bacillus licheniformis* in the thermophile *Bacillus stearothermophilus. J. Gen. Microbiol.* **128:**2997–3000.
12. **Ganesan, S., H. Kamdar, K. Jayaraman, and J. Szulmajster.** 1983. Cloning and expression in *Escherichia coli* of a DNA fragment from *Bacillus sphaericus* coding for biocidal activity against mosquito larvae. *Mol. Gen. Genet.* **189:**181–182.
13. **Gerhardt, P., and R. E. Marquis.** 1989. Spore thermo-resistance mechanisms, p. 43–64. *In* I. Smith, R. A. Slepecky, and P. Setlow (ed.), *Regulation of Procaryotic Development: Structural and Functional Analysis of Bacterial Sporulation and Generation.* American Society for Microbiology, Washington, D.C.
14. **Gonzalez, J. M., Jr., B. J. Brown, and B. C. Carlton.** 1982. Transfer of *Bacillus thuringiensis* plasmids coding for delta-endotoxin among strains of *B. thuringiensis* and *B. cereus. Proc. Natl. Acad. Sci. USA* **79:**6951–6955.
15. **Gottschalk, G., and S. Peinemann.** 1992. The anaerobic way of life, p. 300–311. *In* A. Balows, H. G. Trüper, M. Dworkin, W. Harder, and K. H. Schleifer (ed.), *The Prokaryotes,* 2nd ed. Springer-Verlag, New York.
16. **Graham, J. B., and C. A. Istock.** 1978. Genetic exchange in *Bacillus subtilis* in soil. *Mol. Gen. Genet.* **166:**287–290.

17. **Hanlin, J. H., S. J. Lombardi, and R. A. Slepecky.** 1985. Heat and UV light resistance of vegetative cells and spores of *Bacillus subtilis* Rec^- mutants. *J. Bacteriol.* **163:**774–777.
18. **Hitchins, A. D., and R. A. Slepecky.** 1969. Bacterial sporulation as a modified procaryotic cell division. *Nature* (London) **223:**804–807.
19. **Holt, S. C., and E. R. Leadbetter.** 1969. Comparative ultrastructure of selected aerobic spore-forming bacteria: a freeze-etching study. *Bacteriol. Rev.* **33:**346–378.
20. **Hurst, A.** 1983. Injury, p. 255–275. *In* A. Hurst and G. W. Gould (ed.), *The Bacterial Spore,* vol. 2. Academic Press, Inc., New York.
21. **Imanaka, T., M. Fujii, and S. Aiba.** 1981. Isolation and characterization of antibiotic resistance plasmids from thermophilic bacilli and construction of deletion plasmids. *J. Bacteriol.* **146:**1091–1097.
22. **Kane, M. D., A. Brauman, and J. A. Breznak.** 1991. *Clostridium mayombei* sp. nov., an H_2/CO_2 acetogenic bacterium from the gut of the African soli-feeding termite, *Cubitermes speciosus. Arch. Microbiol.* **156:**99–104.
23. **Kane, M. D., and J. A. Breznak.** 1991. *Acetonema longum* gen. nov. sp. nov., an H_2/CO_2 acetogenic bacterium from the termite, *Pterotermes occidentis. Arch. Microbiol.* **156:**91–98.
24. **Khoury, P. H., S. L. Lombardi, and R. A. Slepecky.** 1987. The perturbation of the heat resistance of bacterial spores by sporulation temperatures and ethanol. *Curr. Microbiol.* **15:**15–19.
25. **Lee, Y.-E., M. K. Jain, C. Lee, S. E. Lowe, and J. G. Zeikus.** 1993. Taxonomic distinction of saccharolytic thermophilic anaerobes: description of *Thermoanaerobacterium xylanolyticum* gen. nov., sp. nov., and *Thermoanaerobacterium saccharolyticum* gen. nov., sp. nov.; reclassification of *Thermoanaerobium brockii, Clostridium thermosulfurogenes,* and *Clostridium thermohydrosulfuricum* E-100–69 as *Thermoanaerobacter brockii* comb. nov., *Thermoanaerobacterium thermosulfurigenes* comb. nov., and *Thermoanaerobacter thermohydrosulfuricus* comb. nov., respectively; and transfer of *Clostridium thermohydrosulfuricum* 39E to *Thermoanaerobacter ethanolicus. Int. J. Syst. Bacteriol.* **43:**41–51.
26. **Madigan, M.** 1992. The family *Heliobacteriaceae,* p. 1981–1992. *In* A. Balows, H. G. Trüper, M. Dworkin, W. Harder, and K. H. Schleifer (ed.), *The Prokaryotes,* 2nd ed. Springer-Verlag, New York.
27. **Marquis, R. E.** 1989. Minerals and bacterial spores, p. 147–161. *In* T. J. Beveridge and R. J. Doyle (ed.), *Bacterial Interactions with Metal Ions.* John Wiley & Sons, Inc., New York.
28. **Martin, P. A. W., J. R. Lohr, and D. H. Dean.** 1981. Transformation of *Bacillus thuringiensis* protoplasts by plasmid deoxyribonucleic acid. *J. Bacteriol.* **145:** 980–983.
29. **Miteva, V. I., N. I. Shivarov, and R. T. Grivorv.** 1981. Transformation of *Bacillus thuringiensis* protoplasts by plasmid DNA. *FEMS Microbiol. Lett.* **12:**253–256.
30. **Moller, B., R. Ossmer, B. H. Howard, G. Gottschalk, and H. Hippe.** 1984. *Sporomusa,* a new genus of gram-negative anaerobic bacteria including *Sporomusa sphaeroides* spec. nov. and *Sporomusa ovata* spec. nov. *Arch. Microbiol.* **139:**388–396.
31. **Murrell, W. G.** 1969. Chemical composition of spores and spore structures, p. 215–273. *In* G. W. Gould and A. Hurst (ed.), *The Bacterial Spore.* Academic Press Ltd., London.

32. **Murrell, W. G.** 1988. Bacterial spores—nature's ultimate survival package, p. 311–346. *In* W. G. Murrell and I. R. Kennedy (ed.), *Microbiology in Action*. John Wiley & Sons, Inc., New York.
33. **Northrop, J., and R. A. Slepecky.** 1967. Sporulation mutations induced by heat in *Bacillus subtilis*. *Science* **155:**838–839.
34. **Omerod, J. T., T. Nesbakken, and Y. Torgersen.** 1990. Phototrophic bacteria that form heat-resistant endospores. *In* M. Baltscheffsky (ed.), *Proceedings of the VIIIth International Congress on Photosynthesis*. Kluwer Academic Publishers, Dordrecht, The Netherlands.
35. **Priest, F. G.** 1993. Systematics and ecology of *Bacillus*, p. 3–16. *In* A. L. Sonenshein, J. A. Hoch, and R. Losick (ed.), *Bacillus subtilis and Other Gram-Positive Bacteria*. American Society for Microbiology, Washington, D.C.
36. **Reanney, D. C., and C. K. Teh.** 1976. Mapping pathways of possible phage-mediated genetic interchange among soil bacilli. *Soil Biol. Biochem.* **8:**305–311.
37. **Rossler, D., W. Ludwig, K. H. Schleifer, C. Lin, T. J. McGill, J. D. Wisotzkey, P. Jurtshuk, Jr., and G. E. Fox.** 1991. Phylogenetic diversity in the genus *Bacillus* as seen by 16S rRNA sequencing studies. *Syst. Appl. Microbiol.* **14:**266–269.
38. **Schink, B.** 1992. Syntrophism among prokaryotes, p. 276–299. *In* A. Balows, H. G. Trüper, M. Dworkin, W. Harder, and K. H. Schleifer (ed.), *The Prokaryotes*, 2nd ed. Springer-Verlag, New York.
39. **Setlow, P.** 1988. Small, acid-soluble spore proteins of *Bacillus* species: structure, synthesis, genetics, function and degradation. *Annu. Rev. Microbiol.* **42:**319–338.
40. **Setlow, P.** 1992. I will survive: protecting and repairing spore DNA. *J. Bacteriol.* **174:**2737–2741.
41. **Siefert, J. L., J. D. Wisotzkey, P. Jurtshuk, Jr., and G. L. Fox.** 1993. 16S rRNA sequence analysis on round-spore forming *Bacillus* species and related non-spore forming bacteria, p. 74. Abstr. 93rd Gen. Meet. Am. Soc. Microbiol. 1993. American Society for Microbiology, Washington, D. C.
42. **Slepecky, R. A.** 1992. What is a *Bacillus?* p. 1–21. *In* R. H. Doi and M. McGloughlin (ed.), *Biology of Bacilli: Applications to Industry*. Butterworth-Heinemann, Boston.
43. **Slepecky, R. A., and H. E. Hemphill.** 1992. The genus *Bacillus*—nonmedical, p. 1663–1696. *In* A. Balows, H. G. Trüper, M. Dworkin, W. Harder, and K. H. Schleifer (ed.), *The Prokaryotes*, 2nd ed. Springer-Verlag, New York.
44. **Slepecky, R. A., and E. R. Leadbetter.** 1977. The diversity of spore-forming bacteria: some ecological implications, p. 869–877. *In* A. N. Barker, J. Wolf, D. J. Ellar, G. J. Bring, and G. W. Gould (ed.), *Spore Research*. Academic Press Ltd., London.
45. **Slepecky, R. A., and E. R. Leadbetter.** 1984. On the prevalence and roles of spore-forming bacteria in nature: some ecological implications, p. 76–99. *In* A. Hurst and G. W. Gould (ed.), *The Bacterial Spore*, vol. 2. Academic Press Ltd., London.
46. **Stackebrandt, E., W. Ludwig, M. Weizenegger, S. Dorn, T. J. McGill, G. E. Fox, C. R. Woese, W. Schubert, and K. H. Schleifer.** 1987. Comparative 16S rRNA oligonucleotide analyses and murine type of round-spore-forming bacilli and non-spore-forming relatives. *J. Gen. Microbiol.* **133:**2523–2529.
47. **Takahashi, W., H. Yamagata, K. Yamaguchi, N. Tsukagoshi, and S. Udake.** 1983. Genetic transformation of *Bacillus brevis* 47, a protein secreting bacterium, by plasmid DNA. *J. Bacteriol.* **156:**1130–1134.

48. **Vary, P. S., J. C. Garbe, M. Franzen, and E. W. Frampton.** 1982. MP13, a generalized transducing bacteriophage for *Bacillus megaterium. J. Bacteriol.* **149:** 112–119.
49. **Vorobjeva, I. P., I. A. Khmel, and L. Alfoldi.** 1980. Transformation of *Bacillus megaterium* protoplasts by plasmid DNA. *FEMS Microbiol. Lett.* **7:**216–263.
50. **Wisotzkey, J. D., P. Jurtshuk, Jr., and G. E. Fox.** 1989. Comparative 16S rRNA analyses on thermophilic and psychrophilic bacillus species, p. 281. Abstr. 89th Annu. Meet. Am. Soc. Microbiol. 1989. American Society for Microbiology, Washington, D.C.
51. **Wisotzkey, J. D., P. Jurtshuk, Jr., G. E. Fox, G. Deinhard, and K. Poralla.** 1992. Comparative sequence analyses on the 16S rRNA (rDNA) of *Bacillus acidocaldarius, Bacillus acidoterrestris,* and *Bacillus cycloheptanicus* and proposal for creation of a new genus, *Alicyclobacillus* gen. nov. *Int. J. Syst. Bacteriol.* **42:** 263–269.
52. **Zamenhof, S.** 1960. Effects of heating dry bacteria and spores on their phenotype and genotype. *Proc. Natl. Acad. Sci. USA* **46:**101–105.
53. **Zhao, H., D. Yang, C. R. Woese, and M. P. Bryant.** 1993. Assignment of fatty acid-b-oxidizing syntrophic bacteria to *Syntrophomonadaceae* fam. nov., on the basis of 16S rRNA sequence analysis. *Int. J. Syst. Bacteriol.* **43:**278–286.

Regulation of Bacterial Differentiation
Edited by P. Piggot et al.

Chapter 11

A Few Good Genes: Developmental Loci in *Bacillus subtilis*

Patrick Stragier

Following the tradition of the last three "Spores" books, this is an inventory of *Bacillus subtilis* developmental genes. Because such a wealth of knowledge has now been accumulated but is scattered among hundreds of papers, I have tried to encapsulate the relevant data in a form as comprehensive and concise as possible. Although this chapter is supposed to be "everything you always wanted to know about *spo* but were afraid to ask," I want to stress that it can only be used as a convenient aide-mémoire and as a starting point for further exploration of the literature. It cannot replace the excellent in-depth reviews that are available, many of which can be found in this book and in the recently published "*Bacillus* bible" (177).

All entries in this chapter are organized in the same way (assuming the data are available). First the genetic location is given, including the nearest known marker, which is often a much more reliable information than the "exact" degree on the map (with the remarkable exception of the 137 kb surrounding the replication origin that have been sequenced by N. Ogasawara and his colleagues, and of some regions for which continuous information is available over 20 to 40 kb). I have usually not included any reference for these data because either they are based on classic genetic mapping (and can be found in the genetic map of the "*Bacillus* bible" [1], although the indicated chromosomal location might be slightly different because of additional physical information), or they come from cloning and sequencing studies that are quoted later. Second, the transcription mode is discussed, including kinetics of expression, identification of the cell type in which the locus is transcribed, nature of the sigma factor involved, and description of any specific regulation. Third, sequencing information is provided, including number of cistrons, size of the prod-

---

Patrick Stragier, Institut de Biologie Physico-Chimique, 13 rue Pierre et Marie Curie, 75005 Paris, France.

uct(s) (prior to potential methionine cleavage), and indication of any remarkable characteristics of the encoded protein(s). I have compared many of the predicted products of these "good genes" to the most recent EMBL data library, and I have analyzed the presence of potential membrane-spanning domains in all of them, using a recently described algorithm (204). Fourth, the phenotype of mutations, which sometimes leads to the elucidation of the function of the locus, is included. I have omitted loci that are not actually required for sporulation although they share regulatory mechanisms with bona fide *spo* genes (e.g., genes involved in competence or some genes induced in response to stationary phase), as well as the *out* loci that are involved in resuming vegetative growth after germination. Conversely, I have included all the loci encoding sigma factors to make the point that some are not required for sporulation. Moreover, they are the best genes!

abrB Located at 4°, upstream of and diverging from *metS* (130a).

Transcribed during vegetative growth from two promoters and turned off at the onset of sporulation (142). Both promoters are negatively autoregulated by AbrB, whereas the downstream promoter is also repressed by Spo0A (142, 189).

Encodes a 94-residue protein (142) which behaves as a hexamer in vitro and binds cooperatively to specific DNA sequences (189, 190).

Null mutations in *abrB* lead to constitutive expression of *spo0E* and *spo0H* and to decreased expression of *hpr* but do not interfere with sporulation (188).They are allelic with *cpsX* and suppress some of the phenotypes associated with mutations in the *spo0* genes (65).

bofA Located at 3°, upstream of the *rrnA* operon.

Transcription starts at T_1, presumably in the mother cell, from a σ^E-dependent promoter (79).

Encodes a 87-residue protein containing three putative membrane-spanning segments (79, 155). The first predicted membrane domain is dispensable for BofA activity (155).

A null mutation in *bofA* leads to a slight defect in sporulation and germination by uncoupling pro-σ^K processing from forespore development and allowing premature expression of late sporulation genes (155). It also exaggerates the sporulation defect created by a *kinA* mutation (*bofA* is allelic with *ski4*) (79). BofA appears to be an inhibitor of the pro-σ^K processing machinery (155).

bofB The *bofB5* and *bofB8* alleles are mutations in the carboxy-terminal part of *spoIVFA* (P257S, and Q259*amber*, respectively) (30).

catA The *catA7* allele is a missense mutation at codon 21 of *hpr* (A21D) (140).

cgeA, cgeB Located at 181° (170a).

Divergent operons transcribed presumably in the mother cell, from two σ^K-dependent promoters requiring the GerE protein (156a).

cgeA contains two cistrons encoding CgeAA (133 residues) and CgeAB (317 residues). *cgeB* contains at least one cistron encoding a 101-residue protein (156a).

Disruption of both *cgeA* and *cgeB* does not interfere with sporulation or germination, but deletion of *cgeA* leads to production of spores with altered surface properties (156a).

cotA Located around 52°. Also known as *pig*.

Transcription starts at T_4, in the mother cell, from a σ^K-dependent promoter (164, 219).

Encodes a 65-kDa protein (35) from the outer coat layer (217). Only the first 37 codons have been sequenced (35).

Disruption of *cotA* does not interfere with sporulation or germination but blocks the formation of the brown pigment characteristic of sporulating colonies on agar plates (35).

cotB Located around 290°.

Transcription starts at T_5, in the mother cell, from a σ^K-dependent promoter requiring the GerE protein (218, 219).

Encodes a 59-kDa protein (35) from the outer coat layer (217). Only the first 23 codons have been sequenced (35).

Disruption of *cotB* does not interfere with sporulation or germination (35).

cotC Located around 168°.

Transcription starts at T_5, in the mother cell, from a σ^K-dependent promoter requiring the GerE protein (218, 219). Transcription of *cotC* is strongly enhanced when sporulation is induced by nutrient exhaustion as compared to induction by resuspension (219). This high level of expression requires the presence of wild-type *spoIVA* and *spoVB* loci (147, 219).

Encodes a 66-residue protein, behaving as a 12-kDa polypeptide in denaturing electrophoresis conditions (35). The CotC protein is rich in tyrosine and lysine residues (35) and appears to be part of the outer coat layer (217). CotC seems to be highly related to an 18-kDa coat protein whose gene has not been identified (35).

Disruption of *cotC* does not interfere with sporulation or germination (35).

cotD Located around 200°.

Transcription starts at T_4, in the mother cell, from a σ^K-dependent promoter activated by the GerE protein (219).

Encodes a 75-residue protein, behaving as an 11-kDa polypeptide in denaturing electrophoresis conditions (35). The CotD protein is rich in histidine and cysteine residues (35) and appears to be part of the inner coat layer (217).

Disruption of *cotD* delays the germination response to L-alanine (35).

cotE Located around 150°.

Transcription starts at T_2, in the mother cell, from a σ^E-dependent promoter and switches around T_3 to a downstream σ^E-dependent promoter requiring the SpoIIID protein (219).

Encodes a 181-residue protein, behaving as a 24-kDa polypeptide in denaturing electrophoresis conditions (217). The CotE protein is rich in acidic residues in its carboxy-terminal part (217) and shows some similarity to heme-containing peroxidases (34a).

Disruption of *cotE* leads to the formation of lysozyme-sensitive, slowly germinating spores that lack the outer coat layer (217). Immunoelectron microscopy experiments indicate that CotE accumulates around the forespore outer membrane, where it could act as a basement protein upon which the outer coat layer is assembled (35a).

cotF Located at 356°.

Transcription starts around T_4, presumably from a σ^K-dependent promoter specifically activated in the mother cell (31).

Encodes a 160-residue protein, the precursor of two polypeptides that are generated from its amino- and carboxy-terminal parts by at least two proteolytic cleavages (31). The *cotF* products behave as 5- and 8-kDa polypeptides in denaturing electrophoresis conditions (31).

Disruption of *cotF* does not interfere with sporulation or germination (31).

cotT Located around 108°.

Expression of *cotT* occurs around stage V and does not require the GerE protein, suggesting that *cotT* is transcribed from a σ^K-dependent promoter, presumably in the mother cell (3).

Encodes an 82-residue protein whose amino terminus is processed to generate a 63-residue mature protein that behaves as an 8-kDa polypeptide in denaturing electrophoresis conditions (15). Mature CotT is a prevalent inner coat protein, rich in tyrosine and proline residues, and containing a glycine-rich C-terminal tail (3). Efficient processing of CotT seems to depend on the assembly of the outer spore coat (15).

Disruption of *cotT* does not interfere with sporulation but reduces the inner coat and delays the germination response to a mixture of L-asparagine, glucose, fructose, and KCl (15).

cotX Located around 107°.

Transcription starts around T_4, presumably in the mother cell, from a σ^K-dependent promoter. The *cotX* gene is part of a cluster of genes controlled by σ^K (2a, 216a).

Encodes a 172-residue protein found in the "insoluble fraction" of spore coats (216a).

Disruption of *cotX* does not interfere with sporulation or germination, but alters the surface hydrophobicity of the spores (216a).

crsA The *crsA47* allele is a missense mutation at codon 290 in *rpoD* (*sigA*) (P290F) (91).

dacB Located at 209°, 10 kb upstream of *aroC*.

Transcription occurs only during sporulation, from a σ^E-dependent promoter (17b).

First gene of a three-cistron operon encoding PBP5* (382 residues) and two proteins of unknown function (196 and 179 residues, respectively) (19, 170a). PBP5* contains an amino-terminal, 27-residue signal sequence which is cleaved off. The mature protein is associated with the mother cell membrane and the outer forespore membrane, presumably through a carboxy-terminal amphiphilic α-helix. PBP5* shares several stretches of similarity with other penicillin-binding proteins with DD-peptidase activity (19).

Disruption of *dacB* leads to production of heat-sensitive, lysozyme-resistant, refractile spores (18). In contrast to *dacA*, the gene encoding the major vegetative penicillin-binding protein (PBP5, which is not required for spore formation), *dacB* appears to play an essential role in cortex synthesis (18).

dacF Located at 211°, between a gene encoding a putative purine nucleoside phosphorylase and *spoIIA*.

Transcription starts after asymmetric septation, in the forespore, from a promoter probably recognized by σ^F and σ^G (168a). It proceeds into the downstream *spoIIA* operon (210).

Encodes a 389-residue protein, with a typical 23-residue, amino-terminal signal sequence, showing extensive similarity to penicillin-binding proteins with DD-carboxypeptidase activity (210).

Disruption of *dacF* does not impair sporulation or germination (210).

ftsAZ Located at 134°, 2 kb downstream of *divIB* (*dds*) and just upstream of *bpr*.

Transcribed from three promoters. Two σ^A-dependent promoters, P1 and P3, are active during vegetative growth and are shut off after T_0. A σ^H-dependent promoter, P2, is active during vegetative growth and strongly induced around T_0 (62, 63).

Two-gene operon encoding FtsA (440 residues) and FtsZ (382 residues), the homologs of enzymes controlling initiation of cell division in *Escherichia coli* (8).

Mutations in *ftsAZ* lead to a filamentous phenotype during vegetative growth and prevent sporulation by blocking asymmetric septum formation. FtsZ is essential (the *ts-1* allele maps in *ftsZ*), whereas an in-frame deletion in *ftsA* leads to sick but viable cells (9, 10). Importance of postexponential, enhanced transcription of *ftsAZ* for asymmetric septation seems to depend on the genetic background (62, 63). The missense mutation *ftsA279*(Ts) impairs transcription of *spoIIG*, suggesting that FtsA could play some regulatory role in addition to its role in septation (90).

gdh Located around 34°.

Transcription starts at $T_{2.5}$, in the forespore, from a σ^G-dependent promoter (129, 154).

Second gene of an operon encoding a 285-residue protein (OrfX) and glucose dehydrogenase, a 260-residue protein (102).

Inactivation of *gdh* (as well as of *orfX*) does not interfere with sporulation or germination (154), although glucose dehydrogenase might be involved in metabolism of the glucose added to germinating spores.

gerA Located at 289°, upstream of and diverging from *citG*.

Transcription starts at T_3, in the forespore, from a σ^G-dependent promoter (49).

Three-gene operon encoding GerAA (480 residues), GerAB (364 residues), and GerAC (373 residues). The three proteins are predicted to contain membrane-spanning domains (5, 10, and 1, respectively), the GerAC unique membrane segment having features of a lipoprotein signal peptide (50, 222).

The *gerA* mutants are defective in their germination response to L-alanine, L-valine, and cycloserine. The blockage is at the earliest stage of germination, suggesting that the *gerA* locus encodes a membrane-located receptor for L-alanine (122).

gerB Located at 314°, close to *lytD*.

Transcription starts at T_3, presumably in the forespore, from a σ^G-dependent promoter (25a).

Three-gene operon encoding GerBA (482 residues), GerBB (367 residues), and GerBC (374 residues). The three proteins are similar to the corresponding proteins of the *gerA* operon, and they share the same hydrophobicity characteristics (25a).

The *gerB* mutants are defective in their germination response to a mixture of L-asparagine, glucose, fructose, and KCl but respond normally to L-alanine (122). The blockage is at the earliest stage of germination, suggesting that the *gerB* locus encodes a membrane-located receptor for germinants other than L-alanine (122).

gerC Located at 204°, between *mtrB* and *ndk*.

Three-gene operon encoding GerCA (251 residues), GerCB (233 residues), and GerCC (348 residues) (69a). All three proteins appear to be hydrophilic. GerCB is similar throughout its length to the product of an *E. coli* open reading frame of unknown function located at 96 min on the *E. coli* genetic map. GerCC contains long stretches of similarity with several bacterial enzymes involved in condensation of precursors for isoprenoid lipids (69a).

The original *gerC58* mutant displays a temperature-sensitive germination response to L-alanine. It contains two mutations, the *gerCC58* mutation itself causing cells to grow poorly on minimal medium and not at all on rich media, whereas a suppressor mutation restores near-normal growth. The unsuppressed mutant shows gross morphological abnormalities during vegetative growth and misplaced additional division septa (120a).

gerD Located at 15°, in the *rrnI-attSPO2* interval (14c).

Transcription starts at $T_{2.5}$, in the forespore, from a σ^G-dependent promoter (92).

Encodes a 185-residue protein containing a putative lipoprotein-like signal peptide (92).

A null mutation in *gerD* leads to a defective germination response to L-alanine and to a mixture of L-asparagine, glucose, fructose, and KCl. Blockage is at an early stage of germination, prior to loss of heat resistance (122).

gerE Located at 251°, 0.6 kb downstream of the *sdhCAB* operon.

Transcription starts at T_4, in the mother cell, from a σ^K-dependent promoter (29).

Encodes a 74-residue protein (27) similar to the C-terminal region of transcriptional activators belonging to the FixJ family (86). GerE stimulates transcription from some σ^K-dependent promoters while repressing transcription from some others (218).

A null mutation in *gerE* abolishes *cotB* and *cotC* transcription and impairs transcription of *cotD* (219). It leads to the production of lysozyme-sensitive, germination-defective spores with aberrant coat ultrastructure (51).

gerF Located around 301°.

Defined by the *ger-21* and *ger-45* mutations that lead to defective germination response to L-alanine and to a mixture of L-asparagine, glucose, fructose, and KCl. Blockage is at an early stage of germination, prior to loss of heat resistance (121). The locus has not been cloned.

gerG Located around 294°.

Encodes phosphoglycerate kinase. Absence of this enzyme leads to inefficient sporulation and poor germination in L-alanine (149). The locus has not been cloned.

gerH Located around 246°.

Status of this locus is uncertain since a preliminary report (146) was not followed by publication of detailed information.

gerI Located around 296°.

Status of this locus is uncertain since a preliminary report (146) was not followed by publication of detailed information. It might be identical to *gerF*.

gerJ Located at 206°.

Transcription starts at $T_{1.5}$ (122).

Germination of a *gerJ* null mutant is blocked after the loss of heat resistance induced by exposure to L-alanine or to a mixture of L-asparagine, glucose, fructose, and KCl. Sporulation is also affected, since resistance properties develop later than normal. Both phenotypes could be due to a defect in cortex biosynthesis (122). Allele *gerJ51* is present in many laboratory strains. The locus has been cloned (122).

gerK Located around 32°.

Encodes a protein similar to GerAC and GerBC (80a).

The *gerK* mutants are defective in their germination response to a mixture of L-asparagine, glucose, fructose, and KCl, but respond normally to L-alanine (122). The blockage is at the earliest stage of germination, suggesting that the *gerK* product is part of a receptor for germinants other than L-alanine (122).

gerM Located at 251°, 2 kb downstream of *gerE*.

Transcription starts at $T_{1.5}$ (161).

Encodes a 210-residue protein containing a putative lipoprotein-like signal peptide (172a).

Defined by a Tn*917* insertion that leads to an oligosporogenous phenotype, some cells being blocked at stage II with multiple polar septa. Spores initiate germination normally but fail to hydrolyze cortex completely (161).

gpr Located around 210°.

Transcription starts at T_2, in the forespore, from a σ^F-dependent promoter. The same promoter is recognized by σ^G after completion of engulfment (135, 197).

Encodes a 368-residue protein, the endoprotease that initiates degradation of the small, acid-soluble spore proteins (SASPs) during the first minutes of germination (197). Gpr is synthesized as an inactive precursor which becomes processed of its first 16 amino acids around stage VI of sporulation and of an additional N-terminal residue early in germination (163). Processing takes place at a site very similar to the sequence recognized by Gpr in SASPs, suggesting that Gpr is able to autoproteolyze itself at a late stage of sporulation (163).

Disruption of *gpr* does not interfere with sporulation or with the first steps of germination. However, it delays outgrowth, a phenotype that is suppressed by inactivation of *sspA* and *sspB*, the genes encoding the major α/β-type SASPs (162).

gsiA Located around 115°.

Transcription is induced by nutrient limitation and initiates at an atypical σ^A-dependent promoter requiring the ComA activator and its cognate histine kinase ComP, but independent of any sporulation-associated gene (125). In nutrient sporulation medium transcription is shut off at T_1 (125).

Two-cistron operon encoding GsiAA (346 residues) and GsiAB (44 residues). There is no evidence that *gsiAB* is expressed.

A null mutation in *gsiA* does not prevent spore formation, but sporulation becomes insensitive to glucose repression (125). It also suppresses a *kinA* defect, suggesting that in the absence of the *gsiA* product(s) Spo0A is efficiently phosphorylated by other kinases than KinA (126).

gsiC The *gsiC82* allele is a missense mutation at codon 288 of *kinA* (W288R) (126).

hpr Located around 75°, in the *glyB-glpD* interval.

Transcription increases during vegetative growth and is maintained during early sporulation (140). Expression is strongly enhanced in a *spo0A* mutant (140), presumably as a consequence of the increased amount of AbrB, an activator of *hpr* transcription (188).

Encodes a 203-residue protein, which binds in vitro to the promoter region of *aprE*, *nprE*, and *sin* (87).

A null mutation in *hpr* leads to overproduction of extracellular alkaline and neutral proteases and renders sporulation insensitive to glucose repression (*hpr* is allelic with *scoC* and *catA*) (140). Overproduction of Hpr severely inhibits sporulation (140).

kinA Located at 118°, 9 kb downstream of *ptsI*.

Transcribed during vegetative growth from a σ^H-dependent promoter (2, 150). Transcription is shut off around T_0 (2, 150), perhaps as a consequence of Spo0A binding downstream of the *kinA* promoter (72).

Encodes a 606-residue protein strongly similar to the transmitter class of histidine kinases (2, 137). KinA is able to autophosphorylate in vitro, a reaction inhibited by *cis*-unsaturated fatty acids, and to transfer its phosphate to Spo0F (20, 187).

A null mutation in *kinA* delays sporulation-associated events and reduces spore formation to a level that strongly depends on the genetic background (64a). *kinA* (previously *spoIIJ*) is allelic with *spoIIF*, *scoB*, *scoD*, and *gsiC* (1, 126).

kinB Located around 277°.

Transcribed during vegetative growth from an atypical σ^A- dependent promoter (202).

First gene of a two-cistron operon encoding KinB (428 residues) and KapB (128 residues). KinB has strong similarity with the transmitter class of histidine kinases and is predicted to contain six membrane-spanning domains (202).

A null mutation in *kinB* does not interfere with sporulation, but it severely reduces spore formation when combined with a *kinA* mutation. A null mutation in *kapB* has the same phenotype (202). KinB is able to phosphorylate Spo0A through a biochemical pathway that requires the presence of Spo0F and Spo0B (72).

scoC The *scoC4* allele is an *amber* mutation at codon 22 of *hpr* (140).

sigA Located at 222°. Also known as *rpoD*.

Transcribed during vegetative growth from tandem σ^A-dependent promoters located upstream of the *sigA* operon. Transcribed during transition to stationary phase by two σ^H-dependent promoters located in the first gene and in the beginning of the second gene of the *sigA* operon (151, 207). The *csh-203* mutation is a Tn*917* insertion between the two σ^H-dependent promoters of *sigA* (64a). A fifth promoter located upstream of the *sigA* operon is activated between T_3 and T_5 (152).

Last cistron of a three-gene operon encoding P23 (a 196-residue protein of unknown function), the DNA primase DnaG (603 residues), and the major sigma factor σ^A (previously σ^{43} or σ^{55}, 371 residues) (206).

Essential gene. The *rpoD47* (previously *crsA47*) mutation is a missense mutation that allows sporulation in the presence of glucose and suppresses the requirement for KinA (108). This phenotype could be due to enhanced transcription of the sporulation activator *spo0A* and decreased transcription of the sporulation inhibitor *sin*, by σ^A(P290F)-associated RNA polymerase (108).

sigB Located at 39°. Transiently known as *rpoF*.

Transcription starts at the onset of stationary phase, from a σ^B-dependent promoter (88). Some transcription also originates from an upstream operon (88).

Third cistron of a four-gene operon encoding RsbV (109 residues), RsbW (160 residues), σ^B (previously σ^{37}, 262 residues), and RsbX (199 residues) (88). σ^B is inactivated by binding of RsbW (12) and is released through the action of RsbV (11, 17), whereas RsbX plays an additional inhibitory role (11, 17). The first three products of the *sigB* operon are similar to their *spoIIA* operon counterparts (88).

Disruption of *sigB* does not interfere with sporulation and does not create any obvious phenotype (13, 38).

sigD Located at 142°.

Transcribed from a σ^A-dependent promoter located upstream of the *sigD* operon (14). Synthesis of the *sigD* product increases during vegetative growth and is shut off around T_1 (20a).

Last cistron of a 30-gene operon, the major *che-fla* locus (14). Allelic with *flaB*. Encodes σ^D (previously σ^{28}, 254 residues) (69).

Disruption of *sigD* prevents flagellar synthesis, motility, and chemotaxis; reduces autolysin synthesis; and induces filamentation. It does not interfere with sporulation (69, 113).

sigE The gene encoding σ^E (previously σ^{29}), *spoIIGB*.

sigF The gene encoding σ^F, *spoIIAC*.

sigG The gene encoding σ^G, *spoIIIG*.

sigH The gene encoding σ^H (previously σ^{30}), *spo0H*.

sigK The gene encoding σ^K (previously σ^{27}), which is created by splicing of *spoIVCB* and *spoIIIC*, after excision of the *skin* element (186). σ^K (221 residues) is produced by processing of the N-terminal 20 amino acids from the inactive precursor pro-σ^K (95, 186).

sigL Located at 295°, in the *cysB-sacB* interval.

Encodes σ^L (436 residues), a member of the σ^{54} family (34).

Disruption of *sigL* prevents transcription of the levanase operon, as well as growth on arginine, ornithine, isoleucine, and valine as sole nitrogen sources, presumably by shutting off transcription of some amino acid permeases. It does not interfere with sporulation (34).

sin Located at 221°.

Transcribed from three promoters (58). P1, located upstream of the *sin* operon, functions at a low level during growth (presumably because of repression by AbrB and Hpr) and is activated around T_0 (apparently through binding of Spo0A) (58, 173, 188). This enhanced transcription leads to higher expression of the first *sin* cistron, whereas the second *sin* cistron is mostly unaffected (58). P2, also located upstream of the *sin* operon, is defined by the appearance at T_2 of new transcripts that could result from processing of mRNAs initiated at P1 (58, 173). P3, located between the two *sin* cistrons, is constitutively active during growth and early sporulation, but the corresponding mRNAs are very poorly translated (58, 110). Both P1 and P3 are σ^A-dependent promoters (173).

Two-gene operon encoding SinI (57 residues) and SinR (previously Sin, 111 residues) (59). *sinR* is allelic with *flaD* (170). SinR contains a helix-turn-helix motif in its amino-terminal part (59), a domain which shares an overall extensive similarity with the corresponding region of bacteriophage ϕ105 repressor (174). SinR has DNA-binding properties in vitro (60). SinI and SinR interact with each other, presumably through a conserved region present in their carboxy-terminal parts (5).

A null mutation in *sinR* leads to earlier and higher transcription of *spoIIA*, *spoIIE*, and *spoIIG* (110). It also reduces competence, motility, and autolysin synthesis, all phenotypes that can be explained by repression or activation of gene expression mediated by binding of SinR to various DNA targets (173). Conversely, an in-frame deletion in *sinI* (or overexpression of *sinR*) leads to reduced expression of *spoIIA*, *spoIIE*, and *spoIIG*, and to an oligosporogenous phenotype, which reflects the antagonistic role played by SinI on SinR function (5).

spl Located at 118°, 0.4 kb downstream of *ptsI*.

Transcription studies have not been reported, but the *spl* product is known to be present in mature spores (46).

Encodes a 342-residue protein, the spore photoproduct lyase, which shows local similarity with various microbial DNA photolyases (46). It is involved in repairing upon germination the damage created by UV irradiation in spore DNA.

Inactivation of *spl,* in conjunction with a mutation in *uvr* (which mediates the general repair pathway), leads to formation of spores that exhibit extreme UV sensitivity (127).

spo0A Located at 218°, downstream of *spoIVB.*

Transcribed during vegetative growth from two promoters, a σ^A-dependent promoter that is turned off around T_0, and a σ^H-dependent promoter that is substantially activated at the onset of stationary phase (22, 150). This promoter switching is controlled by binding of Spo0A itself to the *spo0A* regulatory region (191).

Encodes a 267-residue protein which belongs to the receiver class of two-component regulatory systems (53, 96). Spo0A can be efficiently phosphorylated in vitro by Spo0B~P, presumably at the aspartate residue at position 56 (20). Spo0A can also bind to specific DNA sequences in vitro (167, 192), apparently through its carboxy-terminal region (143).

Null mutations completely block sporulation at the earliest stage. Conversely, many gain-of-function mutations affecting the amino-terminal domain of Spo0A have been described. The *coi* mutations allow sporulation to proceed in catabolite repression conditions, presumably by somehow enhancing the concentration of Spo0A~P (133). The *sof* and *rvtA* mutations suppress null mutations in *spo0B* and *spo0F,* apparently by allowing phosphorylation of Spo0A through an alternate pathway (64a, 178). The *pin* deletions suppress a D56Q mutation in *spo0A* and create a conformational change that makes Spo0A active without phosphorylation (64). The *sad* deletions make Spo0A constitutively active in the absence of the nutritional, cell density, and cell cycle signals normally needed for initiation of sporulation (80).

spo0B Located at 240°, between the *rplU orfX rpmA* and *pheBA* operons.

Transcription occurs during vegetative growth from an atypical σ^A-dependent promoter and is shut off around T_0 (16, 52). Transcription might proceed into the adjacent *pheBA* operon (201).

First cistron of a two-gene operon encoding Spo0B (192 residues) (16, 52) and Obg (428 residues) (201). The Obg protein contains a GTP-binding motif and has GTPase activity (72, 201).

Nonpolar mutations in *spo0B* block sporulation at the earliest stage and are suppressed by secondary mutations in *spo0A* (172, 178). Spo0B is a phosphoprotein which transfers phosphate from Spo0F~P to Spo0A (20). The *obg* gene is essential, and there is no evidence that its product is involved in sporulation (201).

spo0C The *spo0C153* and *spo0C9V* alleles are missense mutations at codon 257 in *spo0A* (A257E and A257V, respectively) (53).

spo0D The *spo0D8* allele is a mutation in *spo0B* (107).

spo0E Located around 115°.

Transcribed from an atypical σ^A-dependent, AbrB-repressed promoter (141). Transcription occurs at a low level during vegetative growth and is induced shortly before the onset of stationary phase (139).

Encodes an 85-residue protein.

Inactivation of *spo0E* does not prevent sporulation, but suppresses a *kinA* mutation and leads to accumulation of Spo$^-$ segregants due to secondary mutations in *spo0A, spo0B,* or *spo0F* (141). Conversely, nonsense mutations in the distal third of *spo0E,* causing synthesis of truncated Spo0E proteins, prevent sporulation, as does over-production of wild-type Spo0E (141). Spo0E appears to play a negative role in the transduction pathway that activates Spo0A, perhaps as a phosphatase for Spo0F~P (72, 141).

spo0F Located at 324°, 0.8 kb downstream of *pyrG* (*ctrA*) and just upstream of *fba1* (*orfY-tsr*).

Mainly transcribed from a σ^H-dependent promoter (150). Transcription occurs during vegetative growth, increases sharply around T_0, and is shut off at T_1 (4, 211). Activation of transcription at T_0 is due to binding of Spo0A to the promoter region (193). Some transcription during exponential growth might also originate from an atypical σ^A-dependent promoter (105).

Encodes a 123-residue protein that belongs to the receiver class of two-component regulatory systems (200, 213).

Null mutations in *spo0F* block sporulation at the earliest stage and can be suppressed by secondary mutations in *spo0A* (73, 178). Spo0F can be efficiently phosphorylated in vitro by KinA and can subsequently transfer its phosphate residue to Spo0B (20). Spo0F is also required for phosphorylation of Spo0A by other histidine kinases than KinA (202). The presence of as few as four copies of *spo0F* severely inhibits sporulation (21), presumably by interfering with the flow of phosphate to Spo0A.

spo0G The *spo0G14* allele is a mutation in *spo0A* (107).

spo0H Located at 9°.

Transcribed from a σ^A-dependent, AbrB-repressed promoter (208). Transcription increases during vegetative growth and reaches a maximum at T_0 (208). Additional posttranslational controls govern the intracellular concentration of the *spo0H* product (68).

Encodes σ^H (218 residues), a nonessential sigma factor involved in expression of vegetative and early stationary-phase genes (81).

A null mutation in *spo0H* blocks sporulation before asymmetric septation, presumably by preventing enhanced expression of several genes required for phosphorylation of Spo0A (150). A direct role of σ^H in asymmetric septum synthesis has not been demonstrated.

spo0J Located at 359°, 8.4 kb downstream of *rnpA*.

Transcription increases during vegetative growth, presumably from an atypical σ^A promoter, and is shut off at the onset of stationary phase. It does not depend on *spo0* genes (17a).

Second cistron of a two-gene operon encoding a 253-residue protein of unknown function and Spo0J (282 residues) (128, 131). The first-cistron product contains one or two putative transmembrane domains and is related to the ParA family of ATPases (from plasmids, phages, or bacteria), which are often involved in chromosome partitioning (124, 131). Spo0J is highly similar to the product of a 283-codon gene located 1.5 kb upstream of *spo0J*, and is related to KorB, a member of the ParB family of proteins, which control the copy number of some plasmids (124, 128, 131). A homolog of the whole *spo0J* operon is found at the same location on the chromosome of *Pseudomonas putida* (131).

The locus is defined by the *spo0J93* and *spoCM-1* alleles, whereas the "*spo0J87*" allele maps in the *spoIIIJ* gene, located 8 kb upstream of *spo0J* (40, 131). Disruption of *spo0J* reduces sporulation 100-fold (128), but the phenotype of mutations in the *spo0J* homolog (*orf283*) or in the first cistron of the *spo0J* operon has not been reported. A null mutation in *spo0J* is suppressed by the uncharacterized *crsF4* mutation, suggesting that this secondary mutation allows enhanced expression of some function compensating for the absence of Spo0J (128).

spo0K Located at 104°, 1.2 kb upstream of and diverging from *trpS*.

Transcribed from a putative σ^A-dependent promoter (160).

Five-gene operon, encoding Spo0KA (or OppA, 545 residues), Spo0KB (or OppB, 311 residues), Spo0KC (or OppC, 305 residues), Spo0KD (or OppD, 355 residues), and Spo0KE (or OppF, 305 residues) (138, 160). The *spo0K* products are similar to the products of the oligopeptide permease (*opp*) operon of *Salmonella typhimurium* and constitute a peptide transport system (138, 160). Spo0KA contains a putative lipoprotein-like signal peptide and is partially released into the medium (138). Spo0KB and Spo0KC contain several predicted transmembrane domains (6 and 7, respectively). Spo0KD and Spo0KE are similar to each other and contain a potential nucleotide-binding motif (138, 160).

Inactivation of any of the first four cistrons reduces spore formation to a level that strongly depends on the genetic background, a phenotype that is partially suppressed by overexpression of *kinA* (160). Inactivation of *spo0KE* has only a minor effect on sporulation but, like mutations in the first four cistrons, strongly reduces competence (138, 160).

spo0L Located around 106°.

Status of this locus is uncertain since a preliminary report (70) was not followed by publication of detailed information.

spoIIA Located at 211°, between *dacF* and *spoVA*.

Transcription is repressed by Sin (110) and starts at $T_{0.5}$, before asymmetric septation (61, 135), from a σ^H-dependent promoter (209) requiring the Spo0A protein (199). A second burst of transcription originates from the *dacF* promoter in the forespore (210).

Three-gene operon encoding SpoIIAA (117 residues), SpoIIAB (146 residues), and σ^F (255 residues) (55, 216). SpoIIAB shows some similarity to the C-terminal part of bacterial histidine kinases, especially KinA. σ^F is inactivated by binding of SpoIIAB before septation and is released through the action of SpoIIAA (37, 120, 136, 168) selectively in the forespore (111). SpoIIAB might also be involved in inhibition of σ^G activity (153).

Null mutations in *spoIIAA* and *spoIIAC* block sporulation at stage II, with a normal-looking septum and accumulation of disporic cells, whereas some missense mutations in *spoIIAC* allow engulfment to proceed to an intermediary stage (77). Null mutations in *spoIIAB* lead to premature and increased σ^F activity and block sporulation at stage 0 (25). Extensive cell lysis during stationary phase in such strains is prevented by secondary mutations reducing σ^F activity (25).

spoIIB Located at 242°, between *comC* and *orfAB mreBCD*.

Transcription starts at T_0, before asymmetric septation, apparently from a σ^A-dependent promoter requiring the Spo0A protein (112).

Encodes a 332-residue protein containing a putative transmembrane domain (112).

A null mutation in *spoIIB* is oligosporogenous, its severity being increased at low temperature and when combined with a *spoVG* mutation. Cells blocked in sporulation present a normal thin septum and display both σ^F and σ^E activity, but no σ^G nor σ^K activity. Cells that undergo complete sporulation release unstable defective spores (112).

spoIIC The *spoIIC298* allele is an *amber* mutation at codon 145 of *spoIID* (94a).

spoIID Located at 320°, in the *narA-glyC* interval, downstream of *murA* (62a).

Transcription starts at T_1, in the mother cell (36), from a σ^E-dependent promoter (158, 184).

Encodes a 343-residue protein containing a putative amino-terminal transmembrane domain (106) and several stretches of similarity with the modifier of the major *B. subtilis* autolysin (100, 103).

A null mutation in *spoIID* prevents complete dissolution of the peptidoglycan layer present in the asymmetric septum and leads to bulging of the forespore into the mother cell without further progression toward engulfment (112). It blocks σ^G and σ^K activity (29, 164, 183).

spoIIE Located at 6°, in the *div-355-cysA* interval (103a).

Transcription is repressed by Sin (110) and starts at $T_{0.5}$, before asymmetric septation (61, 66), from a σ^A-dependent promoter requiring the Spo0A protein (212).

Encodes an 827-residue protein containing 9 to 11 putative transmembrane segments (130a, 214a).

Mutations in *spoIIE* lead to a "straight-and-thick-septum" phenotype (77, 145) and prevent activation of σ^F and of the whole sigma cascade (111).

spoIIF The *spoIIF96* allele is a 107-bp deletion removing the first 23 codons and most of the promoter region of *kinA* (126).

spoIIG Located at 135°, between *bpr* and *spoIIIG*.

Transcription is repressed by Sin (110) and starts at $T_{0.5}$, before asymmetric septation (61, 93), from a σ^A-dependent promoter (94) requiring the Spo0A protein (167). The *spoIIG* mRNA is processed between its two cistrons (14a, 93). Transcription proceeds into the downstream *spoIIIG* gene (119, 183).

Two-gene operon encoding SpoIIGA (309 residues) and pro-σ^E (239 residues) (118, 184, 185). SpoIIGA, a protein containing five putative membrane-spanning domains, appears to be the enzyme that converts pro-σ^E to active σ^E by processing its first 27 amino acids (101, 123a, 184).

Null mutations in *spoIIGA* and *spoIIGB* block sporulation at stage II with a normal-looking septum and lead to accumulation of disporic cells (77).

spoIIH Tn*917* insertion in *spoIIE* (215).

spoIIJ Tn*917* insertion in *kinA* (2).

spoIIK Tn*917* insertion in *spoIIE* (107, 214a).

spoIIL Tn*917* insertion close to the –35 region of the σ^H-controlled promoter of *spo0A* (62b).

spoIIM Located around 212°, in the *spo0A-spoIIA* interval (165).

Transcription starts at $T_{1.5}$ from a σ^E-dependent promoter (176). This transcription mode as well as biochemical fractionation experiments indicates that *spoIIM* is mostly expressed in the mother cell, but genetic evidence suggests that its product is also required in the forespore (176).

Encodes a 215-residue protein containing five putative transmembrane segments (175). *spoIIM* mutants do not complete dissolution of the septal cell wall and do not proceed to engulfment (175). *spoIIM* mutations block σ^G and σ^K activity (175).

spoIIN The *spoIIN279*(Ts) allele is a missense mutation at codon 9 of *ftsA* (S9N) (90).

spoIIP Located around 210°, downstream of *gpr* (57a).

Transcription starts at T_1, presumably in the mother cell, from a σ^E-dependent promoter located in the *gpr-spoIIP* interval (57a).

A null mutation in *spoIIP* prevents complete dissolution of the septal cell wall and leads to bulging of the forespore into the mother cell, without further progression to engulfment. It blocks σ^K activity (57a).

spoIIIA Located at 220°, in the *sin-ahrC* interval, upstream of *fabE.*

Transcription starts at T_1, in the mother cell, from a σ^E-dependent promoter (78). Another σ^E-dependent promoter present in the sixth cistron increases the transcription level of the two last cistrons of the locus (64b).

Eight-gene operon encoding SpoIIIAA (307 residues), SpoIIIAB (171 residues), SpoIIIAC (68 residues), SpoIIIAD (133 residues), SpoIIIAE (399 residues), SpoIIIAF (206 residues), SpoIIIAG (229 residues), and SpoIIIAH (218 residues). All of these proteins are predicted to contain membrane-spanning domains (1, 2, 2, 3 to 4, 9 to 10, 2, 1, 1, respectively) (64b). SpoIIIAA contains a putative nucleotide-binding motif (78).

Nonpolar mutations in each of the eight cistrons block sporulation at stage III, after completion of engulfment, and prevent σ^G (and consequently σ^K) activity (64b).

spoIIIB The *spoIIIB2* mutation was described to be close to but distinct from the *spoIIIA* locus (144). The original allele seems to have been lost.

spoIIIC Located at 231°, downstream of the *skin* element. The *spoIIIC* locus is the 3′ part of the interrupted *sigK* gene (186).

Transcription starts around T_3 (44), when *spoIIIC* is fused to *spoIVCB* by excision of the *skin* element from the mother cell chromosome (186).

Encodes the last 129 residues of σ^K.

The *spoIIIC94* allele is a 6-kb deletion overlapping the *spoIIIC* locus (44, 98). It actually blocks sporulation at stage IV, prevents coat synthesis, and gives rise to phase-gray forespores in which cortex formation is incomplete (145).

spoIIID Located around 312°, upstream of an *mreB* homolog (14b).

Transcription starts around T_2, in the mother cell, from a σ^E-dependent promoter (198) activated by SpoIIID itself (97, 181).

Encodes a 93-residue protein with a helix-turn-helix motif (97, 181) and DNA-binding properties (95). SpoIIID stimulates transcription from some σ^E- and σ^K-dependent promoters, while repressing transcription from some others (95).

Mutations in *spoIIID* prevent transcription of a subset of σ^E-dependent promoters (45, 99) and block pro-σ^K synthesis (109).

spoIIIE Located around 142°.

Transcribed constitutively during growth and sporulation from a weak σ^A-like promoter (56).

Encodes a 787-residue protein containing five to seven putative transmembrane segments and a potential nucleotide binding site (56).

The *spoIIIE36* missense mutation abolishes σ^F-controlled transcription from promoters located at various chromosomal positions but enhances transcription from the same promoters when located at 7° (*ctc* [111]) or 25° (*amyE* [195]). This phenomenon appears to be due to the defective segregation of the forespore chromosome in such a mutant (39a). Strains harboring this mutation complete engulfment, but the forespores are unstable and lyse (182). Null mutations in *spoIIIE* create a similar defect in chromosome segregation but do not interfere with σ^F-controlled transcription (39a).

spoIIIF The *spoIIIF590* allele is a missense mutation at codon 420 of *spoVB* (A420V) (147).

spoIIIG Located at 135°, downstream of *spoIIGB*.

Transcription starts at $T_{0.5}$, before asymmetric septation, from the upstream *spoIIG* operon, but translation is prevented (119, 194). Expression occurs only at T_2, in the forespore, by transcription from a σ^F-dependent promoter located in the *spoIIGB-spoIIIG* interval (194). The same promoter is recognized by σ^G after completion of engulfment (89).

Encodes σ^G (260 residues), the sigma factor that controls transcription in the forespore at late stages of sporulation (89, 119, 196). σ^G activity is delayed until engulfment is completed (183).

Null mutations in *spoIIIG* block late forespore gene expression (196) and prevent activation of σ^K (28).

spoIIIJ Located at 360°, downstream of *rnpA*. Originally defined by the misclassified *spo0J87* allele.

Transcription occurs during vegetative growth from an atypical σ^A-dependent promoter and is shut down around T_0 (40).

First cistron of a two-gene operon encoding SpoIIIJ (260 residues) and Jag (208 residues). SpoIIIJ contains four to six putative transmembrane segments. It is significantly similar to the C-terminal part of the product of the *60K* gene located at the same chromosomal position in *E. coli* and *P. putida* (40, 131).

Null mutations in *spoIIIJ* arrest sporulation at stage III and block σ^G (and consequently σ^K) activity (40). Disruption of *jag* does not interfere with sporulation (40).

spoIVA Located at 204°, upstream of *hbs*.

Transcription starts at $T_{1.5}$, in the mother cell, from two closely spaced σ^E-dependent promoters (157, 180). The downstream promoter is sufficient to support sporulation (157).

Encodes an acidic 492-residue protein, containing a putative nucleotide-binding motif (157, 180).

Mutations in *spoIVA* have no significant effect on gene expression during sporulation, with the exception of a dramatic decrease of *cotC* transcription when sporulation is induced by exhaustion (157). *spoIVA* mutants are impaired in cortex formation and are unable to build the CotE layer around the forespore, a defect which causes misassembly of the coat proteins as swirls in the mother cell cytoplasm (35a).

spoIVB Located at 218°, between *recN* and *spo0A*.

Transcription starts at T_3, in the forespore, from a σ^G-dependent promoter, but requires *spoIIID* expression in the mother cell to reach its wild-type level (26).

Encodes a 425-residue protein with one or two putative transmembrane domain(s) (203).

Null mutations in *spoIVB* prevent processing of pro-σ^K (109) and block cortex and coat formation (26).

spoIVC Originally believed to be a single locus, containing two cistrons (48). Now known to consist of two independent transcription units, *spoIVCA* and *spoIVCB*.

spoIVCA Located at 227°, within the *skin* element, downstream of and convergent with *spoIVCB*.

Transcription starts at T_2 (166), in the mother cell (32), from a σ^E-dependent promoter activated by SpoIIID (94a).

Encodes a 500-residue protein, showing substantial similarity in its N-terminal part with recombinases from the Hin Gin Pin TnpR family (166). SpoIVCA binds in vitro to the recombination sites of the *skin* element (148).

Null mutations in *spoIVCA* prevent the chromosomal rearrangement that creates the *sigK* gene. Therefore they block σ^K formation and subsequent cortex and coat synthesis. The requirement for SpoIVCA in sporulation is bypassed by the presence of a rearranged *sigK* gene (98).

spoIVCB Located at 227°, upstream of and convergent with *spoIVCA*. *spoIVCB* is the 5′ part of the interrupted *sigK* gene. It becomes fused to *spoIIIC* by excision of the *skin* element (186).

Transcription starts around T_3, in the mother cell, from a σ^E-dependent promoter requiring the SpoIIID protein (99). The same promoter is used later by σ^K, first acting in conjunction with SpoIIID (95) then inhibited by GerE (218).

Encodes the first 112 residues of pro-σ^K (186).

Null mutations in *spoIVCB* prevent coat synthesis and give rise to phase-gray forespores in which cortex formation is incomplete (145).

spoIVD The *spoIVD92* allele is a 37-kb deletion that overlaps the *spoIIIC* locus and inactivates the 3′ end of the *sigK* gene. A similar deletion was generated in the strain carrying the *spoIVD*::Tn*917*ΩHU10 transposon insertion (98).

spoIVE The *spoIVE11* allele is a 17-kb deletion that overlaps the *spoIIIC* locus and inactivates the 3′ end of the *sigK* gene (98).

spoIVF Located at 241°, between the *minCD* and *rplU orfX rpmA* operons.

Transcription starts at T_1, presumably in the mother cell, from a σ^E-dependent promoter (30).

Two-gene operon encoding SpoIVFA (264 residues) and SpoIVFB (288 residues). Both proteins contain putative transmembrane domains (1 and 2 to 5, respectively) (30).

Null mutations in *spoIVFB* prevent pro-σ^K processing and give rise to coatless, phase-gray forespores in which cortex formation is incomplete (145). Null, nonpolar mutations in *spoIVFA* create a thermosensitive sporulation phenotype that can be suppressed by secondary mutations in the 3′ region of *spoIVFB* (30). This finding suggests that SpoIVFA is dispensable at low temperature (30°C) and acts by stabilizing the thermolabile SpoIVFB protein (30). However, some recessive mutations in the last codons of *spoIVFA* (*bofB* alleles) allow pro-σ^K processing in the absence of forespore development, a phenotype also observed at low temperature in *spoIVFA* null mutants (28, 30). SpoIVFA appears to control negatively the activity of SpoIVFB in pro-σ^K processing.

spoIVG Located around 97°.

Defined by the *spoIVG5* and *spoIVG25* alleles that lead to coatless phase-gray forespores with incomplete cortex (205). The locus has not been cloned.

spoVA Located at 211°, between *spoIIA* and *lysA*.

Transcription starts at $T_{2.5}$, in the forespore (43), under the control of a σ^G-dependent promoter located in the *spoIIA-spoVA* intergenic region (123).

Six-gene operon encoding SpoVAA (200 residues), SpoVAB (141 residues), SpoVAC (150 residues), SpoVAD (338 residues), SpoVAE (323 residues), and SpoVAF (492 residues) (54, 170a). All of these proteins are predicted to contain several membrane-spanning domains (2 to 3, 4 to 5, 4, 3 to 4, 4 to 5, and 5 to 6, respectively). SpoVAC shows significant similarity to the N-terminal part of SpoVAE (41). SpoVAF is partially similar to GerAA and GerBA (122).

Uncharacterized mutations throughout the *spoVA* operon lead to the production of phase-white spores that are partially resistant to toluene and lysozyme but sensitive to chloroform and heat (42). These immature spores show a normal cortex and are surrounded by coat material (145). Inactivation of *spoVAF* does not prevent sporulation (122).

spoVB Located at 238°, 21 kb downstream of and convergent with *pheA*.
Transcription starts at T_1, presumably in the mother cell, from a σ^E-dependent promoter (147).
Encodes a 518-residue protein containing 14 to 15 putative transmembrane domains (147).
A null mutation in *spoVB* causes the production of heat-sensitive spores containing a defective cortex. It severely reduces transcription of the *cotC* gene (147).

spoVC Located at 5°, downstream of *ctc*.
Might be transcribed during both growth and sporulation (74a).
Encodes a protein whose partial sequence (75) is similar to *E. coli* peptidyl-tRNA hydrolase.
The locus is defined by the *spo-285*(Ts) mutation, which arrests coat formation at an early stage at the nonpermissive temperature (214). It might be an essential gene (74a). The *spo-134* mutation is tentatively placed in the same locus.

spoVD Located at 133°, between *pbp2B* and *murE*.
Transcription starts at T_1, presumably in the mother cell, from a σ^E-dependent promoter (39).
Encodes a 645-residue protein similar to PBP3, the *E. coli pbpB* (*ftsI*) product, an enzyme involved in cross wall biosynthesis (39).
The *spoVD156* mutation leads to the formation of an unusually striated cortex surrounded by incomplete coat layers (145).

spoVE Located at 134°, between *murD* and *murG*.
Transcribed during vegetative growth as part of the *mur* operon. Transcribed during sporulation, shortly after T_0 and around T_3 to T_4, from its own (σ^E-dependent?) promoter (71, 198a).
Encodes a 366-residue protein containing 10 to 11 putative transmembrane domains (85). It is highly similar to FtsW and RodA (76, 85), two proteins of *E. coli* involved in peptidoglycan remodeling.
A null mutation in *spoVE* leads to formation of spores surrounded by well-developed coat layers, whereas cortex is almost entirely absent (85, 145).

spoVF Located at 148°, upstream of the *asd dapG dapA* operon. Also known as *dpa*.
Transcription starts at T_4, in the mother cell, from a σ^K-dependent promoter (33).
Two-gene operon encoding DpaA (297 residues) and DpaB (200 residues), the two subunits of dipicolinate synthetase (33).
Null mutations in *spoVF* lead to formation of heat-sensitive spores, a defect that can be corrected by adding dipicolinic acid to the sporulation medium (6).

spoVG Located at 5°, upstream of *gcaD* (*tms*).

Transcription occurs at a basal level during vegetative growth and is strongly increased around T_0, before asymmetric septation (221). It originates from a σ^H-dependent promoter (220) that is repressed by AbrB (156).

Encodes a 97-residue polypeptide (74).

A null mutation in *spoVG* leads to the formation of minicells during growth (154a) and to a weak oligosporogenous phenotype due to impaired cortex synthesis (159). Severity of the *spoVG* phenotype is strongly enhanced by combination with a *spoIIB* mutation, leading to a nondisporic stage II block (112). Many laboratory strains might harbor a defective *spoVG* locus (112).

spoVH The *spoVH516* and *spoVH518* alleles are misclassified mutations that map in the *spoVA* operon (39).

spoVJ The *spoVJ517* allele is a misclassified mutation that maps in the *spoVK* locus (47).

spoVK Located at 168°.

Transcription starts at $T_{1.5}$, in the mother cell, from a σ^E-dependent promoter requiring the SpoIIID protein, and switches around $T_{3.5}$ to a downstream σ^K-dependent promoter (57). Deletion of the upstream σ^E-dependent promoter results in a 30-min delay in the formation of normal spores (57).

Encodes a 322-residue protein containing a putative nucleotide-binding motif (57).

A null mutation in *spoVK* leads to formation of immature spores that are sensitive to organic solvents, heat, and lysozyme (47).

spoVL Tn*917* insertion in *spoIVFA* (30).

spoVM Located around 145°, upstream of and convergent with *rpmB*.

Transcription starts at T_2, presumably in the mother cell, from a σ^E-dependent promoter activated by the SpoIIID protein (104).

Encodes a 26-residue protein (104).

A null mutation in *spoVM* leads to formation of phase-gray spores that are deficient in cortex and exhibit an aberrantly thin coat (104).

spoVN Located around 279°. Also known as *ald*.

Transcription occurs during vegetative growth from an atypical σ^A-like promoter and increases around T_0 in the absence of alanine (64a).

Encodes alanine dehydrogenase, a 378-residue protein containing a putative nucleotide-binding motif (64a).

A null mutation in *spoVN* leads to a 100-fold decrease in heat resistance, a phenotype that can be partially corrected by addition of pyruvate to the sporulation medium (64a).

spoVP Tn*917* insertion in *spoIVA* (157).

spoVQ Tn*917* insertion in *spoVA* (154a).

spoVIA Located at 255°, in the *gerE-argG* interval.

Defined by the *spo-513* mutation, which leads to the absence of a 36-kDa protein from the outer coats, lysozyme sensitivity, and slow germination (83). The locus has not been cloned.

spoVIB Located at 247°, in the *hemA-leuB* interval.

Defined by the *spo-520, -541, -547,* and *-552* mutations, which delay appearance of sporulation resistance properties and response to germinants, while leading to abnormal assembly of some coat proteins (84). The locus has not been cloned.

spoVIC Located at 294°, in the *cysB* region.

Defined by the *spo-610* mutation, which delays appearance of sporulation resistance properties and response to germinants, while leading to abnormal synthesis and arrangement of some coat proteins (82). The locus has not been cloned.

spoVID Located at 244°, downstream of the *hemAXCDBL* operon.

Transcription starts during the second hour of sporulation, in the mother cell, from a σ^E-dependent promoter (7).

First member of a two-gene operon encoding SpoVID (575 residues), a very acidic protein, and Orf2 (341 residues) (7).

Null mutations in *spoVID* lead to aberrant assembly of the coat proteins and to the release of lysozyme-sensitive, slowly germinating, refractile spores (7). Disruption of *orf2* does not interfere with sporulation (7).

sspA Located around 266°.

Transcription starts at $T_{2.5}$, in the forespore, from a σ^G-dependent promoter (115, 196). Increase of the *sspA* gene dosage leads only to a modest increase of the *sspA* mRNA level and to a simultaneous decrease of the amount of *sspB* mRNA (114).

Encodes SASP-α, a 69-residue protein, which is one of the major SASPs (23). SASP-α binds to the spore DNA, modifies its UV photochemistry, and induces a switch to an A-like conformation (171).

Disruption of *sspA* does not interfere with sporulation or germination, but it leads to production of spores with slightly decreased heat resistance and extreme sensitivity to UV irradiation (116). The latter phenotype is enhanced in a *sspA sspB* double mutant (116).

sspB Located around 66°.

Transcription starts at $T_{2.5}$, in the forespore, from a very strong σ^G-dependent promoter (115, 196). The *sspB* transcript contains a long untranslated leader region having the potential to form a stable secondary structure (130). Increase of the *sspB* gene dosage leads only to a modest increase of the *sspB* mRNA level and to a simultaneous decrease of the amount of *sspA* mRNA (114).

Encodes SASP-β, a 67-residue protein, which is one of the major SASPs (23). SASP-β binds to the spore DNA, modifies its UV photochemistry, and induces a switch to an A-like conformation (171).

Disruption of *sspB* does not interfere with sporulation or germination and allows production of spores with normal resistance to heat and UV irradiation (perhaps because of the parallel increase in SASP-α synthesis) (116). However, it enhances the phenotype of a *sspA* deletion when the two mutations are combined (116).

sspC Located at 182°.

Transcription occurs around T_3 to T_4 (24) and seems to depend on σ^G, as suggested by in vitro experiments (130).

Encodes a 72-residue protein, which is one of the minor α/β-type SASPs (24).

Disruption of *sspC* has not been reported. An increase of the *sspC* gene dosage (from *Bacillus megaterium*) compensates for the absence of SASP-α, suggesting that SspC plays a similar role in UV resistance (117).

sspD Located around 121°.

Transcription starts at $T_{2.5}$, in the forespore, from a σ^G-dependent promoter (115, 196).

Encodes a 64-residue protein, which is one of the minor α/β-type SASPs (23).

Disruption of *sspD* has not been reported. An increase of the *sspD* gene dosage compensates for the absence of SASP-α, suggesting that SspD plays a similar role in UV resistance (117).

sspE Located around 62°.

Transcription starts at $T_{2.5}$, in the forespore, from a σ^G-dependent promoter (115, 196). Increase of the *sspE* gene dosage leads to a comparable increase of the *sspE* mRNA level but is not accompanied by a parallel increase of the *sspE* gene product (114).

Encodes SASP-γ, an 84-residue protein, which is one of the major SASPs (67). SASP-γ is a unique protein, more abundant than either SASP-α or SASP-β. It is not associated with the nucleoid, and it is rapidly degraded to amino acids early in spore germination (171).

Disruption of *sspE* does not interfere with sporulation (67), but it delays the return to vegetative growth upon germination in the absence of external amino acids, a phenotype even more extreme when the *sspE* mutation is combined with *sspA* and *sspB* deletions (171).

sspF Located at 4°.

Transcription starts at T_4, in the forespore, from a σ^G-dependent promoter (134). The *sspF* mRNA is synthesized 1 h later than other *ssp* mRNAs (134). It is very abundant but inefficiently translated (179).

Encodes a 61-residue protein (179), which is presumably one of the minor α/β-type SASPs (171).

Disruption of *sspF* has not been reported.

0.3 kb Original denomination of *sspF* (132).

0.4 kb Original denomination of *spoVG* (169).

I am grateful to all of my colleagues who provided unpublished information and to the editors for their patience. Work in my laboratory is supported by the CNRS (URA 1139) and by a grant from the Human Frontier Science Program.

REFERENCES

1. **Anagnostopoulos, C., P. J. Piggot, and J. A. Hoch.** 1993. The genetic map of *Bacillus subtilis*, p. 425–461. *In* A. L. Sonenshein, J. A. Hoch, and R. Losick (ed.), *Bacillus subtilis and Other Gram-Positive Bacteria: Biochemistry, Physiology, and Molecular Genetics*. American Society for Microbiology, Washington, D.C.
2. **Antoniewski, C., B. Savelli, and P. Stragier.** 1990. The *spoIIJ* gene, which regulates early developmental steps in *Bacillus subtilis*, belongs to a class of environmentally responsive genes. *J. Bacteriol.* **172:** 86–93.

2a. **Aronson, A.** Personal communication.

3. **Aronson, A. I., H.-Y. Song, and N. Bourne.** 1988. Gene structure and precursor processing of a novel *Bacillus subtilis* spore coat protein. *Mol. Microbiol.* **3:**437–444.
4. **Bai, U., M. Lewandowski, E. Dubnau, and I. Smith.** 1990. Temporal regulation of the *Bacillus subtilis* early sporulation gene *spo0F*. *J. Bacteriol.* **172:**5432–5439.
5. **Bai, U., I. Mandic-Mulec, and I. Smith.** 1993. SinI modulates the activity of SinR, a developmental switch protein of *Bacillus subtilis*, by protein-protein interaction. *Genes Dev.* **7:**139–148.
6. **Balassa, G., P. Milhaud, E. Raulet, M. T. Silva, and J. C. F. Sousa.** 1979. A *Bacillus subtilis* mutant requiring dipicolinic acid for the development of heat-resistant spores. *J. Gen. Microbiol.* **110:**365–379.
7. **Beall, B., A. Driks, R. Losick, and C. P. Moran, Jr.** 1993. Cloning and characterization of a gene required for assembly of the *Bacillus subtilis* spore coat. *J. Bacteriol.* **175:**1705–1716.
8. **Beall, B., M. Lowe, and J. Lutkenhaus.** 1988. Cloning and characterization of *Bacillus subtilis* homologs of *Escherichia coli* cell division genes *ftsZ* and *ftsA*. *J. Bacteriol.* **170:**4855–4864.
9. **Beall, B., and J. Lutkenhaus.** 1991. FtsZ in *Bacillus subtilis* is required for vegetative septation and for asymmetric septation during sporulation. *Genes Dev.* **5:**447–455.
10. **Beall, B., and J. Lutkenhaus.** 1992. Impaired cell division and sporulation of a *Bacillus subtilis* strain with the *ftsA* gene deleted. *J. Bacteriol.* **174:**2398–2403.
11. **Benson, A. K., and W. G. Haldenwang.** 1992. Characterization of a regulatory network that controls σ^B expression in *Bacillus subtilis*. *J. Bacteriol.* **174:**749–757.
12. **Benson, A. K., and W. G. Haldenwang.** 1993. *Bacillus subtilis* σ^B is regulated by a binding protein (RsbW) that blocks its association with core RNA polymerase. *Proc. Natl. Acad. Sci. USA* **90:**2330–2334.

13. **Binnie, C., M. Lampe, and R. Losick.** 1986. Gene encoding the σ^{37} species of RNA polymerase σ factor from *Bacillus subtilis. Proc. Natl. Acad. Sci. USA* **83:**5943–5947.
14. **Bischoff, D. S., and G. W. Ordal.** 1992. *Bacillus subtilis* chemotaxis: a deviation from the *Escherichia coli* paradigm. *Mol. Microbiol.* **6:**23–28.
14a. **Bonamy, C.** Personal communication.
14b. **Bosma, A.** Personal communication.
14c. **Bott, K.** Personal communication.
15. **Bourne, N., P. C. FitzJames, and A. I. Aronson.** 1991. Structural and germination defects of *Bacillus subtilis* spores with altered contents of a spore coat protein. *J. Bacteriol.* **173:**6618–6625.
16. **Bouvier, J., P. Stragier, C. Bonamy, and J. Szulmajster.** 1984. Nucleotide sequence of the *spo0B* gene of *Bacillus subtilis* and regulation of its expression. *Proc. Natl. Acad. Sci. USA* **81:**7102–7106.
17. **Boylan, S. A., A. Rutherford, S. M. Thomas, and C. W. Price.** 1992. Activation of *Bacillus subtilis* transcription factor σ^B by a regulatory pathway responsive to stationary-phase signals. *J. Bacteriol.* **174:**3695–3706.
17a. **Bramucci, M.** Personal communication.
17b. **Buchanan, C. E.** Personal communication.
18. **Buchanan, C. E., and A. Gustafson.** 1992. Mutagenesis and mapping of the gene for a sporulation-specific penicillin-binding protein in *Bacillus subtilis. J. Bacteriol.* **174:**5430–5435.
19. **Buchanan, C. E., and M.-L. Ling.** 1992. Isolation and sequence analysis of *dacB,* which encodes a sporulation-specific penicillin-binding protein in *Bacillus subtilis. J. Bacteriol.* **174:**1717–1725.
20. **Burbulys, D., K. A. Trach, and J. A. Hoch.** 1991. Initiation of sporulation in *Bacillus subtilis* is controlled by a multicomponent phosphorelay. *Cell* **64:**545–552.
20a. **Chamberlin, M.** Personal communication.
21. **Chapman, J. W., and P. J. Piggot.** 1987. Analysis of the inhibition of sporulation of *Bacillus subtilis* caused by increasing the number of copies of the *spo0F* gene. *J. Gen. Microbiol.* **133:**2079–2088.
22. **Chibazakura, T., F. Kawamura, and H. Takahashi.** 1991. Differential regulation of *spo0A* transcription in *Bacillus subtilis:* glucose represses promoter switching at the initiation of sporulation. *J. Bacteriol.* **173:**2625–2632.
23. **Connors, M. J., J. M. Mason, and P. Setlow.** 1986. Cloning and nucleotide sequence of genes for three small acid-soluble proteins of *Bacillus subtilis* spores. *J. Bacteriol.* **166:**417–425.
24. **Connors, M. J., and P. Setlow.** 1985. Cloning of a small, acid-soluble spore protein gene from *Bacillus subtilis* and determination of its complete nucleotide sequence. *J. Bacteriol.* **161:**333–339.
25. **Coppolecchia, R., H. DeGrazia, and C. P. Moran, Jr.** 1991. Deletion of *spoIIAB* blocks endospore formation in *Bacillus subtilis* at an early stage. *J. Bacteriol.* **173:**6678–6685.
25a. **Corfe, B., and A. Moir.** Personal communication.
26. **Cutting, S., A. Driks, R. Schmidt, B. Kunkel, and R. Losick.** 1991. Forespore-specific transcription of a gene in the signal transduction pathway that governs pro-σ^K processing in *Bacillus subtilis. Genes Dev.* **5:**456–466.
27. **Cutting, S., and J. Mandelstam.** 1986. The nucleotide sequence and the transcription during sporulation of the *gerE* gene of *Bacillus subtilis. J. Gen. Microbiol.* **132:**3013–3024.

28. **Cutting, S., V. Oke, A. Driks, R. Losick, S. Lu, and L. Kroos.** 1990. A forespore checkpoint for mother cell gene expression during development in *B. subtilis*. *Cell* **62:**239–250.
29. **Cutting, S., S. Panzer, and R. Losick.** 1989. Regulatory studies on the promoter for a gene governing synthesis and assembly of the spore coat in *Bacillus subtilis*. *J. Mol. Biol.* **207:**393–404.
30. **Cutting, S., S. Roels, and R. Losick.** 1991. Sporulation operon *spoIVF* and the characterization of mutations that uncouple mother cell from forespore gene expression in *Bacillus subtilis*. *J. Mol. Biol.* **221:**1237–1256.
31. **Cutting, S., L. Zheng, and R. Losick.** 1991. Gene encoding two alkali-soluble components of the spore coat from *Bacillus subtilis*. *J. Bacteriol.* **173:**2915–2919.
32. **Dancer, B., and J. Mandelstam.** 1981. Complementation of sporulation mutations in fused protoplasts of *Bacillus subtilis*. *J. Gen. Microbiol.* **123:**17–26.
33. **Daniel, R. A., and J. Errington.** 1993. Cloning, DNA sequence, functional analysis and transcriptional regulation of the genes encoding dipicolinic acid synthetase required for sporulation in *Bacillus subtilis*. *J. Mol. Biol.* **232:**468–483.
34. **Débarbouillé, M., I. Martin-Verstraete, F. Kunst, and G. Rapoport.** 1991. The *Bacillus subtilis sigL* gene encodes an equivalent of σ^{54} from Gram-negative bacteria. *Proc. Natl. Acad. Sci. USA* **88:**9092–9096.
34a. **Deits, T.** Personal communication.
35. **Donovan, W., L. Zheng, K. Sandman, and R. Losick.** 1987. Genes encoding spore coat polypeptides from *Bacillus subtilis*. *J. Mol. Biol.* **196:**1–10.
35a. **Driks, A.** Personal communication.
36. **Driks, A., and R. Losick.** 1991. Compartmentalized expression of a gene under the control of sporulation transcription factor σ^E in *Bacillus subtilis*. *Proc. Natl. Acad. Sci. USA* **88:**9934–9938.
37. **Duncan, L., and R. Losick.** 1993. SpoIIAB is an anti-σ factor that binds to and inhibits transcription by regulatory protein σ^F from *Bacillus subtilis*. *Proc. Natl. Acad. Sci. USA* **90:**2325–2329.
38. **Duncan, M. L., S. S. Kalman, S. M. Thomas, and C. W. Price.** 1987. Gene encoding the 37,000-dalton minor sigma factor of *Bacillus subtilis* RNA polymerase: isolation, nucleotide sequence, chromosomal locus, and cryptic function. *J. Bacteriol.* **169:**771–778.
39. **Errington, J.** 1993. Sporulation in *Bacillus subtilis:* regulation of gene expression and control of morphogenesis. *Microbiol. Rev.* **57:**1–33.
39a. **Errington, J.** Personal communication.
40. **Errington, J., L. Appleby, R. A. Daniel, H. Goodfellow, S. R. Partridge, and M. Yudkin.** 1992. Structure and expression of the *spoIIIJ* gene of *Bacillus subtilis:* a vegetatively expressed gene that is essential for σ^G activity at an intermediate stage of sporulation. *J. Gen. Microbiol.* **138:**2609–2618.
41. **Errington, J., P. Fort, and J. Mandelstam.** 1985. Duplicated sporulation genes in bacteria: implication for simple developmental systems. *FEBS Lett.* **188:**184–188.
42. **Errington, J., and J. Mandelstam.** 1984. Genetic and phenotypic characterization of a cluster of mutations in the *spoVA* locus of *Bacillus subtilis*. *J. Gen. Microbiol.* **130:**2115–2121.
43. **Errington, J., and J. Mandelstam.** 1986. Use of a *lacZ* gene fusion to determine the dependence pattern and the spore compartment expression of the sporu-

lation operon *spoVA* in *spo* mutants of *Bacillus subtilis*. *J. Gen. Microbiol.* **132:**2977–2985.

44. **Errington, J., S. Rong, M. S. Rosenkrantz, and A. L. Sonenshein.** 1988. Transcriptional regulation and structure of the *Bacillus subtilis* sporulation locus *spoIIIC*. *J. Bacteriol.* **170:**1162–1167.
45. **Errington, J., L. Wooten, J. C. Dunkerley, and D. Foulger.** 1989. Differential gene expression during sporulation in *Bacillus subtilis:* regulation of the *spoVJ* gene. *Mol. Microbiol.* **3:**1053–1060.
46. **Fajardo-Cavazos, P., C. Salazar, and W. L. Nicholson.** 1993. Molecular cloning and characterization of the *Bacillus subtilis* spore photoproduct lyase (*spl*) gene, which is involved in repair of UV radiation-induced DNA damage during spore germination. *J. Bacteriol.* **175:**1735–1744.
47. **Fan, N., S. Cutting, and R. Losick.** 1992. Characterization of the *Bacillus subtilis* sporulation gene *spoVK*. *J. Bacteriol.* **174:**1053–1054.
48. **Farquhar, R., and M. D. Yudkin.** 1988. Phenotypic and genetic characterization of mutations in the *spoIVC* locus of *Bacillus subtilis*. *J. Gen. Microbiol.* **134:**9–17.
49. **Feavers, I. M., J. Foulkes, B. Setlow, D. Sun, W. Nicholson, P. Setlow, and A. Moir.** 1990. The regulation of transcription of the *gerA* spore germination operon of *Bacillus subtilis*. *Mol. Microbiol.* **4:**275–282.
50. **Feavers, I. M., J. S. Miles, and A. Moir.** 1985. The nucleotide sequence of a spore germination gene (*gerA*) of *Bacillus subtilis* 168. *Gene* **38:**95–102.
51. **Feng, P., and A. I. Aronson.** 1986. Characterization of a *Bacillus subtilis* germination mutant with pleiotropic alterations in spore coat structure. *Curr. Microbiol.* **13:**221–226.
52. **Ferrari, F. A., K. Trach, and J. A. Hoch.** 1985. Sequence analysis of the *spo0B* locus reveals a polycistronic transcription unit. *J. Bacteriol.* **161:**556–562.
53. **Ferrari, F. A., K. Trach, D. LeCoq, J. Spence, E. Ferrari, and J. A. Hoch.** 1985. Characterization of the *spo0A* locus and its deduced product. *Proc. Natl. Acad. Sci. USA* **82:**2647–2651.
54. **Fort, P., and J. Errington.** 1985. Nucleotide sequence and complementation analysis of a polycistronic sporulation operon, *spoVA,* in *Bacillus subtilis*. *J. Gen. Microbiol.* **131:**1091–1105.
55. **Fort, P., and P. J. Piggot.** 1984. Nucleotide sequence of the sporulation locus *spoIIA* in *Bacillus subtilis*. *J. Gen. Microbiol.* **130:**2147–2153.
56. **Foulger, D., and J. Errington.** 1989. The role of the sporulation gene *spoIIIE* in the regulation of prespore-specific gene expression in *Bacillus subtilis*. *Mol. Microbiol.* **3:**1247–1255.
57. **Foulger, D., and J. Errington.** 1991. Sequential activation of dual promoters by different sigma factors maintains *spoVJ* expression during successive developmental stages of *Bacillus subtilis*. *Mol. Microbiol.* **5:**1363–1373.

57a. **Frandsen, N.** Personal communication.

58. **Gaur, N. K., K. Cabane, and I. Smith.** 1988. Structure and expression of the *Bacillus subtilis sin* operon. *J. Bacteriol.* **170:**1046–1053.
59. **Gaur, N. K., E. Dubnau, and I. Smith.** 1986. Characterization of a cloned *Bacillus subtilis* gene which inhibits sporulation in multiple copies. *J. Bacteriol.* **170:**860–869.
60. **Gaur, N. K., J. Oppenheim, and I. Smith.** 1991. The *Bacillus subtilis sin* gene, a regulator of alternate developmental processes, codes for a DNA-binding protein. *J. Bacteriol.* **173:**678–686.

61. **Gholamhoseinian, A., and P. J. Piggot.** 1989. Timing of *spoII* gene expression relative to septum formation during sporulation of *Bacillus subtilis*. *J. Bacteriol.* **171:**5747–5749.
62. **Gholamhoseinian, A., Z. Shen, J.-J. Wu, and P. Piggot.** 1992. Regulation of transcription of the cell division gene *ftsA* during sporulation of *Bacillus subtilis*. *J. Bacteriol.* **174:**4647–4656.
62a. **Glaser, P.** Personal communication.
62b. **Gonzy-Tréboul, G.** Personal communication.
63. **Gonzy-Tréboul, G., C. Karmazyn-Campelli, and P. Stragier.** 1992. Developmental regulation of transcription of the *Bacillus subtilis ftsAZ* operon. *J. Mol. Biol.* **224:**967–979.
64. **Green, B. D., G. Olmedo, and P. Youngman.** 1991. A genetic analysis of Spo0A structure and function. *Res. Microbiol.* **142:**825–830.
64a. **Grossman, A. D.** Personal communication.
64b. **Guérout-Fleury, A.-M.** Personal communication.
65. **Guespin-Michel, J. F.** 1971. Phenotypic reversion in some early blocked sporulation mutants of *Bacillus subtilis*. Genetic studies of polymyxin-resistant partial revertants. *Mol. Gen. Genet.* **112:**243–254.
66. **Guzman, P., J. Westpheling, and P. Youngman.** 1988. Characterization of the promoter region of the *Bacillus subtilis spoIIE* operon. *J. Bacteriol.* **170:**1598–1609.
67. **Hackett, R. H., and P. Setlow.** 1987. Cloning, nucleotide sequencing, and genetic mapping of the gene for small, acid-soluble spore protein γ of *Bacillus subtilis*. *J. Bacteriol.* **196:**1985–1992.
68. **Healy, J., J. Weir, I. Smith, and R. Losick.** 1991. Posttranscriptional control of a sporulation regulatory gene encoding transcription factor σ^H in *Bacillus subtilis*. *Mol. Microbiol.* **5:**477–488.
69. **Helmann, J. D., L. M. Marquez, and M. J. Chamberlin.** 1988. Cloning, sequencing, and disruption of the *Bacillus subtilis* σ^{28} gene. *J. Bacteriol.* **170:** 1568–1574.
69a. **Henner, D. J.** Personal communication.
70. **Henner, D. J., and J. A. Hoch.** 1980. The *Bacillus subtilis* chromosome. *Microbiol. Rev.* **44:**57–82.
71. **Henriques, A. O., H. de Lencastre, and P. J. Piggot.** 1992. A *Bacillus subtilis* morphogene cluster that includes *spoVE* is homologous to the *mra* region of *Escherichia coli*. *Biochimie* **74:**735–748.
72. **Hoch, J. A.** 1993. *spo0* genes, the phosphorelay, and the initiation of sporulation, p. 747–755. *In* A. L. Sonenshein, J. A. Hoch, and R. Losick (ed.), *Bacillus subtilis and Other Gram-Positive Bacteria: Biochemistry, Physiology, and Molecular Genetics*. American Society for Microbiology, Washington, D.C.
73. **Hoch, J. A., K. Trach, F. Kawamura, and H. Saito.** 1985. Identification of the transcriptional supressor *sof-1* as an alteration in the *spo0A* protein. *J. Bacteriol.* **161:**552–555.
74. **Hudspeth, D. S. S., and P. S. Vary.** 1992. *spoVG* sequence of *Bacillus megaterium* and *Bacillus subtilis*. *Biochim. Biophys. Acta* **1130:**229–231.
74a. **Igo, M.** Personal communication.
75. **Igo, M., M. Lampe, and R. Losick.** 1988. Structure and regulation of a *Bacillus subtilis* gene that is transcribed by the $E\sigma^B$ form of RNA polymerase holoenzyme, p. 151–156. *In* A. T. Ganesan and J. A. Hoch (ed.), *Genetics and Biotechnology of Bacilli*, vol. 2. Academic Press, Inc., San Diego, Calif.

76. **Ikeda, M., T. Sato, M. Wachi, H. K. Jung, F. Ishino, Y. Kobayashi, and M. Matsuhashi.** 1989. Structural similarity among *Escherichia coli* FtsW and RodA proteins and *Bacillus subtilis* SpoVE protein, which function in cell division, cell elongation, and spore formation, respectively. *J. Bacteriol.* **171:**6375–6378.
77. **Illing, N., and J. Errington.** 1991. Genetic regulation of morphogenesis in *Bacillus subtilis:* roles of σ^E and σ^F in prespore engulfment. *J. Bacteriol.* **173:** 3159–3169.
78. **Illing, N., and J. Errington.** 1991. The *spoIIIA* operon of *Bacillus subtilis* defines a new temporal class of mother-cell-specific sporulation genes under the control of the σ^E form of RNA polymerase. *Mol. Microbiol.* **5:**1927–1940.
79. **Ireton, K., and A. D. Grossman.** 1992. Interactions among mutations that cause altered timing of gene expression during sporulation in *Bacillus subtilis. J. Bacteriol.* **174:**3185–3195.
80. **Ireton, K., D. Z. Rudner, K. J. Siranosian, and A. D. Grossman.** 1993. Integration of multiple developmental signals in *Bacillus subtilis* through the Spo0A transcriptional factor. *Genes Dev.* **7:**283–294.
80a. **Irie, R.** Personal communication.
81. **Jaacks, K. J., J. Healy, R. Losick, and A. D. Grossman.** 1989. Identification and characterization of genes controlled by the sporulation regulatory gene *spo0H* in *Bacillus subtilis. J. Bacteriol.* **171:**4121–4129.
82. **James, W., and J. Mandelstam.** 1985. *spoVIC,* a new sporulation locus in *Bacillus subtilis* affecting spore coats, germination and the rate of sporulation. *J. Gen. Microbiol.* **131:**2409–2419.
83. **Jenkinson, H. F.** 1981. Germination and resistance defects in spores of a *Bacillus subtilis* mutant lacking a coat polypeptide. *J. Gen. Microbiol.* **127:**81–91.
84. **Jenkinson, H. F.** 1983. Altered arrangement of proteins in the spore coat of a germination mutant of *Bacillus subtilis. J. Gen. Microbiol.* **129:**1945–1958.
85. **Joris, B., G. Dive, A. Henriques, P. J. Piggot, and J. M. Ghuysen.** 1990. The life-cycle proteins RodA of *Escherichia coli* and SpoVE of *Bacillus subtilis* have very similar primary structures. *Mol. Microbiol.* **4:**513–517.
86. **Kahn, D., and G. Ditta.** 1991. Modular structure of FixJ: homology of the transcriptional activator domain with the –35 domain of sigma factors. *Mol. Microbiol.* **5:**987–997.
87. **Kallio, P. T., J. E. Fagelson, J. A. Hoch, and M. A. Strauch.** 1991. The transition state regulator Hpr of *Bacillus subtilis* is a DNA-binding protein. *J. Biol. Chem.* **266:**13411–13417.
88. **Kalman, S., M. Duncan, S. Thomas, and C. W. Price.** 1990. Similar organization of the *sigB* and *spoIIA* operons encoding alternative sigma factors of *Bacillus subtilis* RNA polymerase. *J. Bacteriol.* **172:**5575–5585.
89. **Karmazyn-Campelli, C., C. Bonamy, B. Savelli, and P. Stragier.** 1989. Tandem genes encoding σ-factors for consecutive steps of development in *Bacillus subtilis. Genes Dev.* **3:**150–157.
90. **Karmazyn-Campelli, C., L. Fluss, T. Leighton, and P. Stragier.** 1992. The *spoIIN279(ts)* mutation affects the FtsA protein of *Bacillus subtilis. Biochimie* **74:**689–694.
91. **Kawamura, F., L.-F. Wang, and R. H. Doi.** 1985. Catabolite-resistant sporulation (*crsA*) mutations in the *Bacillus subtilis* RNA polymerase σ^{43} gene (*rpoD*) can suppress and be suppressed by mutations in *spo0* genes. *Proc. Natl. Acad. Sci. USA* **82:**8124–8128.

92. **Kemp, E. H., R. L. Sammons, A. Moir, D. Sun, and P. Setlow.** 1991. Analysis of transcriptional control of the *gerD* spore germination gene of *Bacillus subtilis*. *J. Bacteriol.* **173:**4646–4652.
93. **Kenney, T. J., and C. P. Moran, Jr.** 1987. Organization and regulation of an operon that encodes a sporulation-essential sigma factor in *Bacillus subtilis*. *J. Bacteriol.* **169:**3329–3339.
94. **Kenney, T. J., K. York, P. Youngman, and C. P. Moran, Jr.** 1989. Genetic evidence that RNA polymerase associated with σ^A uses a sporulation-specific promoter in *Bacillus subtilis*. *Proc. Natl. Acad. Sci. USA* **86:**9109–9113.
94a. **Kobayashi, Y.** Personal communication.
95. **Kroos, L., B. Kunkel, and R. Losick.** 1989. Switch protein alters specificity of RNA polymerase containing a compartment-specific sigma factor. *Science* **243:**526–529.
96. **Kudoh, J., T. Ikeuchi, and K. Kurahashi.** 1985. Nucleotide sequences of the sporulation gene *spo0A* and its mutant genes of *Bacillus subtilis*. *Proc. Natl. Acad. Sci. USA* **82:**2665–2668.
97. **Kunkel, B., L. Kroos, H. Poth, P. Youngman, and R. Losick.** 1989. Temporal and spatial control of the mother-cell regulatory gene *spoIIID* of *Bacillus subtilis*. *Genes Dev.* **3:**1735–1744.
98. **Kunkel, B., R. Losick, and P. Stragier.** 1990. The *Bacillus subtilis* gene for the developmental transcription factor σ^K is generated by excision of a dispensable DNA element containing a sporulation recombinase gene. *Genes Dev.* **4:**525–535.
99. **Kunkel, B., K. Sandman, S. Panzer, P. Youngman, and R. Losick.** 1988. The promoter for a sporulation gene in the *spoIVC* locus of *Bacillus subtilis* and its use in studies of temporal and spatial control of gene expression. *J. Bacteriol.* **170:**3513–3522.
100. **Kuroda, A., M. H. Rashid, and J. Segikuchi.** 1992. Molecular cloning and sequencing of the upstream region of the major *Bacillus subtilis* autolysin gene: a modifier protein exhibiting sequence homology to the major autolysin and the *spoIID* product. *J. Gen. Microbiol.* **138:**1067–1076.
101. **LaBell, T. L., J. E. Trempy, and W. G. Haldenwang.** 1987. Sporulation-specific σ factor σ^{29} of *Bacillus subtilis* is synthesized from a precursor protein, P^{31}. *Proc. Natl. Acad. Sci. USA* **84:**1784–1788.
102. **Lampel, K. A., B. Uratani, G. R. Chaudhry, R. F. Ramaley, and S. Rudikoff.** 1986. Characterization of the developmentally regulated *Bacillus subtilis* glucose dehydrogenase gene. *J. Bacteriol.* **166:**238–243.
103. **Lazarevic, V., P. Margot, B. Soldo, and D. Karamata.** 1992. Sequencing and analysis of the *Bacillus subtilis lytRABC* divergon: a regulatory unit encompassing the structural genes of the *N*-acetylmuramoyl-L-alanine amidase and its modifier. *J. Gen. Microbiol.* **138:**1949–1961.
103a. **Levin, P. A.** Personal communication.
104. **Levin, P. A., N. Fan, E. Ricca, A. Driks, R. Losick, and S. Cutting.** 1993. An unusually small gene required for sporulation by *Bacillus subtilis*. *Mol. Microbiol.* **9:**761–771.
105. **Lewandoski, M., E. Dubnau, and I. Smith.** 1986. Transcriptional regulation of the *spo0F* gene of *Bacillus subtilis*. *J. Bacteriol.* **168:**870–877.
106. **Lopez-Diaz, I., S. Clarke, and J. Mandelstam.** 1986. *spoIID* operon of *Bacillus subtilis:* cloning and sequence. *J. Gen. Microbiol.* **132:**341–354.

107. **Losick, R., P. Youngman, and P. J. Piggot.** 1986. Genetics of endospore formation in *Bacillus subtilis. Annu. Rev. Genet.* **20:**625–669.

108. **Louie, P., A. Lee, K. Stansmore, R. Grant, C. Ginther, and T. Leighton.** 1992. Roles of *rpoD, spoIIF, spoIIJ, spoIIN,* and *sin* in regulation of *Bacillus subtilis* stage II sporulation-specific transcription. *J. Bacteriol.* **174:**3570–3576.

109. **Lu, S., R. Halberg, and L. Kroos.** 1990. Processing of the mother-cell σ factor, σ^K, may depend on events occurring in the forespore during *Bacillus subtilis* development. *Proc. Natl. Acad. Sci. USA* **87:**9722–9726.

110. **Mandic-Mulec, I., N. Gaur, U. Bai, and I. Smith.** 1992. Sin, a stage specific repressor of cellular differentiation. *J. Bacteriol.* **174:**3561–3569.

111. **Margolis, P., A. Driks, and R. Losick.** 1991. Establishment of cell type by compartmentalized activation of a transcription factor. *Science* **254:**562–565.

112. **Margolis, P., A. Driks, and R. Losick.** 1993. Sporulation gene *spoIIB* from *Bacillus subtilis. J. Bacteriol.* **175:**528–540.

113. **Marquez, L. M., J. D. Helmann, E. Ferrari, H. M. Parker, G. W. Ordal, and M. J. Chamberlin.** 1990. Studies of σ^D-dependent functions in *Bacillus subtilis. J. Bacteriol.* **172:**3435–3443.

114. **Mason, J. M., P. Fajardo-Cavazos, and P. Setlow.** 1988. Levels of mRNAs which code for small, acid-soluble spore proteins and their *lacZ* gene fusions in sporulating cells of *Bacillus subtilis. Nucleic Acids Res.* **16:**6567–6582.

115. **Mason, J. M., R. H. Hackett, and P. Setlow.** 1988. Regulation of expression of genes coding for small, acid-soluble proteins of *Bacillus subtilis* spores: studies using *lacZ* gene fusions. *J. Bacteriol.* **170:**239–244.

116. **Mason, J. M., and P. Setlow.** 1986. Essential role of small, acid-soluble spore proteins in resistance of *Bacillus subtilis* spores to UV light. *J. Bacteriol.* **167:**174–178.

117. **Mason, J. M., and P. Setlow.** 1987. Different small, acid-soluble proteins of the α/β type have interchangeable roles in the heat and UV radiation resistance of *Bacillus subtilis* spores. *J. Bacteriol.* **169:**3633–3637.

118. **Masuda, E. S., H. Anaguchi, T. Sato, M. Takeuchi, and Y. Kobayashi.** 1990. Nucleotide sequence of the sporulation gene *spoIIGA* from *Bacillus subtilis. Nucleic Acids Res.* **18:**657.

119. **Masuda, E. S., H. Anaguchi, K. Yamada, and Y. Kobayashi.** 1988. Two developmental genes encoding sigma factor homologs are arranged in tandem in *Bacillus subtilis. Proc. Natl. Acad. Sci. USA* **85:**7637–7641.

120. **Min, K.-T., C. M. Hilditch, J. Errington, and M. D. Yudkin.** σ^F, the first compartment specific transcription factor of *Bacillus subtilis,* is regulated by an anti-sigma factor which is also a protein kinase. *Cell,* in press.

120a. **Moir, A.** Personal communication.

121. **Moir, A., E. Laffert, and D. A. Smith.** 1979. Genetic analysis of spore germination mutants of *Bacillus subtilis* 168: the correlation of phenotype with map location. *J. Gen. Microbiol.* **111:**165–180.

122. **Moir, A., and D. Smith.** 1990. The genetics of bacterial spore germination. *Annu. Rev. Microbiol.* **44:**531–553.

123. **Moldover, B., P. J. Piggot, and M. D. Yudkin.** 1991. Identification of the promoter and the transcriptional start site of the *spoVA* operon of *Bacillus subtilis* and *Bacillus licheniformis. J. Gen. Microbiol.* **137:**527–531.

123a. **Moran, C. P., Jr.** Personal communication.

124. **Motallebi-Veshareh, M., D. A. Rouch, and C. M. Thomas.** 1990. A family of ATPases involved in active partitioning of diverse bacterial plasmids. *Mol. Microbiol.* **4:**1455–1463.
125. **Mueller, J. P., G. Bukusoglu, and A. L. Sonenshein.** 1992. Transcriptional regulation of *Bacillus subtilis* glucose-starvation inducible genes: control of *gsiA* by the ComP-ComA signal transduction system. *J. Bacteriol.* **174:**4361–4373.
126. **Mueller, J. P., and A. L. Sonenshein.** 1992. Role of the *Bacillus subtilis gsiA* gene in regulation of early sporulation gene expression. *J. Bacteriol.* **174:**4374–4383.
127. **Munakata, N.** 1969. Genetic analysis of a mutant of *Bacillus subtilis* producing ultraviolet-sensitive spores. *Mol. Gen. Genet.* **104:**258–263.
128. **Mysliwiec, T. H., J. Errington, A. B. Vaidya, and M. G. Bramucci.** 1991. The *Bacillus subtilis spo0J* gene: evidence for involvement in catabolite repression of sporulation. *J. Bacteriol.* **173:**1911–1919.
129. **Nakatani, Y., W. L. Nicholson, K.-D. Neitzke, P. Setlow, and E. Freese.** 1989. Sigma-G RNA polymerase controls forespore-specific expression of the glucose dehydrogenase operon in *Bacillus subtilis. Nucleic Acids Res.* **17:**999–1017.
130. **Nicholson, W. L., D. Sun, B. Setlow, and P. Setlow.** 1989. Promoter specificity of σ^G-containing RNA polymerase from sporulating cells of *Bacillus subtilis:* identification of a group of forespore-specific promoters. *J. Bacteriol.* **171:** 2708–2718.
130a. **Ogasawara, N.** Personal communication.
131. **Ogasawara, N., and H. Yoshikawa.** 1992. Genes and their organization in the replication origin of the bacterial chromosome. *Mol. Microbiol.* **6:**629–634.
132. **Ollington, J. F., and R. Losick.** 1981. A cloned gene that is turned on at an intermediate stage of spore formation in *Bacillus subtilis. J. Bacteriol.* **147:**443–451.
133. **Olmedo, G., E. G. Ninfa, J. Stock, and P. Youngman.** 1990. Novel mutations that alter the regulation of sporulation in *Bacillus subtilis:* evidence that phosphorylation of regulatory protein Spo0A controls the initiation of sporulation. *J. Mol. Biol.* **215:**359–372.
134. **Panzer, S., R. Losick, D. Sun, and P. Setlow.** 1989. Evidence for an additional temporal class of gene expression in the forespore compartment of sporulating *Bacillus subtilis. J. Bacteriol.* **171:**561–564.
135. **Partridge, S. R., and J. Errington.** 1993. The importance of morphological events and intercellular interactions in the regulation of prespore-specific gene expression during sporulation in *Bacillus subtilis. Mol. Microbiol.* **8:**945–955.
136. **Partridge, S. R., D. Foulger, and J. Errington.** 1991. The role of σ^F in prespore-specific transcription in *Bacillus subtilis. Mol. Microbiol.* **5:**757–767.
137. **Perego, M., S. P. Cole, D. Burbulys, K. Trach, and J. A. Hoch.** 1989. Characterisation of the gene for a protein kinase which phosphorylates the sporulation-regulatory proteins Spo0A and Spo0F of *Bacillus subtilis. J. Bacteriol.* **171:** 6187–6196.
138. **Perego, M., C. F. Higgins, S. R. Pearce, M. P. Gallagher, and J. A. Hoch.** 1991. The oligopeptide transport system of *Bacillus subtilis* plays a role in the initiation of sporulation. *Mol. Microbiol.* **5:**173–185.
139. **Perego, M., and J. A. Hoch.** 1987. Isolation and sequence of the *spo0E* gene: its role in initiation of sporulation in *Bacillus subtilis. Mol. Microbiol.* **1:**125–132.

140. **Perego, M., and J. A. Hoch.** 1988. Sequence analysis and regulation of the *hpr* locus, a regulatory gene for protease production and sporulation in *Bacillus subtilis. J. Bacteriol.* **170:**2560–2567.
141. **Perego, M., and J. A. Hoch.** 1991. Negative regulation of *Bacillus subtilis* sporulation by the *spo0E* gene product. *J. Bacteriol.* **173:**2514–2520.
142. **Perego, M., G. B. Spiegelman, and J. A. Hoch.** 1988. Structure of the gene for the transition state regulator *abrB:* regulator synthesis is controlled by the *spo0A* sporulation gene in *Bacillus subtilis. Mol. Microbiol.* **2:**689–699.
143. **Perego, M., J.-J. Wu, G. B. Spiegelman, and J. A. Hoch.** 1991. Mutational dissociation of the positive and negative regulatory properties of the Spo0A sporulation transcription factor of *Bacillus subtilis. Gene* **100:**207–212.
144. **Piggot, P. J.** 1973. Mapping of asporogenous mutations of *Bacillus subtilis:* a minimum estimate of the number of sporulation operons. *J. Bacteriol.* **114:** 1241–1253.
145. **Piggot, P. J., and J. G. Coote.** 1976. Genetic aspects of bacterial endospore formation. *Bacteriol. Rev.* **40:**908–962.
146. **Piggot, P. J., A. Moir, and D. A. Smith.** 1981. Advances in the genetics of *Bacillus subtilis* differentiation, p. 29–39. *In* H. S. Levinson, A. L. Sonenshein, and D. J. Tipper (ed.), *Sporulation and Germination.* American Society for Microbiology, Washington, D.C.
147. **Popham, D. L., and P. Stragier.** 1991. Cloning, characterization and expression of the *spoVB* gene of *Bacillus subtilis. J. Bacteriol.* **173:**7942–7949.
148. **Popham, D. L., and P. Stragier.** 1992. Binding of the *Bacillus subtilis spoIVCA* product to the recombination sites of the element interrupting the σ^K-encoding gene. *Proc. Natl. Acad. Sci. USA* **89:**5991–5995.
149. **Prasad, C., M. Diesterhaft, and E. Freese.** 1972. Initiation of spore germination in glycolytic mutants of *Bacillus subtilis. J. Bacteriol.* **119:**805–810.
150. **Predich, M., G. Nair, and I. Smith.** 1992. *Bacillus subtilis* early sporulation genes *kinA, spo0F* and *spo0A* are transcribed by the RNA polymerase containing σ^H. *J. Bacteriol.* **174:**2771–2778.
151. **Qi, F.-X., and R. H. Doi.** 1990. Localization of a second sigH promoter in the *Bacillus subtilis sigA* operon and regulation of *dnaE* expression by the promoter. *J. Bacteriol.* **172:**5631–5636.
152. **Qi, F.-X., X. S. He, and R. Doi.** 1991. Localization of a new promoter, P5, in the *sigA* operon of *Bacillus subtilis* and its regulation in some *spo* mutant strains. *J. Bacteriol.* **173:**7050–7054.
153. **Rather, P. N., R. Coppolecchia, H. DeGrazia, and C. P. Moran, Jr.** 1990. Negative regulator of σ^G-controlled gene expression in stationary-phase *Bacillus subtilis. J. Bacteriol.* **172:**709–715.
154. **Rather, P. N., and C. P. Moran, Jr.** 1988. Compartment-specific transcription in *Bacillus subtilis:* identification of the promoter for *gdh. J. Bacteriol.* **170:**5086–5092.
154a. **Resnekov, O.** Personal communication.
155. **Ricca, E., S. Cutting, and R. Losick.** 1992. Characterization of *bofA,* a gene involved in intercompartmental regulation of pro-σ^K processing during sporulation in *Bacillus subtilis. J. Bacteriol.* **174:**3177–3184.
156. **Robertson, J. B., M. Gocht, M. A. Marahiel, and P. Zuber.** 1989. AbrB, a regulator of gene expression in *Bacillus,* interacts with the transcription initiation regions of a sporulation gene and an antibiotic biosynthesis gene. *Proc. Natl. Acad. Sci. USA* **86:**8457–8461.

156a. **Roels, S.** Personal communication.

157. **Roels, S., A. Driks, and R. Losick.** 1992. Characterization of *spoIVA*, a sporulation gene involved in coat morphogenesis in *Bacillus subtilis*. *J. Bacteriol.* **174:**575–585.

158. **Rong, S., M. S. Rosenkrantz, and A. L. Sonenshein.** 1986. Transcriptional control of the *Bacillus subtilis spoIID* gene. *J. Bacteriol.* **165:**771–779.

159. **Rosenbluh, A., C. D. Banner, R. Losick, and P. C. Fitz-James.** 1981. Identification of a new developmental locus in *Bacillus subtilis* by construction of a deletion mutation in a cloned gene under sporulation control. *J. Bacteriol.* **148:**341–351.

160. **Rudner, D. Z., J. R. LeDeaux, K. Ireton, and A. D. Grossman.** 1991. The *spo0K* locus of *Bacillus subtilis* is homologous to the oligopeptide permease locus and is required for sporulation and competence. *J. Bacteriol.* **173:**1388–1398.

161. **Sammons, R. L., G. M. Slynn, and D. A. Smith.** 1987. Genetical and molecular studies on *gerM*, a new developmental locus of *Bacillus subtilis*. *J. Gen. Microbiol.* **133:**3299–3312.

162. **Sanchez-Salas, J.-L., M. L. Santiago-Lara, B. Setlow, M. D. Sussman, and P. Setlow.** 1992. Properties of *Bacillus megaterium* and *Bacillus subtilis* mutants which lack the protease that degrades small, acid-soluble proteins during spore germination. *J. Bacteriol.* **174:**807–814.

163. **Sanchez-Salas, J.-L., and P. Setlow.** 1993. Proteolytic processing of the protease which initiates degradation of small, acid-soluble proteins during germination of *Bacillus subtilis* spores. *J. Bacteriol.* **175:**2568–2577.

164. **Sandman, K., L. Kroos, S. Cutting, P. Youngman, and R. Losick.** 1988. Identification of the promoter for a spore coat protein gene in *Bacillus subtilis* and studies on the regulation of its induction at a late stage of sporulation. *J. Mol. Biol.* **200:**461–473.

165. **Sandman, K., R. Losick, and P. Youngman.** 1987. Genetic analysis of *Bacillus subtilis spo* mutations generated by Tn*917*-mediated insertional mutagenesis. *Genetics* **117:**603–617.

166. **Sato, T., Y. Samori, and Y. Kobayashi.** 1990. The *cisA* cistron of *Bacillus subtilis* sporulation gene *spoIVC* encodes a protein homologous to a site-specific recombinase. *J. Bacteriol.* **172:**1092–1098.

167. **Satola, S., P. A. Kirchman, and C. P. Moran, Jr.** 1991. Spo0A binds to a promoter used by σ^A RNA polymerase during sporulation in *Bacillus subtilis*. *Proc. Natl. Acad. Sci. USA* **88:**4533–4537.

168. **Schmidt, R., P. Margolis, L. Duncan, R. Coppolecchia, C. P. Moran, Jr., and R. Losick.** 1990. Control of developmental transcription factor σ^F by sporulation regulatory proteins SpoIIAA and SpoIIAB in *Bacillus subtilis*. *Proc. Natl. Acad. Sci. USA* **87:**9221–9225.

168a. **Schuch, R., and P. J. Piggot.** Personal communication.

169. **Segall, J., and R. Losick.** 1977. Cloned *B. subtilis* DNA containing a gene that is activated early during sporulation. *Cell* **11:**751–761.

170. **Sekiguchi, J., H. Ohsu, A. Kuroda, H. Moriyama, and T. Akamatsu.** 1990. Nucleotide sequences of the *Bacillus subtilis flaD* locus and a *B. licheniformis* homologue affecting the autolysin level and flagellation. *J. Gen. Microbiol.* **136:**1223–1230.

170a. **Serror, P.** Personal communication.

171. **Setlow, P.** 1993. Spore structural proteins, p. 801–809. *In* A. L. Sonenshein, J. A. Hoch, and R. Losick (ed.), *Bacillus subtilis and Other Gram-Positive Bacteria:*

Biochemistry, Physiology, and Molecular Genetics. American Society for Microbiology, Washington, D.C.

172. **Shoji, K., S. Hiratsuka, F. Kawamura, and Y. Kobayashi.** 1988. New suppressor mutation *sur0B* of *spo0B* and *spo0F* mutations in *Bacillus subtilis*. *J. Gen. Microbiol.* **134:**3249–3257.

172a. **Slynn, G., and B. Corfe.** Personal communication.

173. **Smith, I.** 1993. Regulatory proteins that control late-growth development, p. 785–800. *In* A. L. Sonenshein, J. A. Hoch, and R. Losick (ed.), *Bacillus subtilis and Other Gram-Positive Bacteria: Biochemistry, Physiology, and Molecular Genetics*. American Society for Microbiology, Washington, D.C.

174. **Smith, I., I. Mandic-Mulec, and N. Gaur.** 1991. The role of negative control in sporulation. *Res. Microbiol.* **142:**831–839.

175. **Smith, K., M. E. Bayer, and P. Youngman.** 1993. Physical and functional characterization of the *Bacillus subtilis spoIIM* gene. *J. Bacteriol.* **175:**3607–3617.

176. **Smith, K., and P. Youngman.** 1993. Evidence that the *spoIIM* gene of *Bacillus subtilis* is transcribed by RNA polymerase associated with σ^E. *J. Bacteriol.* **175:**3618–3627.

177. **Sonenshein, A. L., J. A. Hoch, and R. Losick (ed.).** 1993. *Bacillus subtilis and Other Gram-Positive Bacteria: Biochemistry, Physiology, and Molecular Genetics*. American Society for Microbiology, Washington, D.C.

178. **Spiegelman, G., B. Van Hoy, M. Perego, J. Day, K. Trach, and J. A. Hoch.** 1990. Structural alterations in the *Bacillus subtilis* Spo0A regulatory protein which suppress mutations at several *spo0* loci. *J. Bacteriol.* **172:**5011–5019.

179. **Stephens, M. A., N. Lang, K. Sandman, and R. Losick.** 1984. A promoter whose utilization is temporally regulated during sporulation in *Bacillus subtilis*. *J. Mol. Biol.* **176:**333–348.

180. **Stevens, C. M., R. Daniel, N. Illing, and J. Errington.** 1992. Characterization of a sporulation gene, *spoIVA*, involved in spore coat morphogenesis in *Bacillus subtilis*. *J. Bacteriol.* **174:**586–594.

181. **Stevens, C. M., and J. Errington.** 1990. Differential gene expression during sporulation in *Bacillus subtilis:* structure and regulation of the *spoIIID* gene. *Mol. Microbiol.* **4:**543–552.

182. **Stragier, P.** 1989. Temporal and spatial control of gene expression during sporulation: from facts to speculations, p. 243–254. *In* I. Smith, R. A. Slepecky, and P. Setlow (ed.), *Regulation of Prokaryotic Development*. American Society for Microbiology, Washington, D.C.

183. **Stragier, P.** 1992. Establishment of forespore-specific gene expression during sporulation of *Bacillus subtilis*, p. 297–310. *In* J. A. Cole, F. Mohan, and C. Dow (ed.), *Procaryotic Structure and Function*. Society for General Microbiology, Cambridge.

184. **Stragier, P., C. Bonamy, and C. Karmazyn-Campelli.** 1988. Processing of a sporulation sigma factor in *Bacillus subtilis:* how morphological structure could control gene expression. *Cell* **52:**697–704.

185. **Stragier, P., J. Bouvier, C. Bonamy, and J. Szulmajster.** 1984. A developmental gene product of *Bacillus subtilis* homologous to the sigma factor of *Escherichia coli*. *Nature* (London) **312:**376–378.

186. **Stragier, P., B. Kunkel, L. Kroos, and R. Losick.** 1989. Chromosomal rearrangement generating a composite gene for a developmental transcription factor. *Science* **243:**507–512.

187. **Strauch, M. A., D. de Mendoza, and J. A. Hoch.** 1992. *cis*-Unsaturated fatty acids specifically inhibit a signal-transducing protein kinase required for initiation of sporulation in *Bacillus subtilis*. *Mol. Microbiol.* **6:**2909–2917.

188. **Strauch, M. A., and J. A. Hoch.** 1993. Transition-state regulators: sentinels of *Bacillus subtilis* post-exponential gene expression. *Mol. Microbiol.* **7:**337–342.

189. **Strauch, M. A., M. Perego, D. Burbulys, and J. A. Hoch.** 1989. The transition state transcription regulator AbrB of *Bacillus subtilis* is autoregulated during vegetative growth. *Mol. Microbiol.* **3:**1203–1210.

190. **Strauch, M. A., G. B. Spiegelman, M. Perego, W. C. Johnson, D. Burbulys, and J. A. Hoch.** 1989. The transition state transcription regulator AbrB of *Bacillus subtilis* is a DNA binding protein. *EMBO J.* **8:**1615–1621.

191. **Strauch, M. A., K. A. Trach, J. Day, and J. A. Hoch.** 1992. Spo0A activates and represses its own synthesis by binding at its dual promoters. *Biochimie* **74:**619–626.

192. **Strauch, M. A., V. Webb, G. Spiegelman, and J. A. Hoch.** 1990. The Spo0A protein of *Bacillus subtilis* is a repressor of the *abrB* gene. *Proc. Natl. Acad. Sci. USA* **87:**1801–1805.

193. **Strauch, M. A., J.-J. Wu, R. H. Jonas, and J. A. Hoch.** 1993. A positive feedback loop controls transcription of the *spo0F* gene, a component of the sporulation phosphorelay in *Bacillus subtilis*. *Mol. Microbiol.* **7:**967–974.

194. **Sun, D., R. M. Cabrera-Martinez, and P. Setlow.** 1991. Control of transcription of the *Bacillus subtilis spoIIIG* gene, which codes for the forespore specfic transcription factor σ^G. *J. Bacteriol.* **173:**2977–2984.

195. **Sun, D., P. Fajardo-Cavazos, M. D. Sussman, F. Tovar-Rojo, R. M. Cabrera-Martinez, and P. Setlow.** 1991. Effect of chromosome location of *Bacillus subtilis* forespore genes on their *spo* gene dependence and transcription by $E\sigma^F$: identification of features of good $E\sigma^F$-dependent promoters. *J. Bacteriol.* **173:**7867–7874.

196. **Sun, D., P. Stragier, and P. Setlow.** 1989. Identification of a new σ-factor involved in compartmentalized gene expression during sporulation of *Bacillus subtilis*. *Genes Dev.* **3:**141–149.

197. **Sussman, M. D., and P. Setlow.** 1990. Cloning, nucleotide sequence, and regulation of the *Bacillus subtilis gpr* gene which codes for the protease that initiates degradation of small, acid-soluble proteins during spore germination. *J. Bacteriol.* **173:**291–300.

198. **Tatti, K. M., C. H. Jones, and C. P. Moran, Jr.** 1991. Genetic evidence for interaction of σ^E with the *spoIIID* promoter in *Bacillus subtilis*. *J. Bacteriol.* **173:**7828–7833.

198a. **Theeragool, G., A. Miyao, K. Yamada, T. Sato, and Y. Kobayashi.** 1993. In vivo expression of the *Bacillus subtilis spoVE* gene. *J. Bacteriol.* **175:**4071–4080.

199. **Trach, K., D. Burbulys, M. Strauch, J.-J. Wu, N. Dhillon, R. Jonas, C. Hanstein, P. Kallio, M. Perego, T. Bird, G. Spiegelman, C. Fogher, and J. A. Hoch.** 1991. Control of the initiation of sporulation in *Bacillus subtilis* by a phosphorelay. *Res. Microbiol.* **142:**815–823.

200. **Trach, K., J. W. Chapman, P. J. Piggot, and J. A. Hoch.** 1985. Deduced product of the stage 0 sporulation gene *spo0F* shares homology with the Spo0A, OmpR, and SfrA proteins. *Proc. Natl. Acad. Sci. USA* **82:**7260–7264.

201. **Trach, K., and J. A. Hoch.** 1989. The *Bacillus subtilis spo0B* stage 0 operon encodes an essential GTP-binding protein. *J. Bacteriol.* **171:**1362–1371.

202. **Trach, K. A., and J. A. Hoch.** 1993. Multisensory activation of the phosphorelay initiating sporulation in *Bacillus subtilis:* identification and sequence of the protein kinase of the alternate pathway. *Mol. Microbiol.* **8:**69–79.
203. **Van Hoy, B. E., and J. A. Hoch.** 1990. Characterization of the *spoIVB* and *recN* loci of *Bacillus subtilis. J. Bacteriol.* **172:**1306–1311.
204. **Von Heijne, G.** 1992. Membrane protein structure prediction. Hydrophobicity analysis and the positive-inside rule. *J. Mol. Biol.* **225:**487–494.
205. **Waites, W. M., D. Kay, I. W. Dawes, D. A. Wood, S. C. Warren, and J. Mandelstam.** 1970. Sporulation in *Bacillus subtilis.* Correlation of biochemical events with morphological changes in asporogenous mutants. *Biochem. J.* **118:**667–676.
206. **Wang, L.-F., and R. H. Doi.** 1986. Nucleotide sequence and organization of *Bacillus subtilis* RNA polymerase major sigma (σ^{43}) operon. *Nucleic Acids Res.* **14:**4293–4307.
207. **Wang, L.-F., and R. H. Doi.** 1987. Promoter switching during development and the termination site of the σ^{43} operon of *Bacillus subtilis. Mol. Gen. Genet.* **207:**114–119.
208. **Weir, J., M. Predich, E. Dubnau, G. Nair, and I. Smith.** 1991. Regulation of *spo0H,* a gene coding for the *Bacillus subtilis* σ^{H} factor. *J. Bacteriol.* **173:**521–529.
209. **Wu, J.-J., P. J. Piggot, K. M. Tatti, and C. P. Moran, Jr.** 1991. Transcription of the *Bacillus subtilis spoIIA* operon. *Gene* **101:**113–116.
210. **Wu, J.-J., R. Schuch, and P. J. Piggot.** 1992. Characterization of a *Bacillus subtilis* sporulation operon that includes genes for an RNA polymerase σ factor and for a putative DD-carboxypeptidase. *J. Bacteriol.* **174:**4885–4892.
211. **Yamashita, S., H. Yoshikawa, F. Kawamura, H. Takahashi, T. Yamamoto, Y. Kobayashi, and H. Saito.** 1986. The effect of *spo0* mutations on the expression of *spo0A-* and *spo0F-lacZ* fusions. *Mol. Gen. Genet.* **205:**28–33.
212. **York, K., T. J. Kenney, S. Satola, C. P. Moran, Jr., H. Poth, and P. Youngman.** 1992. Spo0A controls the σ^{A}-dependent activation of *Bacillus subtilis* sporulation-specific transcription unit *spoIIE. J. Bacteriol.* **174:**2648–2658.
213. **Yoshikawa, H., J. Kazami, S. Yamashita, T. Chibazakura, H. Sone, F. Kawamura, M. Oda, M. Isaka, Y. Kobayashi, and H. Saito.** 1986. Revised assignment for the *B. subtilis spo0F* gene and its homology with *spo0A* and with two *Escherichia coli* genes. *Nucleic Acids Res.* **14:**1063–1072.
214. **Young, M.** 1976. Use of temperature-sensitive mutants to study gene expression during sporulation in *Bacillus subtilis. J. Bacteriol.* **126:**928–936.
214a. **Youngman, P.** Personal communication.
215. **Youngman, P., J. B. Perkins, and R. Losick.** 1984. A novel method for the rapid cloning in *Escherichia coli* of *Bacillus subtilis* chromosomal DNA adjacent to Tn*917* insertions. *Mol. Gen. Genet.* **195:**424–433.
216. **Yudkin, M. D.** 1987. Structure and function in a *Bacillus subtilis* sporulation-specific sigma factor: molecular nature of mutations in *spoIIAC. J. Gen. Microbiol.* **133:**475–481.
216a. **Zhang, J., P. C. Fitz-James, and A. I. Aronson.** 1993. Cloning and characterization of a cluster of genes encoding polypeptides present in the insoluble fraction of the spore coat of *Bacillus subtilis. J. Bacteriol.* **175:**3757–3766.
217. **Zheng, L., W. P. Donovan, P. C. Fitz-James, and R. Losick.** 1988. Gene encoding a morphogenic protein required in the assembly of the outer coat of the *Bacillus subtilis* endospore. *Genes Dev.* **2:**1047–1054.

218. **Zheng, L., R. Halberg, S. Roels, H. Ichikawa, L. Kroos, and R. Losick.** 1992. Sporulation regulatory protein GerE from *Bacillus subtilis* binds to and can activate or repress transcription from promoters for mother-cell specific genes. *J. Mol. Biol.* **226:**1037–1050.
219. **Zheng, L., and R. Losick.** 1990. Cascade regulation of spore coat gene expression in *Bacillus subtilis. J. Mol. Biol.* **212:**645–660.
220. **Zuber, P., J. Healy, H. L. Carter III, S. Cutting, C. P. Moran, Jr., and R. Losick.** 1989. Mutation changing the specificity of an RNA polymerase sigma factor. *J. Mol. Biol.* **206:**605–614.
221. **Zuber, P., and R. Losick.** 1983. Use of a *lacZ* fusion to study the role of the *spo0* genes of *Bacillus subtilis* in developmental regulation. *Cell* **35:**275–283.
222. **Zuberi, A. R., A. Moir, and I. M. Feavers.** 1987. The nucleotide sequence and gene organization of the *gerA* spore germination operon of *Bacillus subtilis* 168. *Gene* **51:**1–11.

INDEX

The page numbers for entries occurring within tables are followed by a t.